Sickness and Society

Sickness and Society

RAYMOND S. DUFF, M.D.

and

AUGUST B. HOLLINGSHEAD, Ph.D.

✦✦

Harper & Row, Publishers

New York, Evanston,

and London

LIBRARY OF CONGRESS CATALOG CARD NUMBER: 68-15988

This book is dedicated to our families.
All have known sickness in the course of their lives.

CONTENTS

PART V. IMPACT OF THE ILLNESS

PART VI. A LAST LOOK

FOREWORD

I rarely have read a more exciting book than *Sickness and Society*. In this book the authors describe the drama of sickness in an unnamed but easily identifiable medical center, enacted by patients, their families, hospital administrators, nurses, community physicians, and the faculty and students of a medical school. In some respects it reminds me of a book that I was privileged to publish as coauthor with August B. Hollingshead ten years ago. It took courage then to look objectively at one's own profession; it takes possibly even more courage to examine some of the medical activities at "Eastern University." Such an objective examination, however, is in the best tradition of Eastern University. *Social Class and Mental Illness* was greeted with critical dismay by some segments of the profession; yet, finally, it was accepted and had a salutary impact on the field. I predict that this will also happen to *Sickness and Society* and that it will become a milestone in the development of better medical care.

This book focuses on the relationship between the care of hospitalized medical and surgical patients and the social environment of a university and community hospital. Do the patients receive optimal care? Does the social system hinder or enhance such care? Is the psychosocial environment sufficiently considered in rendering such care?

By studying the medical care of three "social classes" of patients—those in ward, semiprivate, and private accommodations—through detailed interviews and observations, the authors provide answers to these questions. I do not agree with all their answers, and I do not agree with some of their implicit assumptions. It is impossible for me to accept the fact that medical teaching and research are not compatible with good medical care. I do not believe that an inherent antagonism exists among physicians, hospital administrators, and nurses or that hospitals are run for the benefit of physicians. When the authors describe the awesome, complex, and often confused transactions among

ix

patients, families, and members of the health professions, the reader may draw an unnecessarily negative picture; yet the main message of the book is powerful, clear, and essentially correct: *The patient's care is far from what it could and should be!* Possibly one of the most alarming aspects of this report is the fact that the medical center under scrutiny has been ranked nationally among the best. It is safe to assume that the conditions described in this report prevail in other centers and that these problems are by no means the result of local inefficiency or lassitude.

After this critical statement, I should like to conclude on an optimistic note. Much has changed since the data for this book were collected. Society itself is producing some of these changes. The ward patient is becoming a private patient. The faculties of many medical schools have become more interested in good clinical care and health delivery. A change in health ethics is inducing the professions to pay more attention to the needs and rights of the community of patients. In such a cultural climate the book ought to be of enormous interest not only to the health professions but also to the consumer—the patient. To meet the challenge will require a calm appraisal of what we are doing for the ill and infirm. Perhaps a reappraisal of the delivery of health services should accompany pure biomedical research. Certainly more adequate funding of medical education is needed. The staggering deficits encountered by the hospital in the care of the poor have to be balanced by a more adequate system of funding.

The first step in the solution of a problem is to recognize its existence. Based on the explored facts, efforts have been made to introduce drastic improvements and things have started to change in the Medical Center of Eastern University. Its leaders should feel, with gratitude and pride, that Duff and Hollingshead have carried the torch and are lighting the path of progress.

F. C. Redlich, M.D., Dean
Yale University School of Medicine

PREFACE

At some time in the life history of each individual, sickness strikes within his immediate family and interferes with the daily activities carried out in the fulfillment of social roles. Society has developed elaborate institutions to cope with illness in its manifold forms. In our society if the illness is serious the afflicted individual is likely to seek professional help. To define a sickness, individuals functioning within health institutions—physicians' offices, hospitals, and schools of medicine—interact with one another as well as with the affected person and family members. In accordance with their respective social roles, they decide what should be done about the problems the patient presents. Sickness, thus, reflects the judgments of several different people as they respond to physical symptoms in the body or to the behavior of a person who is defined by his society as *sick*.

The demands of patients and families and the responses of the representatives of different institutions to sickness may be viewed as a drama. The socially defined and self-defined roles of each player—patients, physicians, nurses, hospital administrators, and family members—have an influence on the ways the drama is enacted. Each member of the cast has a role to play, and each may have a different objective as he makes decisions in behalf of the sick person. The aims of each actor may be in harmony or in discord with those of other actors. Lack of communication among the players often complicates the performance. Patients may or may not report their symptoms to family members, physicians, or nurses; they may or may not trust others; they may or may not desire to know "the truth" about their illness. Family members may or may not know what is wrong with the patient. Physicians may or may not know what ails the patient; even when they know the nature of the problems, they may or may not decide to tell the patient "the truth." The several dramatis personae may wear masks; they may even be enacting a play within a play. In these and other ways society influences sickness, and sickness, in turn, affects society. This interrelationship is suggested in our title *Sickness and Society*.

xi

The research reported in this book traces linkages between sickness and social factors as observed in the illnesses of persons admitted to a general hospital. The central focus is the "career" of the patient from the time he first sought help for the illness we followed through the hospitalization and convalescence or death. The study was directed and carried out by a physician and a sociologist who worked together from the time the research was just an idea until the book was completed. In brief, our report aims at helping professional and general readers understand the social processes entailed in becoming, being, and having been sick enough to be hospitalized. We believe these objectives are best achieved by focusing upon the data we collected. Therefore, we have avoided footnote references that may or may not be pertinent to this study.

Every person who participated in the study knew we were carrying out a research project. We were careful to tell each one that eventually our findings would be published. To facilitate the presentation of personal data we have assigned fictitious names to each family. To protect the privacy of the family, details have been changed and a composite picture constructed. However, essential facts, particularly the medical and social conditions, have not been altered.

We acknowledge our obligations to the patients, their families, physicians, nurses, and other persons less closely associated with them during the course of the patients' illnesses. We are deeply indebted to the general hospital in which we centered our research, as well as to the faculty of the School of Medicine affiliated with it. We especially thank the members of the Advisory Committee who consulted with us during the months we planned the research.

We acknowledge with special gratitude Public Health Service Research Grant No. NU 00012 to the hospital from the Division of Nursing, Bureau of Health Manpower. This grant enabled us to carry out the research.

Yale University's general support of research enabled the authors to devote time to the multiple tasks entailed in the study from its beginning until the manuscript was published.

We wish to express our personal thanks to Katharine Campbell, Susan La France, Barbara McCrone, and Louise Silverman who worked long hours in crisis situations gathering essential data for the study. They were exposed to illness without being able to offer assistance. As they asked questions, observed, listened, and recorded in the sick room and the family home, they were variously welcomed, blamed, ignored, avoided, and sometimes invited to leave. These primary data collectors found this to be a difficult and demanding role. However, they discovered that their many tasks were personally as rewarding and meaningful as they were difficult.

Margaret Plymire and Robert West assisted us in designing the project and testing the schedules in the pilot study. Transcription, filing of data, and typing of reports and manuscripts were carried out by Belle Greenberg, Gail Snider, and Ann Tabor. Others who assisted in one phase or another of this research include: Barbara Almond, M.D., Priscilla Baxter, Carol Cofrancesco, Jane Duff, Joyce Duff, Richard Fletcher, Charlotte Mitchell, Gilbert Merkx, Lois Richards, Lillian Smith, Charlotte Stadler, Ellen Steele, and Joyce Williams. Max Pepper, M.D., Lloyd Rogler, and Robert Wilson provided consultation at the beginning of the research. Robert W. Hetherington and John Kramer, Jr. were particularly helpful in the analysis of the statistical data. We extend our special thanks to the Executive Director of the hospital for his continued support from the inception of the study through financing, design, data gathering, data analysis, and, finally, the completion of the manuscript.

We acknowledge with deep gratitude our many obligations to Janet Turk. Mrs. Turk has worked with Professor Hollingshead on three major books during the past decade. She typed and retyped this manuscript; read, reread, and edited copy; gave sage advice; and indexed the book.

Finally, Raymond S. Duff wishes to make special acknowledgment to Mrs. Duff and their children who faced more uncertainties than usual while he pursued a research career which was not exactly medicine and not necessarily sociology.

R.S.D.

A.B.H.

New Haven, Connecticut
December 15, 1967

PART I PROBLEMS AND PROCEDURES

CHAPTER 1 INTRODUCTION

THIS BOOK FOCUSES ATTENTION UPON INTERRELATIONS between the care hospitalized medical and surgical patients receive and the social environment in which it is administered. The authors studied a single illness experience from the time each patient was admitted to a general hospital until he returned home and completed his convalescence or died. We directed our efforts toward securing answers to five general questions: (1) Did the illnesses of sick persons reflect factors operative in their effective social environment? (2) Was the care patients received related to the organization of medical institutions? (3) Did sick persons influence their own care? (4) Did the role relations of the several lay and professional groups involved in the processes of patient care influence the delivery of medical services to the sick person? (5) What was the impact of the illness on the sick person and on his family?

The key concepts involved in each of these questions were delimited before we began our research. In the first question the central concept is the *effective social environment.* The effective social environment is conceived as being encompassed primarily by the immediate family, but also it includes members of the kinship group, work associates, friends, neighbors, and others who are meaningful to the sick person. Individuals who are in interaction with one another are continually in the process of reciprocally evaluating one another within a framework of culturally defined *role expectations.* Role expectations are premised on the person's position in the family as well as on his age and sex. Each person customarily plays a number of different roles in daily life and may, or may not, satisfactorily fulfill the norms associated with the roles he is expected or required to play. Other dimensions of the effective environment include such diverse things as: the physical aspects of the home and neighborhood; abilities, motivations, aspirations, state of health; and opportunities and limitations associated with class status.

3

The *organization of medical institutions* is presumably a primary factor entailed in the care a patient receives during the course of his illness. In our society the hospital has come to be viewed by the public and the medical profession as the most appropriate institution for the diagnosis and treatment of many types of acute and chronic illness. The general hospital is an indispensable adjunct to the practice of medicine today; it may be viewed as an extension of medical practice since both physicians and patients look to it for the care of persons too ill for home or office treatment. In the words of one of our subjects, "The hospital is the place to go for repairs." Patients ordinarily come to the hospital from their homes and return to their homes after discharge from the hospital. In due course they may resume customary family and work roles. Hospitals are viewed also as essential to the training of physicians and for research into the nature and control of disease.

During the twentieth century divisions have developed within medicine to permit the specialization necessary for the application of the growing knowledge and techniques developed from the physical and biological sciences. A concomitant of specialization has been the focusing of attention on a single disease, a specialized type of a particular disease, or a single organ or process. As a consequence the practice of medicine in general hospitals is specialized medicine. Although the practice of medicine outside the hospital is concentrated in the offices of private practitioners, the private practitioners also tend to be specialists. The general practitioner belongs to a declining segment of organized medicine with staff privileges in the hospital.

The sick person is the primary actor in the patient-care process. He presumably plays an important role in the way it is carried out in the physician's office, the hospital, and his home. Patients, for reasons of their own, may mislead family members and physicians concerning their symptoms and problems. While the physician relies upon a personal history as well as more or less objective data derived from physical examination and laboratory findings to provide appropriate diagnosis and therapy for his patient s ailment, he may not communicate this aspect of the diagnostic process to the patient.

Herein lies a potential for confusion regarding the patient's medical problem. However, the patient's influences on the processes entailed in his care are not limited to this aspect of the diagnostic process. The patient may or may not "cooperate" with the physician in the application of the therapy he prescribes for the illness. To confuse the situation even further, some patients deceive their physicians by leading them to believe they are complying with their treatment recommendations when, in fact, they are assiduously avoiding their orders. In these situations neither the patient nor the physician may be aware of this influence in the overall treatment process. When the physician does not take into account the influence of the patient's own actions, the consequences may possibly be discernible on the outcome of the illness; but no one involved—the patient, the physician, hospital personnel, or members of the patient's family—understands what has occurred.

Hospitalized patients are cared for by persons who bring to bear the art and science of medicine to relieve them of pain and hopefully to cure them of their afflictions. When the sick person is admitted to the hospital he presumably becomes the central figure in a social group. The primary reason for the group's existence is to care for the patient's medical, personal, and social needs while he is in the hospital. The patient's spouse, other members of his family, the physician responsible for his care, nurses, technicians, students of medicine and nursing, and hospital administrators play diverse but related roles in this social group. The patient ordinarily interacts with several members of the group at some time during his stay in the hospital. When we began our research we depicted the role relations of the group involved in the care of each patient in the following terms:

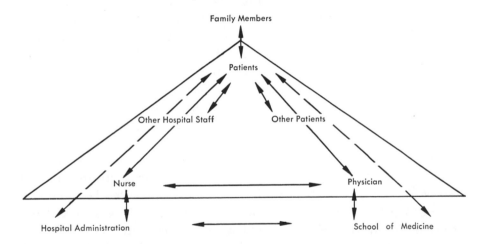

Persons within the triangle—patients, physicians, nurses, technicians, and other hospital personnel—usually interact with one another on the floor of the hospital where care is administered. Persons occupying role positions outside the triangle visit the patient-care divisions from time to time and interact with the patient in various ways. Family members usually interact with the patient but they have minimal responsibility for his care. Although hospital administrators rarely interact with the patient, they have an important role in providing and supervising the care the patient receives. The School of Medicine is affiliated with the hospital where we did our research, and it has a strong influence on patient care; we shall demonstrate this point in later chapters. The direction of the arrows symbolizes the flow of communication and activity between the different members of the group during the course of their daily activities. Each member of the group represented in the diagram contributes to the illness experiences of the patient. In turn, the patient accepts the care and uses the advice the staff imparts to him. We postulate that the institutional representatives with whom the patient interacts are relevant to his experiences as a sick person. Other studies have shown that each institutional representative plays a characteristic role as he performs his activities from hour to hour and day to day in the care of the patient.[1]

From the viewpoint of the patient, the first consideration is the care he receives for his illness. We define "care" in terms of what is useful to the patient in achieving health goals. Potential health goals may fail to be achieved or sacrifices of other life goals may occur because essentially nonmedical factors are involved in the processes of caring for the patient. For example, the medical history may be incomplete because professional personnel have too little time, limited interviewing skill, or a lack of knowledge to prepare an adequate history; or the medical history may be inadequate because a patient is reluctant to communicate his real problem to a physician, is unable to do so, or may mislead those responsible for his care. Lack of information or contradictory statements may influence subsequent thinking about diagnosis and, hence, may affect the treatment the patient receives.

From the perspective of theoretical medicine, the best patient care is derived from the classic model which ties diagnosis and treatment into a sequential relationship. Ideally, the processes of diagnosis and treatment should be appropriate and specific for each patient. This model assumes, first, that optimal care of the patient will follow the most accurate diagnosis in terms of the existing criteria for that diagnosis and, second, that the physician responsible for the patient's care will prescribe and administer the appropriate treatment for the diagnosis. Stated in terms of research design, the processes of diagnosis and treatment are viewed as independent variables and the care of the patient as the dependent variable.

This classic model, however, appeared to be too simple to explain the realities of behavior in the care of patients we observed while planning this study. Intervening variables were suspected. We postulated that mediating factors might alter the diagnosis, the treatment given, and the care received by the patient. Stated otherwise, we believed there are variables, which interfere with the care of patients, between what is asserted in the theoretical model and what happens in practice. To be specific, intervening variables which may influence patient care include: (1) the internal structure of the patient's family; (2) the organization of the medical profession; (3) the organization of the hospital; (4) the organization of medical education; (5) perceptions physicians have of the patient; (6) perceptions the patient has of the physician; (7) perceptions the patient's family have of the patient; and (8) perceptions patients have of themselves. The interrelationship between the independent and the dependent variables of the theoretical model, in combination with selected intervening variables, was thought to be worthy of study.

Before a person is admitted to the hospital in which we made this study, he is examined by a physician and a financial officer, who make the crucial decisions regarding the admissibility of the supposedly sick person to the hospital. To be eligible to sponsor patients for admission to the hospital a physician has to have staff privileges. The admission may be recommended for diagnostic determinations or for treatment of a previously diagnosed condition. The medical decision for admission is based upon the knowledge and judgment of the sponsoring physician. The person to be admitted has to vouch for his own ability to pay the hospital bill, or some other person or agency has to underwrite the charges. The financial requisite is derived from the fact that the hospital is a nonprofit, essentially unendowed, private institution. To remain in operation it must ascertain that the charges built up during the hospitalization will be paid. The responsibility of assessing the prospective patient's ability to meet the charges for his hospitalization rests with the hospital; it is a financial decision. Thus, the sponsoring physician and the admissions officer may be viewed as gatekeepers for the hospital.

Is the medical decision to admit or not to admit the patient related to the financial decision? Two factors are involved in this question and its answers: the socioeconomic status of the sick person and the organization of health services in the community. These factors are likely to be more or less independent of the patient's disease condition. However, the socioeconomic status of the patient and the organization of health services may not be independent of one another. There may be a linkage between socioeconomic status in the community, as reflected in the accommodations provided for patient care by the hospital, and the organization of medical care, as seen in the sponsorship of patients by physicians. These organizational factors are intervening variables; they may be associated with the medical care the patient receives.

The impact of the illness is of primary importance to the patient, but other persons are vitally concerned—the spouse and members of the immediate family, in particular. The responsible physician has a professional interest in the outcome of his efforts. Ideally, all persons who are involved in the interactional network should be interested in the results of the care the sick person receives. In Part V we shall focus attention on this point to determine who, in fact, is concerned with the impact of the illness on the patient and the family. Two of the questions we shall consider are: How does the patient view the treatment he recieves? How do family members react to the patient's illness?

Research studies in general hospitals have tended to focus on a disease,[2] the organization of the hospital,[3] and the functioning of different specialized groups—nurses[4] and physicians[5] especially. Few studies have been made of patients, particularly as they relate to physicians, nurses, other hospital personnel, and members of their families.[6] We hasten to add that there are good reasons for the paucity of research on the care of patients. The study of the patient in the treatment setting of a general hospital is not an easy one. The various specialists—physicians, nurses, and technicians—are comfortable in their everyday behavior "doing something" for sick people. Physicians usually see little to be gained by the study of the social behavior of persons involved in the care of patients. They are oriented toward research in "the biological sphere"; this is where the advances in medicine have been made. Physicians know little about the behavioral sciences; when they do mention them they tend to deprecate the possible contributions these sciences may make to an understanding of the care of patients. Nurses are busy people and reluctant to give their time to studies they define as "peripheral." Finally, the patients themselves see little to be gained by researchers asking questions and observing what the specialists are doing to them and how they are doing it. Few persons, professionals or patients, enjoy being "bugs on a pin," especially when they cannot perceive the relevance of "the pin" to their well-being. To ask a person to expose his most vulnerable self to intensive inquiry is a research problem in and of itself.

The physician-patient relationship is of special importance to the doctor; presumably, it is to the patient also. The physician-patient relationship is a confidential one, and its strength as well as its mystery arises from this fact. The patient offers his body to the physician for treatment, usually with apprehension. This, however, is countered by hope that the physician will cure him of his problem. The physician may be reluctant to grant permission for "outsiders" to study his relationship with his patient. He derives much of his status from this special relationship. For him to discuss his patient and his patient's family may breach the physician-patient relationship. Conversely, to approach the patient and ask him to talk about his relationship with his confidential agent—the physician—is outside the normal course of treatment. To ask a sick person to offer his self—what he is, what he feels, what he hopes for, what he has been, and what he thinks—for a study that is not essential to the treatment of his present illness is a formidable act on the part of the researcher. All the researcher has to offer in return is hope that the information he gathers will help others in need at some future time. Speaking more broadly, faith in future knowledge is the one recompense the researcher is able to offer a suffering patient and all those responsible for his support, treatment, and care.

To the members of the group involved in the direct care of the patient, researchers are "outsiders." What goes on *inside* the group is the concern of the group. It is protected by such phrases as "the physician-patient relationship," "the nursing process," "the privacy of the patient," "the welfare of the patient." To understand what is entailed in the experiences of a hospitalized patient it is necessary to penetrate the curtain of confidentiality that is draped around the group. Thus, the paucity of studies involving interpersonal relations in patient care may be attributed, in part at least, to our reluctance to probe sensitive areas of behavior.

The emphasis on specialization probably plays a part also in the reluctance of each group of specialists to consider that its activities can be understood adequately by a nonspecialist. Specialization in its most complex forms is found in medical centers where patient care, teaching, and research function side by side. The hospital in which we centered our research is part of a modern medical center. In this medical center, particularly in the hospital, specialization of interests and activities is readily seen. However, the impact of specialization of interests, and its attendant technology, upon the experiences of patients is not so readily visible. While specialization is necessary in the diagnosis and treatment of disease, we should not lose sight of the fact that the patient is the one whom the complex of specialized knowledge, technology, and structures is designed to help.

In sum, the questions we raised when we began this research, combined with the theoretical position we adopted to answer them, have served as guides to our thoughts and activities as we moved through the several phases of this study. Our research, in a few words, is concerned with assessing the medical and social factors that influenced the care each patient received during the course of a single illness experience—before he entered the hospital but also especially within the hospital and during the convalescent period. The general objective is to increase our knowledge of factors which have discernible effects on the care of sick persons.

NOTES

1. Talcott Parsons, *The Social System,* Free Press of Glencoe, New York, 1951, pp. 436–437. Henry E. Sigerist, *On the Sociology of Medicine,* Milton J. Roemer (ed.), M. D. Publications, New York, 1960, pp. 9–22. William Caudill, *The Psychiatric Hospital as a Small Society,* Harvard University Press, Cambridge, 1958, pp. 231–265.
2. Henry E. Sigerist, *On the History of Medicine,* Felix Marte-Ibañez (ed.), M.D. Publications, New York, 1960, especially p. 235.

3. John H. Knowles (ed.), *Hospitals, Doctors, and the Public Interest,* Harvard University Press, Cambridge, 1965. Lewis E. Weeks and John R. Griffith (eds.), *Progressive Patient Care: An Anthology,* University of Michigan Press, Ann Arbor, 1964; this anthology contains an excellent bibliography on the organization of hospitals for patient care, pp. 369–385. Temple Burling, Edith M. Lentz, and Robert N. Wilson, *The Give and Take in Hospitals,* Putnam's, New York, 1956. Robert N. Wilson, "The Social Structure of a General Hospital," *The Annals of the American Academy of Political and Social Science, 346* (1963), 67.

4. James K. Skipper and Robert C. Leonard, *Social Interaction and Patient Care,* Lippincott, Philadelphia, 1965. Esther Lucile Brown, *Newer Dimensions of Patient Care,* Russell Sage Foundation, New York, 1962. Ida J. Orlando, *The Dynamic Nurse-Patient Relationship: Function, Process, and Principles,* Putnam's, New York, 1961.

5. Samuel W. Bloom, *The Doctor and His Patient,* Russell Sage Foundation, New York, 1963. Howard S. Becker, Blanche Geer, Everett C. Hughes, and Anselm L. Strauss, *Boys in White: Student Culture in Medical School,* University of Chicago Press, Chicago, 1961. Ray E. Trussell, *Hunterdon Medical Center,* Harvard University Press, Cambridge, 1965, pp. 109–114, 174–212. Robert K. Merton, George G. Reeder, and Patricia L. Kendall (eds.), *The Student-Physician,* Harvard University Press, Cambridge, 1957.

6. Rose Laub Coser, *Life in the Ward,* Michigan State University Press, East Lansing, 1962. Clark E. Vincent, "The Family in Health and Illness: Some Neglected Areas," *The Annals of the American Academy of Political and Social Science, 346* (1963), 109. Henry B. Richardson, *Patients Have Families,* The Commonwealth Fund, New York, 1948. Eliot Friedson, *Patients' Views of Medical Practice—A Study of Subscribers to a Prepaid Medical Plan in the Bronx,* Russell Sage Foundation, New York, 1961.

The way a research project is conducted is as essential to its outcome as are the questions it is designed to answer. Moreover, the discerning reader wants to know how the researchers reached the conclusions they set forth in their report. With these considerations in mind, we present in this chapter the main outlines of the development of this study from its inception until its completion.

All phases of the research were carried out by the authors, assisted by nurses, sociologists, and physicians, none of whom had worked together before. Experience indicated that from five to seven years' time would have to be invested in the study we envisaged. Therefore, the authors agreed that before they committed themselves to a major piece of research one of the first issues they would have to settle was whether or not the physician and the sociologist could work together. To help us clarify our thinking and as an aid to working out research procedures that would give us the kinds of information we desired and, at the same time, be tolerated by patients, physicians, nurses, and members of the patients' families, we decided to make an exploratory study.

Our first step was a series of personal observations on the patient-care units in which the medical and surgical services are housed in the hospital. Our presence "on the floor" immediately became of concern to physicians, nurses, and ancillary personnel. The physician-researcher was recognized, but no one knew why he was making rounds and talking with patients, registered nurses, licensed practical nurses, medical students, house staff, and attending physicians. The sociologist, too, made rounds, observed patients, spent time on the floor, and talked with the staff. Our explanation that we were interested in studying staff-patient relationships eased our relations with patients and ancillary staff but it increased the anxieties of nurses and younger physicians. A role that was acceptable to most of the nurses and many members of the house staff was soon developed by a graduate student in sociology, working

11

on the project, who was also a registered nurse. She validated her presence by saying simply that she was "working on a thesis." (This was a true statement.) She mingled with the nurses, went to lunch with them, and visited in the nurse's station, up and down the corridors, and in the patients' rooms.

Our informal contacts with staff members gave us considerable insight into the way nonmedical research was viewed in the hospital. We were told pointedly that the study of "other peoples' affairs" was not welcomed. One head nurse told us that "a professor at Eastern" had been denied a request to do "behavioral" research in the hospital. Another told us "an anthropologist went into the psychiatric hospital as a patient and not even the head nurse knew he was a fake." During the time we were establishing ourselves, we employed a former head nurse to work on the project, but we soon learned that she felt like a traitor to her fellow nurses. She made numerous references to the anthropologist mentioned above, calling the research he had done "very sneaky." She appeared to be concerned about how hospital personnel would view her. Over a period of several weeks, this nurse's tensions increased considerably, and we decided to release her from the project. The suspicions of personnel about our presence reinforced a decision we had made earlier—not to try to cover up any of our work.

Some interns and assistant residents showed anxiety about our presence on the patient-care divisions. This was more than balanced by the help we received from established physicians. One surgeon, insistent that we wear white coats and appear on the floor like medical personnel, said:

> It is bad for the patients to see someone in civilian clothes along with the doctor. If you wear a white coat the doctors as well as the patients will know you and recognize you as someone who is interested in them. Everyone here wears a uniform of some kind. It is important, at night particularly, that you wear a white coat.

We did wear white coats, and we were invited on rounds by several physicians. We were concerned only as observers, not participants; we did not interfere with the activities of the floor, and we held scrupulously to this role.

After three months of preliminary observation and experience, the authors decided that they could work together and that the study was feasible. For the next twelve months we drafted schedules, made preliminary tests of each one on patients, and clarified our objectives. During this time we studied twenty patients and families—ten on the medical service and ten on the surgical service of the hospital. Also, nine physicians and eleven nurses were interviewed, and an analysis was made of the hospital's statistics on admissions and discharges of patients. Particular attention was given to the patients' condition, the procedures carried out, and their relationships with physicians, nurses, and family members. We were concerned especially with decisions on the care of patients, changes in their physical status from better to worse and from worse to better, and their discharge from the hospital or death. The roles played by the several persons involved in the group around the patients were observed directly. Preliminary assessments were made of the influence exerted on patients by each principal role player—family member, physician, and nurse.

Information was gathered to determine how the decision was made to seek medical care, why this hospital was selected in contrast to some other one, who made the decision to admit the sick person, and so on. We determined what information was exchanged between the physicians, nurses, and members of the family and how useful it was to the patient. Factors influencing the decision to discharge the patient from the hospital were examined. The convalescent period was studied in terms of gains toward the recovery of the patient from the illness. Another objective was the determination of the impact of the illness on the individual and his family.

Our questions were directed toward: the diagnosis "of the illness condition"; the technical treatment prescribed; the care administered; the professional persons who administered the care, primarily physicians and registered nurses; and perceptions the patient had of his illness, his treatment, the hospital, and the care he was receiving. We interviewed family members to elicit their thoughts and judgments about the patient, his illness, and the treatment received, and their attitudes toward being in the study. Each patient was followed from his admission to the hospital until his discharge. Some patients were followed for several weeks after their discharge from the hospital, and appropriate data were gathered during our visits to the patients' homes.

For each patient we attempted to determine: attitudes toward hospitals and physicians, nurses, and other health personnel; patterns of use of health resources; achievement of potential health goals through the hospitalization; whether or not unnecessary sacrifice of other goals by the patient had occurred as a consequence of his care; and what adaptations occur in a family when a member becomes a patient in the hospital. Further, we ascertained the family's relationship to the patient, the hospital staff, and other patients.

The pilot study taught us two things: first, it *is* possible to observe patients, physicians, nurses, and other hospital personnel as they perform their roles in the hospital; second, it *is* possible to use schedules to interview patients, family members, and hospital personnel. Viewed generally, the questions on the schedules we developed during the planning and pilot phases of the study are concerned with the patient; his illness; his physician; his admission to the hospital; his experiences in the hospital; his family, nurses, and other hospital personnel; and his release from the hospital, his convalescence, and his post-hospital experience. The schedules are divided into four groups:

1. *Admission interview with and about the patient.* (a) Admission to the hospital; (b) patient's physician; (c) patient and spouse.

2. *Observation Schedule.* This schedule was designed to gather information on all activities that involved the patient during four 20-minute periods of three days of hospitalization. Four observations were made on the first day, four on the third day, and four on the fifth day. The hours chosen were 9 to 10 A.M., 12 NOON to 1 P.M., 3 to 4 P.M., and 7 to 8 P.M. The first was concerned with morning care; the second, lunch; the third, afternoon visiting; and the last, evening visits. The first two were chosen to enable us to observe the interactions between the patient and hospital personnel primarily; the later time periods were directed toward the activities of family and friends who came to the hospital to see the patient. In addition, we observed each surgical patient from the time preoperative medication was given until he was in the operating room. In approximately one half of the surgical cases we entered the operating room and made detailed notes on the operation as it was initiated. In all instances we stayed with the patient until he was under anesthesia. During our observations we recorded conversations at the time they took place.

3. *Schedules on hospital care.* (a) Patient, personal history; (b) the family, background; (c) patient, diagnostic; (d) patient, therapeutic; (e) spouse, therapeutic; (f) discharge; (g) home visit; (h) follow-up visit; (i) physician, diagnostic; (j) physician, therapeutic; (k) physician, discharge; (l) nurse, therapeutic; (m) nurse, discharge; (n) ancillary personnel, therapeutic.

4. *Hospital records.* (a) Admission form: provides the patient's name, address, marital status, religious affiliation, age, race, sex, and hour of admission, nursing unit, patient accommodation, and hospital service; (b) discharge form: provides date of discharge, diagnosis, and fact of survival or death at discharge; (c) financial: patients' ledger cards filed in the accounting office were available to us; (d) medical record: access to medical records is a question of law and hospital policy; the medical record of each patient was available to us at all times. (Legally, a patient may have access to his own medical records; theoretically, the record for each patient is a complete statement of medical and/or surgical findings, but if a few sheets were removed one would hardly know that this had been done because the record is by no means continuous.)

The interview schedules followed a planned sequence that began with the admission of the patient to the hospital, moved through the diagnosis and treatment of the illness to the discharge, and concluded with a home visit subsequent to the patient's hospital experience.

Apart from the schedules used for individual patients, a schedule was developed specifically for interviews with physicians, nurses, and hospital administrators. The questions were directed toward the elicitation of the respondents' views of the contributions of attending physicians, interns, residents, registered staff nurses, registered private-duty nurses, aides, other ancillary staff, and hospital administrators in the care of patients. The questions in these interviews were directed toward the respondent's perceptions of roles and role relations rather than toward specific patients. We queried each respondent on his views of the chief shortcomings of each person involved in one way or another in the care of patients. Finally, we raised questions regarding the ways the respondent thought the contributions and shortcomings of the different persons and services had influenced their goals as physician, nurse, or administrator. (This schedule was administered, in due course, to 45 physicians, 9 hospital administrators, 36 staff registered nurses, 9 private-duty nurses, and 15 licensed practical nurses. Each respondent was interviewed privately, either in the project's or the interviewee's office, subsequent to the completion of data collection in the hospital. These tape-recorded interviews took about an hour and a half; some were completed in one hour, but some lasted three hours. In addition, we also had numerous discussions with registered nurses, licensed practical nurses, nurse's aides, nursing supervisors, nursing administrators, house officers, private practitioners, faculty in the School of Medicine, and hospital administrators.)

We decided to select from among the patients admitted to the medical and surgical services of the hospital a study group who met the following specifications: *age*—40 through 64 years; *sex*—equal numbers; *race* —white only; *marital status*—married and living with spouse; *residence*— within the state; *time of admission*—Sunday through Thursday; *illness status* —conscious on admission; *length of stay*—probably two days or longer; *service*—one half on Medicine and one half on Surgery; *accommodation*—at least twenty on each accommodation: private, semiprivate, and ward.

Age limitations were imposed so that the study group would cover the upper range of the productive years of adult life. The sexes were balanced to learn if sex influences the care a patient receives. Race was limited to whites because the races are unequally distributed in the accommodations the hospital provides for inpatients. The specification *married and living with spouse* increased the probability that both members of the spouse pair would be involved in the hospitalization experience. Residence within the state made it convenient for us to interview the patient and a family member after the patient's release from the hospital. (The hospital draws the vast majority of its patients from residents of the state and three out of four from within 25 miles of the hospital.) The days of admission covered the period of the week on which most admissions occur. The admission of patients to the hospital follows a general cycle of in-on-Sunday and out-on-Friday or -Saturday; emergencies, of course, are admitted at any time, but relatively few admissions are emergencies. This cycle is planned, in part, by the hospital administration, but physicians and patients also enter into the scheduling process. Illness condition on admission was included to eliminate unconscious persons who might not be able to communicate with us. Length of stay was important as we were concerned that the patient be in the hospital long enough for the nurses and other staff to become acquainted with him. We controlled service and accommodation so we could compare medical with surgical patients in each of the three accommodations the hospital provides for its clientele.

Statistical data the hospital maintains on Hollerith cards were analyzed for the year immediately preceding the date we started to choose patients for the final study. The hospital's statistical data indicated that a sample of 225 persons would approximate one patient out of twenty who met our criteria during the two years we planned the intake phase of the study. We estimated a sample of this size would be large enough so that we could make meaningful comparisons between groups, yet it would be small enough for us to make individual case studies.

When we had completed the design of the study, the specifications of the sample, the development of schedules, and preliminary analysis of the data from the pilot study, we met with the Advisory Committee. We presented our plans, discussed with the committee what we intended to do to implement these plans, and we were assured of their cooperation. (We realized, of course, that eliciting the support of any physician was our responsibility.) The next step was to put our plans into operation in the different sections of the hospital.

In each unit of the hospital we held a series of meetings with the appropriate officials. The meetings were usually brief and to the point, as they took place during regular working hours. We asked for suggestions on how to present the project to the staff on the floor. Almost every person had something to offer in the way of suggestions, and we tried to incorporate the volunteered information into our behavior. The cooperation of physicians was essential to our project since we would not approach a patient until we had secured the permission of his physician. One chief of service assured us he could "deliver the cooperation" of a majority of physicians on his service. Another volunteered to contact reluctant colleagues and attempt, if necessary, to obtain their cooperation. A third suggested we prepare a letter to be sent to physicians affiliated with the hospital. We followed this suggestion and prepared a statement that explained the study briefly. We discussed it with the Director of the hospital and the Medical Board, all of whom endorsed the statement. In due course it was mailed on hospital stationery to all surgeons and internists with staff privileges in the hospital.

Some eighteen months of preliminary work in the hospital led us to believe the hospital personnel knew us well. We assumed also that all staff persons on the medical and surgical services knew we planned to study particular patients. However, until we made the selection of a patient the staff had no knowledge of which patients would be studied. We were concerned that the very fact of a patient being in the study might influence the physician-patient, nurse-patient, and ancillary personnel–patient social interactions. Moreover, we thought the behavior of all persons in the interactional network of the hospital and the family might be affected by the study. To control for the possible contaminating factor of selection for study, we divided the study group into two categories: full study and partial study. (See pages 23–24 for a more detailed explanation.) The partial-study families were divided, in turn, into two categories: partial-study I's and partial-study II's. Full-study families (161) were interviewed and observed intensively from the beginning of their hospitalization until after their discharge. Partial-study I's (thirty-two patients and families) were examined in the hospital but less intensively than the full-study group. The partial-study II's (thirty-two patients and families) were observed informally, but no systematic data were collected from them until after their discharge from the hospital. By limiting our interviews and observations on the partial-study I's and II's, we hoped to control the possible effects of inclusion in the full study. The general design and the number of patients (and families) in each category are as follows:

Interview and Observation Procedures in Data Collection	Study Group		
	Full-Study	Partial-Study I	Partial-Study II
Number of families	161	32	32
Patient and family in hospital	x		
Focused observations in hospital	x		
Staff interviews	x	x	
General observations in hospital	x	x	x
Visits in home	x	x	x
Medical records	x	x	x
Accounting records	x	x	x

From data gathered by the admissions officer, each patient was selected at random within the specified limits of age, sex, race, marital status, residence, illness status, time of admission, accommodation, and estimated minimum length of stay. The number of patients selected on any given date was determined by our needs at that particular time. This stemmed from the fact that we balanced by service and accommodation the number of families being studied at one time. By systematically gathering data in several different sections of the hospital simultaneously, we avoided becoming too conspicuous in any one area. Determination of which person became a full-study or a partial-study patient was a matter of chance.

Immediately after a family had been selected for study, Duff contacted the physician who had sponsored the admission to the hospital. The physician was told that this patient had been drawn in our sample, and permission to include him in our study was requested. If the physician's permission was granted Duff then visited the patient, explained the purpose of the study briefly, and asked for the patient's permission to include him in the research. Data were collected only with the knowledge and consent of the physician, the patient, and the spouse. The explanation of the project to persons of different interests, education, and motivation eventuated in a high level of sophistication on the part of our staff as to its presentation, particularly to individuals under the stress of illness and hospitalization. Acceptance of the study was usually granted in the first three to four hours of hospitalization. After the physician and patient had agreed to participate in the study we lost no families—that is we did not have to terminate data collection because a spouse or other family member refused to accept the project after a patient had accepted it. This is not to say that we did not have a certain amount of tension during the data collection; this point will be discussed in the presentation of data in later chapters.

The patient and the spouse, or other family members, were told they would be asked questions and observed, especially early in the hospital stay. They were told we planned to visit the home after the patient had been released from the hospital. They were assured that the project staff would not have a service role in the patient's care. After explaining the project's purpose to the patient and usually also to the spouse, Duff then explained that the actual questioning and visits to the patient's bed and later to his home would be carried out by a member of our staff.

The data for each patient and family were gathered by a minimum of three different members of the research staff: the senior physician, Duff, the primary data collector, and an evening observer. Duff was general supervisor of the day-to-day operation of the staff; he was the contact between physicians, patients, family members, and the hospital. The primary data collector was responsible for assembling most of the interview and observation data from the patient and his family during the hospitalization, and she was expected to make the home visits to the families assigned to her. The responsibility of the observer was to make the evening observations in the patients' rooms. In a free in their communications with us. We gave consistent supervision to each data collector and to all of them collectively. We were available at all times to help a member of the staff if any difficulty arose. For help on problems that they did not consider significant enough to raise with the physician or the sociologist, the primary data collectors turned to one another.

The illness condition of the patient, as judged by the patient himself or sometimes by his physician, a nurse, or the spouse, was of primary importance, and the collection of data had to be subordinated to it. Although this principle was requisite to the patient's well-being and to the success of the project, it placed a heavy burden on our staff who had to pace their work to our understanding of and respect for the stressful situations faced by patients, their families, and hospital staff. Beyond these general points, most of the approaches to the interviews and observations had to be developed *ad hoc* around the special situation of each respondent, whether a patient, a family member, or a staff person in the hospital.

We attempted to create a staff which would work toward commonly recognized goals. Staff meetings were held weekly to discuss any questions that arose. The meetings were valuable in bringing into the open questions that appeared to be bothering a given individual. The different members of the staff talked freely of their difficulties and successes of the week; often sharp disagreements occurred between discussants. Since the project required the continued participation of physicians, patients and their families, hospital staff, and the Advisory Committee, we were faced continuously with delicate questions involving humans under stress in crisis situations. Under these conditions the staff meetings became an effective form of group therapy. They were also a seminar in which we learned from one another.

The collection of data from patients, their spouses and other family members, physicians, nurses, and ancillary staff was a time-consuming enterprise. We spent, on the average, 125 hours on each full-study patient and his family; the mean number of hours consumed on the partial-study I families was 90, and on the partial-study II families some 30 hours. The primary data collectors were in direct face-to-face contact with the patient, the spouse, and the family some 35 to 40 hours out of the total devoted to a family. These direct-contact hours were spent in conversation, observation, and interviews. The remaining time spent on a family was given over to abstracting records; planning home visits; recording interviews, observational data, and conversations; and planning the next steps in the study's relations with the family and the hospital staff. Some five to six hours were given over to interviews with physicians, nurses, and hospital staff who were caring for the patient. A considerable proportion of this time was consumed in arranging interviews with doctors and nurses. We used from four to twelve hours on each of the inter-

sense each of these researchers was a data collector but, for conve
designating role responsibilities, we differentiated between the gene
of the primary data collectors and the physician, and the specialized
of the evening observer.

Once a patient was assigned to a particular data collector, Duff accor
her to the patient's bed and introduced the patient to her. Duff also
each patient from time to time as if on rounds. He made notes on ea
and this information became a part of the data on each family. Near tl
clusion of the work on each family Duff met with the primary data col
reviewed the data, and drew up a concluding statement about the pa
illness, hospitalization, and family situation.

Each primary data collector and evening observer was trained in our
before she was allowed to visit the patients and their families. Special emp
was given to the history of the project and our efforts to operationalize
study of patients and families so that all members of the research staff w
be familiar with our interests. Each primary data collector worked through
schedule, question by question, with the authors and then with another prim
data collector. Each one was encouraged to ask questions and to discuss w
us anything she did not understand thoroughly. We felt that an awareness
the aim of each question was necessary before the data collector worked with
family because we wanted uniform interpretation from one data collector
another, from patient to patient, and from spouse to spouse. Primary dat
collectors were taught how to approach physicians, nurses, hospital staff, pa
tients, spouses of patients, and other family members. We were interested ir
seeing that each primary data collector and evening observer had a professional
orientation, technical competence, and thorough understanding of the project
in order to convey empathy in their contacts with respondents, whether patients,
other family members, or hospital personnel. To avoid confusion in identity,
on the one hand, and to facilitate data collection, on the other, our staff members were taught to present themselves to persons in charge of an area in the
hospital before they began to see patients. The persons in training were taken
on tours of the hospital. We stressed the necessity of avoiding talk about their
work in elevators, at lunch, at social gatherings, and so forth. This was
essential because of the confidentiality of the data and to ensure that major
embarrassments would not occur.

Another problem we discussed on numerous occasions with the primary data
collectors was the importance of giving the respondents a chance to ask questions about the project. We stressed the necessity of the data collector's
establishing rapport and clarifying the purpose of the interview before going
ahead with any schedule. We wanted each respondent to feel comfortable with
our primary data collectors. We needed also to have the data collectors feel

views with physicians, nurses, and hospital administrators regarding their views on the care of patients in the hospital. This time was given over to arranging the interview, actually conducting and recording it, and the preparation of a summary of the discussion.

The many kinds of data collected from the patients, spouses and other family members, physicians, nurses, ancillary staff, and the hospital records were prepared for analysis by two different procedures. Specific items of information, such as age, the amount charged for board and room in the hospital, or the accommodation in which the patient was housed, were coded for punching on data-processing machines. The individual items constitute valuable facts of the research data, but they are inadequate for the comprehension of many facets of behavior.

Grasping the meaning of often isolated, casual, and sometimes indirect remarks to an understanding of a person and a family is more difficult than coding individual items, but it is often far more rewarding. To take advantage of the vast quantity of vivid experiences related to us by respondents and revealed by behavior we had observed and by tales of family activities, we decided on an *assessment schedule*, rather than responses to our direct questions to a respondent, designed to provide answers we asked of our data; this was essential to the utilization of the masses of insightful information we had gathered. The assessment schedule was developed by the authors and tested on the information we had accumulated during the pilot study.

We spent some three to four months reading and rereading all the information we had gathered on the families in the pilot study, asking ourselves questions, then seeing if we could find answers in the family and patient records. Eventually we developed a forty-eight-question schedule. Each question on this schedule is designed to give us an answer derived from a synthesis of all the data we had accumulated on the patient, the spouse, and the family. The data to answer each question were derived from the two authors' independent readings of the entire record. When we had completed the study of a family, we directed our attention to dictating our answers to each of the forty-eight questions. In this process we often read and reread the record again, discussed specific points, and, where we disagreed, re-examined the record. Thus, the answers reflect consensus. We followed the policy of summarizing the answers to a particular question into a category that could be coded for the data-processing machines. For instance, we asked this question: *What is the degree of urgency for hospital admission?* We summarized the answers as follows: (1) very urgent; (2) some delay tolerable—up to two days; (3) admission optional by time, but necessary; (4) admission optional. When we had decided on the appropriate answer the category to be punched was circled. Then a brief statement was dictated detailing the need for and the circumstances of admission. When the assessment schedule was completed on each of the patients and their families, we punched the specific, summarized, categorical answers on Hollerith cards for analysis by statistical procedures.

We selected the 5 per cent level of confidence as the criterion of significance, that is the probability is less than five chances in one hundred that the distribution of the figures in a table can be attributable to chance. Two types of statistical procedures are used to determine significance: We use the *t-test* when the data are in variable form, such as the age of the patient or the dollar cost of the hospitalization. We use *chi-square* to measure the significance of a distribution when the data are expressed in the form of attributes—for example, no change, improved, worse, much worse. We do not differentiate between the use of the *t-test* or *chi-square* in the presentation of data in a particular table. We simply signify when the distribution is or is not significant by the symbols $p < .05$ (significantly different) and $p > .05$ (not significantly different). The coefficient of contingency is used in appropriate tables to measure association between two sets of interrelated attributes. Where it is used, the measure of association is derived from chi-square and corrected for the broad grouping of the categories. The nearer the corrected coefficient of contingency approaches 1, the stronger the association.

We analyze the data in terms of three structural dimensions that are built into the organization of the hospital: accommodation, service, and sex. Each patient is housed in a bed located in one of the three accommodations provided by the hospital for its clientele. The accommodations—private, semiprivate, and ward—are subdivided, in turn, into specialized treatment services, in the instance of this research the medical and surgical services. Within the structure of accommodation and service, each patient, if not alone in a private room, is placed in a room occupied by others of the same sex.

Since we did not ask a patient to enter the study until his physician had given us his permission to do so, the physician was able to screen patients who might be in the study. Eleven physicians denied us permission to study a total of sixteen patients; however, each physician who asked us not to study a particular patient gave us permission on a different occasion to approach another of his patients who was selected for study. The sixteen persons we were not given permission to include in the study had four things in common: (1) they were all of relatively high socioeconomic status; (2) they were private patients —twelve on the medical service and four on the surgical service; (3) they were all seriously ill—two were involved in terminal illnesses; and (4) their physician-sponsors protected them from our questions and observations. They were equally divided between males and females.

Five additional patients refused to participate in the study after their physician-sponsors had given us permission to approach them. All were private patients; four were women, one a man; three were on the surgical service. These persons faced major personal or social problems, and four out of the five were afflicted with serious diseases—one who had advanced heart disease and a diseased gall bladder later died in the hospital; one had psoriasis and advanced arthritis; two were suffering from cancer, frightened, confused, and in pain. Four gave us hope for a day or two that they would cooperate, but as the enormity of their problems engulfed them they felt they could not tolerate our work. We believe they rejected us because they were so burdened with anxiety and exhausted from illness they felt further intrusions would be intolerable. One rejected us out of hand. He was a downwardly mobile, severely deteriorated alcoholic with advanced cirrhosis of the liver. To be hospitalized was an insult to his dignity; to have us invade his "privacy" was beyond his endurance.

The 21 patients we were not permitted to study represent 8.5 per cent of 246 persons selected for possible study; 6.5 per cent were physician rejections and 2 per cent were patient rejections. Stated otherwise, 76 per cent of the rejections were by physicians in behalf of their patients and 24 per cent were patient rejections after the physician had given his consent for us to study them. It is significant that all of the rejections were among the private patients. Moreover, even within the private accommodation category they were in the higher socioeconomic groups.

We were able to make comparisons between the study group and all hospital patients admitted during the twenty-four months we were selecting the sample because the hospital records information on punched cards about admission, treatment, discharge, and payment of bills. The data summarized in Table 1 demonstrate that the 225 patients in the study did not differ significantly by age, sex, hospital service, or residence from the larger universe of patients admitted to the hospital during the months we were choosing the sample. Other comparisons reveal no significant differences between the patients in the study group and the remaining patients on any attribute or variable we utilized as a selection criterion. We conclude that our sample is representative of all patients who might have been included in the study. Therefore, one may generalize from the sample to the larger population of patients who were treated in the hospital during the two years of patient intake into the study.

By gathering data with three different levels of intensity we were in a position to determine if the quality of the data is influenced by participation in the study. To test for the interference effects of our research on the normal processes of care of patients, we compared the attributes of full-study patients with the same attributes in the partial-study I and partial-study II groups. (See page 17). The analytical procedures in this phase of the study were

TABLE 1. DISTRIBUTION OF PATIENTS BY SERVICE, SEX, AGE, AND
PLACE OF RESIDENCE

| | Patients | |
Distribution Factor	In Study	In Hospital
A. Hospital Serivce		
Medicine	46%	47%
Surgery	54	53
B. Sex		
Male	50	51
Female	50	49
C. Age		
40–49 years	40	40
50–59 years	42	41
60–64 years	18	18
D. Place of Residence		
The city	39	36
The city's suburbs	37	40
Southern part of the state	17	18
Other parts of the state	7	5
For all sections, N =	(225)	(3,912)
p > .05		

divided into two steps. First, the full-study patients were compared with the partial-study I patients to see if there were any significant differences. This step was taken because these patients and families knew they were in the study while they were in the hospital, as did their physicians, their nurses, and other hospital personnel. However, no one except the researchers was told there was any difference in the intensity with which we were gathering data on these patients. In our comparisons of full-study patients with partial-study I patients, we are attempting to assess the effects of intensive study of human relations in the care of patients versus limited contacts by the researchers. If differences significant in extent appear between the full-study and the partial-study I patients, then we may infer that our detailed study of the full-study group did influence the activities of the patients, spouses, physicians, nurses, and so on. However, if no meaningful differences appear we may conclude that the intensive study of patients did not interfere with the normal processes of patient care.

In the second step we tested the possibility of interference with the patient-care process in both the full-study and the partial-study I groups by comparing the full-study group with the partial-study II group. The partial-study II patients were not interviewed or observed systematically until after they left the hospital. Moreover, the nurses who cared for them and others relevant in the patient-care process were unaware of the inclusion of these patients in our project until after their discharge from the hospital. This precaution was taken to reduce the possibility that knowledge of a given person's inclusion in the study might influence his care and attitudes toward his illness experience, the hospital, physicians, nurses, and so on. If this was occurring, the answers we received would compromise the meaning of our findings for the study as a whole. In sum, the two categories of partial-study patients were established to give us information on the possible effects that being a study patient might have had on the human group revolving around the patient during the hospitalization period.

After all data were collected on the 225 patients and families, we made a series of comparisons between the full-study, partial-study I, and partial-study II patients to determine if our study did, in fact, have discernible influences on human relations while the patient was in the hospital. The items selected for detailed examination in these comparisons are of two kinds: those that are objective and external to the patient and those in which participation in the project may have influenced patient-care processes. The first group includes: (1) method of referral to the hospital; (2) hour of admission; (3) residence of the patient; (4) socioeconomic status of the family; (5) payment of hospital bill; (6) total dollar cost of the hospitalization; and (7) length of hospital stay. Detailed comparisons on each of these items between the full-study patients and the partial-study I patients, on the one hand, and the full-study patients and the partial-study II patients, on the other hand, reveal *no significant difference* on any item.

Fifteen items, which might possibly have been influenced by full participation in the project in comparison with partial participation, were compared one with another. They are as follows: (1) patient's comprehension of actions by physicians; (2) patient's comprehension of actions by nurses; (3) patient's comprehension of communications between himself and doctors; (4) patient's comprehension of communications between himself and nurses; (5) patient's level of satisfaction with the nursing care he received in the hospital; (6) patient's reported level of satisfaction with care he received from physicians while he was in the hospital; (7) registered nurse's level of understanding of the nature of the patient's illness; (8) registered nurse's rating of the cooperativeness of a patient with her efforts to care for him; (9) nurse's report of the patient's tendency to complain; (10) nurse's report of the patient's ability to express his needs; (11) registered nurse's satisfaction in caring for the patient; (12) cooperativeness of the patient as reported by the physician; (13) patient's tendency to complain as reported by the physician; (14) patient's ability to express his needs as seen by the physician; and (15) physician's satisfaction in caring for the patient.

No significant differences are found between the full-study and the partial-study I patients or between the full-study and the partial-study II patients on any of the fifteen human relations items as reported by the patient, the nurse, or the physician. In addition, we find no significant differences when we compare the attitudes of the patients toward their hospitalization in the three segments of the study group, that is the full-study, the partial-study I, and the partial-study II patients. All patients, whether they were studied in the hospital or after their discharge, had similar attitudes toward the hospital, nurses, and physicians.

We were able to compare the opinions of the physicians and the registered nurses toward only the full-study and the partial-study I patients because there were no physician or registered nurse interviews on the partial-study II patients. We found no significant differences between the attitudes of either the physicians or the registered nurses toward the full-study and partial-study I patients. The comparisons we made between the answers full-study and partial-study I patients as well as the full-study and partial-study II patients made to our questions led us to conclude that *being in the study did not discernibly affect the patient-care process within the hospital.* When we had satisfied ourselves on this point we decided to proceed with the analysis of the data on the full-study patients and drop further analysis of the partial-study patients. Hereinafter, we concern ourselves only with the 161 full-study patients and their families.

To facilitate the presentation of data, fictitious names are given to families. To protect further the privacy of the families studied, critical identifying characteristics have been altered. We use family data to illustrate the processes and problems associated with illness and how these, in turn, are linked to more general social processes operative in our society.

Summary

In this chapter we have outlined the way this study developed from its initial stages through the analysis of the data. Some seven years were given to the research from its beginning until the manuscript was drafted. We devoted 18 months to the planning phases of preliminary observations and the pilot study, schedule drafting, and testing. Three years were focused on the collection of data in the hospital and from the families. Two years were spent on the analysis of the materials we had assembled. Our analysis demonstrates that we have a representative sample of patients. Moreover, the full-study patients show no significant effects of selection for the study in comparisons with either the partial-study I or the partial-study II patients.

In brief, the methodological procedures we developed and followed are discussed to help the reader evaluate the answers we assembled from the data to permit us to answer the five basic questions around which this research is built.

PART II THE SOCIAL SETTING

T<small>HE</small> <small>HOSPITAL WHERE WE CENTERED THIS RESEARCH IS A</small> constituent unit in a modern medical center. The Medical Center contains within it three organizations that have functioned as health resources for the people of the community for more than a century: a hospital, a school of medicine, and practitioners of medicine. Medical practitioners were the creators of the School of Medicine and of the hospital. The hospital has been associated with the Eastern University School of Medicine since its founding and, in turn, these institutions have been interlinked with organized medical practitioners in the area.

The School of Medicine traces its founding to the passage of an act by the General Assembly of the state which granted a charter to the Medical Institution of Eastern College. Thus authorized, "the Medical Institution" was established under the joint supervision of the college and the State Medical Society, and the first degrees were conferred in 1814. Twelve years later leaders in the State Medical Society convinced the State Legislature of the need for a hospital in which men could be taught the science and art of medicine. Four physicians pledged $100 a year for five years to the state-chartered General Hospital Society to purchase land and start planning a hospital building. This pledged sum of $2,000 was supplemented through additional private gifts and appropriations from the State Legislature. In a few years enough money was raised to purchase land and to construct a building with beds and other facilities adequate for inpatient care. From the opening of the building in 1833 to the present, the hospital has performed the dual functions of caring for the sick and training physicians.

A revision of the original charter in 1844 by the State Legislature, with the approval of the State Medical Society, changed the name of the Medical Institution to the Medical School of Eastern College and placed it under the control of the college. Three years later, Eastern College became Eastern University, and the Medical School became a constituent unit in the university. Fifty years ago the Medical School became the School of Medicine, Eastern University. It has retained this title to the present.

The Medical Institution and the hospital began as separate corporate bodies, and they have remained legally independent of each other. This point needs to be remembered as some problems of both the hospital and the School of Medicine are related to it.

The hospital continued as a teaching center and a facility for the care of inpatients until well after the Civil War. An act of the State Legislature in 1872 provided for the care of outpatients by the establishment of a dispensary for "the purpose of supplying medicines and medical advice and assistance to such as may be sick and needy in the city and vicinity." This legislative act provided that "free access to any dispensary that may be opened by said corporation shall be afforded at reasonable hours and under proper regulations to such students in the Medical Institution of [Eastern] College as may be designated by the faculty." The Dispensary which was located adjacent to the Medical Institution and the hospital was viewed as closely associated with the Medical Institution, but its association with the hospital was not specified. Through agreements with the governing boards of the Medical Institution and the hospital, clinical instruction for medical students and ambulatory service to patients in the Dispensary were made possible. Cooperation between the School of Medicine and the hospital in the functioning of the Dispensary continued without interruption until 1952 when the Dispensary became an integral part of the hospital.

Four years after the founding of the Dispensary the State Legislature chartered the State Training School for Nurses as a diploma school for the basic training of professional nurses. It was affiliated with the hospital. The State Training School for Nurses was closed in the middle 1920's because Eastern University established a program in basic nursing.

In the early 1890's community leaders reached the conclusion that a second hospital, independent of the School of Medicine and Eastern University, was necessary to meet the needs of the rapidly growing community. A charter was obtained from the State Legislature to establish a new hospital and a school of nursing. This hospital, with a constituent training program for nurses, was opened in 1897. Located approximately one half-mile from the old hospital and the School of Medicine, it was an independent, nonprofit, general hospital, essentially under the control of private practitioners of medicine. This hospital and its school of nursing grew and prospered until the prolonged economic depression of the 1930's. During World War II community leaders decided on the consolidation of the hospital facilities; thus, in 1945, the two hospitals were incorporated as a single community hospital.

Plans were developed by the leaders of the newly created community hospital to abandon the buildings put up in the 1890's and to construct a building adjacent to the hospital and School of Medicine. To actuate the plans and administer the proposed hospital complex, a full-time hospital administrator was appointed to the position of Director of the combined hospitals. The plans for a new building to replace the hospital structure a half-mile away became an actuality in 1953 when an eight-story X-shaped building was opened. This new building, across the street from the buildings of the School of Medicine, is connected to the older complex by underground tunnels and electrical, plumbing, and communication lines. Adjacent to this building and on the same block of land the hospital then constructed a dormitory and educational building for the School of Nursing it had taken over when the two hospitals merged. When the new building was in full operation the more distant hospital building was closed and the University-Community Hospital, as projected in 1945, was a reality.

The next step in the development of the hospital complex was taken in 1958 when the School of Medicine and the School of Nursing, Eastern University, joined with the hospital to form the Eastern University–Community Hospital Medical Center. However, the hospital remained a separate legal corporation with its own board of directors and responsible for its own financing. Currently, the Medical Center is composed of a general hospital with its Community Division and University Division, two psychiatric hospitals, a school of medicine, and a series of health-related educational programs. Also located in the Medical Center complex are departments of Eastern University whose subject matter is related closely to medical science.

The Medical Center has three manifest goals: education, research, and the diagnosis and treatment of the illnesses of people who seek help. Viewed historically, the Medical Center has evolved around the central function of training medical students to become physicians. The hospital was founded primarily by physicians, who taught in the Medical Institution, so their students would have a place in which to learn the art of medicine on "clinical material," that is on sick members of society. The training of physicians continues to be the fulcrum about which the program of education for health care turns. However, there are twelve additional educational programs maintained in the Medical Center. Professional groups rely upon the graduates of these thirteen programs to help fill the constantly increasing need for trained personnel in the many specialized areas of health care. The hospital and the School of Medicine work together in the operation of these programs.

The School of Medicine has from 315 to 320 students enrolled in the undergraduate years. One half of these students are involved in the academic work of the preclinical years while the other half, in the clinical years of their training, work with patients who are undergoing treatment in the hospital. Postgraduate medical education is an important part of the program of the School of Medicine; interns, residents, and clinical fellows outnumber the undergraduate medical student group, but the postgraduate physicians, some 400, are appointees of the hospital.

Eleven nonphysician-training programs are carried on in the Medical Center. The School of Medicine supports a two-year program leading to a master's degree for the training of hospital administrators. The School of Medicine also has a series of programs at the master's or doctoral levels for nonclinicians who expect to become specialists in some area of public health.

The hospital carries in conjunction with the State University a joint program for the training of physical therapists; this is a one-year training experience for students who are working toward a baccalaureate degree. The hospital carries also a postbaccalaureate one-year internship that trains persons as dietitians, a one-year program for inhalation therapists, a two-year program for X-ray technicians, and a one-year baccalaureate program for medical technologists.

The student nurse programs are an important part of the training function of the Medical Center. The School of Nursing, Eastern University, is a graduate program; its students have completed the baccalaureate degree and the basic training required of registered nurses before matriculation. This is a small program, oriented toward research in nursing. Nursing students of the State University, during their junior and senior years of college, train in the hospital. The nursing students in this program receive clinical experience in the basic professional course which prepares them for the baccalaureate degree and for registration as a nurse. Approximately 150 young women received part or all of their clinical experience in the hospital during the two years we were gathering data on patients.

An undergraduate school of nursing is organized under the Board of Directors of the hospital. Upon completion of the curriculum the students are awarded diplomas and are then eligible to apply to the State Board of Examiners for Nursing for licensure as registered nurses. During the course of a single year about 200 young women are involved in some phase of their three years of training. A licensed practical nurse course is conducted by the State Department of Education as a part of its statewide vocational program. The first three months of the one-year course are spent in a regional vocational technical school located in the community; the next nine months are given over to clinical nursing experience in the hospital. The licensed practical nurse trainees work forty hours a week during the months they are gaining experience in the hospital. After a year of training the student is eligible to take the examination leading to certification. Approximately forty-five persons completed this training program each year we were collecting data. A very high proportion of the trainees in this program are residents of the community. Moreover, from 85 to 90 per cent of those who successfully complete the course and become licensed find employment in this hospital.

In addition to the formal courses of instruction the School of Medicine, the University School of Nursing, and the hospital sponsor seminars, symposia, and short courses for physicians, nurses, and other specialists in the health field. No figures are available to enable us to estimate how many of these less formal experiences contribute to the realization of the educational goals of the constituent units that compose the Medical Center, but during the course of a year approximately 1,000 students in the various programs receive technical or professional training.

The discovery of new knowledge through basic research is identified with the School of Medicine. On the whole, employees of the hospital are too busy with their day-to-day tasks to have time or energy to plan and execute research programs. Research to them is often an unwelcome imposition by the School of Medicine. The research goal is associated almost exclusively with the full-time faculty of the School of Medicine and most recently with the University School of Nursing.

The divergent interests of persons affiliated with the Medical Center give rise to difficulties when unresolved issues interfere with the conduct of care of patients. Although physicians are concerned about this divergence of interests and objectives, the administrators and heads of departments in the hospital, such as admitting, nursing, social service, accounting, and medical records, are most aware of conflicts of interest between constituent units in the Medical Center. Turnover of personnel, characteristic of teaching hospitals, is a recurrent source of friction, since patients do not come and go on the same cycle as the students. From 150 to 160 medical students work in the clinical departments of the hospital during the school year. They rotate from service to service in accordance with a schedule established by the School of Medicine. As students, they come and go with the calendar of the University year. Each June some 75 young persons are graduated from the School of Medicine. Then too, from 175 to 200 young physicians leave the house staff; on July 1, or near this date, a new contingent of approximately the same size enters into house-staff status. Each September a new group of 75 to 80 students starts work on their clinical years. This same type of turnover of students is experienced by each of the educational programs in the Medical Center. Turnover of students from one year to the next and from program to program presents the hospital with severe staffing problems on the patient-care divisions. This creates problems in the care of patients.

Responsibility for medical staffing differs in different parts of the hospital.

The full-time faculty of the School of Medicine controls the University Division of the hospital. Most of the patients in this section of the hospital are sponsored by physicians who are either full-time faculty in the School of Medicine or residents, interns, or medical students under the direct authority of full-time faculty members. Community practitioners of medicine who are appointed to the hospital's medical staff are responsible for the care of patients they sponsor in the Community Division.

Representatives of the hospital, the School of Medicine, and the private practice of medicine are joined in a single policy-making organization—the Medical Board. The board consists of sixteen members, each occupying a key position in the structure of the medical staff of the hospital. The School of Medicine is represented by the Dean, the chairmen of five clinical departments of the University Division (Medicine, Surgery, Pediatrics, Obstetrics and Gynecology, and Psychiatry), and the chiefs of Clinical Laboratories, Anesthesiology, Pathology, and Radiology. Each of these persons except the Dean has major hospital responsibilities and is at the same time a professor in the School of Medicine.

The private practice of medicine is represented by five specialists who are the chiefs in the Community Division: Surgery, Medicine, Pediatrics, Obstetrics and Gynecology, and Dentistry. Each is an attending physician in the hospital and a clinical professor in the School of Medicine.

The hospital's Executive Director represents the hospital even though he is a professor in the School of Medicine (Hospital Administration). We note that the School of Medicine has ten representatives on the Medical Board; medical practitioners in the community are represented by five physicians. The Executive Director of the hospital is identified primarily with the hospital rather than with the School of Medicine or with the organized practice of medicine in the community.

During the interval of planning and data collection for this study the Chief of Staff of the Medical Board was also the Chief of Surgery for the Community Division. Likewise, the Deputy Chief of Staff was simultaneously the Chief of Medicine on the University Division. The Chief of Staff was a surgeon in private practice in the community; the Deputy Chief of Staff was a professor and Chairman of the Department of Medicine in the School of Medicine.

Except for the Dean of the School of Medicine, each member of the Medical Board has at least two appointments: one to the medical staff of the hospital and one to the faculty of the School of Medicine. The professors in the School of Medicine are given a staff position in the hospital. Reciprocally, the private practitioners are given a courtesy title in the School of Medicine. This interdigitation of titles, functions, and institutional identifications creates overlapping loyalties and obligations between institutions and institutional goals that may, in fact, run counter to one another.

The Medical Board is composed entirely of physicians; it is the most influential body in the hospital in the area of patient care. It is the creation of the Board of Directors of the hospital, but members of the Medical Board do not sit on the Board of Directors of the hospital nor do the members of the Board of Directors sit on the Medical Board. The Medical Board meets monthly to discuss policy questions, make recommendations, and communicate these to the Board of Directors of the hospital, to the relevant departments in the School of Medicine, to the operating departments in the hospital, and to practitioners accredited to the hospital. Members of the hospital's administrative staff ordinarily sit as observers in the room while the Medical Board is in session. They may present matters to the Medical Board, argue their point, and discuss the issues, but they may not vote. The main liaison between the Medical Board and the Board of Directors of the hospital rests in the person of the Executive Director. There is, however, a monthly meeting of selected members of the Medical Board and the Board of Directors of the hospital. During these meetings actions of the Medical Board are discussed. Within the hospital, the policies voted by the Medical Board are carried out by one or more, possibly all, of the operating departments.

The major specialties of Medicine, Surgery, Pediatrics, Obstetrics and Gynecology, Radiology, and Psychiatry are represented on the patient-care divisions of the hospital's constituent units. Its physical facilities include a special infant-care unit, two clinical research centers, a 6-million-electron-volt linear accelerator, and a van de Graff generator for X-ray therapy, highly sophisticated attached apparatus in the clinical laboratory, equipment for cardiovascular radiography, and so on. The specialized knowledge and skills of the full-time faculty in the Eastern University School of Medicine are a resource limited to a leading university teaching hospital. Physicians have these specialists available for consultation. The hospital owns and occupies 750,000 square feet of building space and in 1962 it contained 840 beds. In size and bed capacity it is larger than 98 per cent of the general hospitals in the United States.

The School of Medicine and the hospital have struggled for generations with the issue of who should or should not be paid a fee for the service of caring for a hospitalized patient. From the founding of the hospital until about 1920, professors in the School of Medicine were both faculty and private practitioners. Since 1920 the dominant faculty of the School of Medicine has been full-time with few exceptions. The full-time faculty are on the medical staff of the hospital but their salaries are paid by the University. Their center of interest is the training of medical students and the house staff;

research is also an essential activity. For professors it may be said that the practice of medicine or surgery is ancillary to education and research. However, in order to train students and do research, clinical material is indispensable. Private practitioners, on the other hand, earn their livelihoods by caring for patients. Their economic connection with their patients is embodied into the *mos* of the private practitioner—a fee for a service. The practice of medicine in the community has been left to the specialists and generalists who maintain private offices.

Three types of accommodations are provided for inpatients: ward or service, semiprivate, and private. The private and semiprivate accommodations are concentrated largely in the Community Division, while most of the ward accommodations are located in the University Division.

Remarkable differences exist among the three types of accommodations. The private accommodations in the Community Division are centered on the west side of the new building away from the noise and clutter of the downtown area. Most windows provide a view of residential sections of the city, the distant hills, or the sea. The rooms contain a built-in clothes closet, private toilet, washbasin, and in some rooms a bath. The room is bright and tastefully decorated; it is furnished with a single bed, a lounge chair, and a reading table; there are outlets for lamps, radios, television, and telephone. The general impression is one of light, airiness, and quiet.

A special unit of private accommodations is provided in the University Division. It is located in what used to be the private pavilion of the hospital before the Community Division was built. The unit has been reconstructed recently. The new rooms are as large as those in the private sector of the Community Division. They are as tastefully decorated and as lavishly furnished. The corridors are lushly carpeted from wall to wall, and attractive oil paintings adorn the walls. The patients housed here are almost exclusively under the care of faculty members of the School of Medicine. This unit is referred to informally as a "plush setup."

Accommodations strictly limited to semiprivate patients are centered in the Community Division. They are on the east side of the building, facing the downtown area, the industrial districts, and a superhighway. The rooms are equipped with two, three, or four beds. The semiprivate accommodations have 60 per cent more beds in the same floor space than the private accommodations. This results in more crowding in the rooms, sharing of facilities by the patients, and the need for interpersonal adjustments over the use of such items as the bathroom and radios.

Semiprivate accommodations in the University Division are determined, in part, by the interests of the faculty and, in part, by what is available at a particular time. A bed occupied one day by a ward patient may be assigned to a semiprivate patient, or rarely to a private patient, the next day. These floors are referred to as *mixed*.

Strictly ward accommodations for medical patients are in a building that has been characterized by the hospital authorities as obsolete. The halls are narrow and the rooms are dark. There are no private toilets or bathrooms and no clothes closets. The floors are worn in uneven ripples by the many feet that have traversed them over the years. The halls are cluttered with trolleys of equipment, baskets of dirty linen, boxes of supplies, and well-worn stretchers on trucks. The rooms are filled with beds which show the years of hard usage they have received. Noises and smells of the sick room and the human animal in distress pervade the atmosphere. The two exclusively ward units on which surgical patients are housed are little different from the two given over to medical patients. They are simply in another old building. In both areas of service, the ward accommodations are crowded with equipment and people, sick and well.

The question of the admission of patients to accommodations is related to several factors: availability of beds, the disease of the patient, the urgency for admission, the organization of medicine in the community and in the hospital, and the socioeconomic status of the patient. To repeat a point we raised in Chapter 1, before a patient is admitted to the hospital he has to be certified by two institutional gatekeepers: a physician and an admissions officer. The physician who certifies the medical need for admission must be a member of the medical staff of the hospital. If he is not so affiliated but is a licensed physician in this state or some other state, he may make a referral of the patient to a physician who is a member of the hospital's staff, or he may refer the patient to the emergency service. The principal concern of the physician is with the patient's medical condition. The primary objectives of the admissions officer who is an employee of the hospital are the coordination of bed assignments and the planning of financial arrangements with patients. (The hospital is interested in keeping its beds in use, but it is a rare day, indeed, when a bed cannot be found for an emergency admission.) The admissions officer is faced with the task of evaluating the competence of the proposed patient to pay the bills that will be engendered by his entrance into the hospital. In brief, before an admission is made to the hospital the certifying officers have to be satisfied with the patient's medical need and his financial responsibility.

If the prospective patient has a private physician who is a member of the hospital's staff, the physician either telephones the hospital and directs the admissions officer to admit the patient or, in the case of an emergency, arranges to meet the patient at the hospital. In case of an accident with the patient coming directly to the Emergency Room for help, the emergency service then calls the patient's physician.

The patients of private physicians are admitted to the Community Division unless there is a special reason for them to be sent to the University Division. The type of accommodations utilized by the patient may be controlled by what is available. However, if a patient and his physician request a private room, one can usually be found. If one is not available at the time, the patient may be placed temporarily in a semiprivate room in the Community Division, then transferred when a private room is available. The opposite procedure could occur but seldom does, as very few patients go into private rooms to await transfer to semiprivate rooms; ordinarily such patients are able and willing to wait for a semiprivate accommodation.

Admission to the ward accommodations is confined largely to persons who do not have a private physician and cannot afford to pay for one. Ward patients are certified by an assistant resident or resident who is assigned the responsibility of assessing the urgency for hospitalization. Ward patients enter the hospital largely from the ambulatory clinics or through the emergency service. A particular ward patient may be referred to the clinics or the emergency service by a private physician who, for one reason or another, does not chose to treat him. A patient, so referred, may be admitted to the hospital as an inpatient if the examining physician judges his condition to be so serious as to need hospitalization. The admissions officer makes a very careful effort to determine the prospective patient's financial ability to pay for the recommended hospitalization. She asks: Is the patient a welfare case? Does the patient have a resource that can be utilized for his hospital expenses? Does the patient have some form of private insurance that will cover part or all of the costs of hospitalization? Can the patient's family be relied upon to pay the bill?

The hospital is responsible for the bills it accrues, and it, in turn, has to accept the onus for a patient who cannot or will not pay for the care he receives. Patients who are urgently in need of hospitalization are admitted even though no satisfactory answers can be found to the question of who is going to pay the hospital bill. The house officers and the admissions officers realize that they cannot allow a patient to die in the hall or on the street because of real indigence. The admissions officers, medical and administrative, are compelled by humanitarian values to admit a dead beat rather than have a dead body on the doorstep of the hospital.

While the hospital charges for its services to ward patients and makes every effort to collect for these services, the physicians who care for the ward patients are not allowed by the hospital's rules to charge for their services.[1]

Patients in semiprivate and private accommodations are charged by the hospital for the services performed by the hospital and, in addition, their physicians may, and almost all do, charge a fee for their services. This fee is charged privately by the physician and paid privately by the patient. The hospital transaction and the physician transaction are separate items. They are recognized as such by the patient, the physician, and the hospital. The ward patient does not have a personal physician; he is a service case. This fact is known by the patient, the physician, and the hospital personnel.

Patients who are recommended by clinic physicians for hospitalization on the ward service but whose time of admission is optional are required generally by the admissions officer to pay the estimated cost of their hospitalization in cash at the time they are admitted to the hospital. For example, a woman who is in need of surgery which requires hospitalization but which can be postponed elects to enter the hospital when a bed is available. She may be told by the admissions officer that the hospital bill will be about $100 in excess of insurance coverage and that to be admitted she must bring this sum in cash to the hospital with her.

Private patients are not screened with such care. Their physician-sponsors, in a sense, are surrogates for their credit. Admissions officers have a keen sense of social status and a practiced eye for the well-to-do and the provident. Semiprivate patients are screened financially less carefully than ward patients; the admissions officers are not likely to ask for cash in advance. However, the semiprivate patient may be embarrassed occasionally by an admissions officer who questions the patient and/or a spouse too closely in his efforts to decide if the patient is, in fact, a good risk or a member of that segment of the community who are referred to as the "good poor," those who are self-supporting but medically indigent.

Marked socioeconomic differences exist between the types of patients admitted to the accommodations offered by the hospital. Individuals who select private rooms are drawn largely from the upper third of the socioeconomic structure. Persons attracted to the semiprivate rooms are, in the main, from the blue-collar, manual-work occupational groups. Patients admitted to the ward accommodations primarily come from the poorest segments of the socioeconomic structure of the community. These gross differences are recognized by physicians, nurses, other hospital personnel, and the patients themselves. Early in the data-collection period, we saw a letter written by a physician to the hospital protesting the efforts of the administrators and a group of faculty in the School of Medicine to mitigate some of the differences between accommodations. The physician wrote bluntly: "There are three classes of patients who use the hospital—the unwashed, the washed, and the washed-and-perfumed."

Within the hospital the ward patients are often viewed as "the unwashed," and in many cases they are literally unwashed. Many patients found on the wards would like to be hospitalized in the Community Division in a semiprivate room but are not able to pay for it. They are unhappy with their ward accommodations. When adversity strikes the "good poor" they are forced to associate with and accept accommodations prepared for the "undeserving poor." Sometimes patients are "dumped" upon the ward service by practitioners in the community because they realize that the patient cannot afford either better accommodations or their fee. Sometimes physicians explain to the family and to the patient that in this way they will be spared additional medical expenses. The "good poor" are often dismayed by the fact that their loved ones have to be hospitalized on the wards. However, they have no resources with which to fight against this decision.

University-Community Hospital is a nondenominational, nonprofit, privately owned institution with little endowment. It has no direct affiliations with the local, state, or federal governments and is responsible for its own financing. The financing of the hospital has a long history, but for present purposes we confine our discussion of financial problems to the situation as it was when we started our study and during the months we collected data. By the late 1950's the annual deficit of the hospital had become a severe problem —over $400,000 for the care of indigent and medically indigent outpatients plus an additional loss of above $100,000 per year for inpatient care. Recurrent appeals to potential donors for private gifts were not closing the gap between expenditures and receipts.

A specially qualified committee of the Board of Directors of the hospital was appointed and directed to examine a number of questions pertinent to the financing of the hospital. This committee made a careful review of the economy and efficiency of the hospital's operation, the financial relationshps between the hospital and the School of Medicine, problems of third-party reimbursement, capital fund requirements, and the organization of the Board itself. The findings and recommendations of this group defined clearly the serious financial problems facing the hospital in its relationship with the local community and state governments. The committee found that the hospital was providing about 25 per cent of the hospitalization for all welfare patients in voluntary hospitals in the state and was receiving grossly inadequate reimbursement from welfare agencies for this service. Because this practice required use of the hospital's meager endowment income to subsidize the care of welfare agency clients and because the huge volume of such services regularly exhausted endowment income, the additional loss had to be balanced by increasing charges to private patients to a figure substantially in excess of the cost of services they received.

The report focused attention also on the problem of the medically indigent patient who, although able to pay part of the cost of his service, cannot pay full costs and under current welfare laws is ineligible for public assistance. The very substantial deficit caused by these patients had to be subsidized through another surcharge against the paying patient rather than through participation by the whole community.

The Board of Directors reached the conclusion that excessively high charges to private patients to offset losses incurred by indigent and medically indigent patients were no longer the solution to mounting deficits. In the spring of 1958 the Chairman of the Executive Committee of the Board of Directors wrote to the president of the Community Council asking for help to "explore means of attacking these problems on a community level."

Early in 1959 the Community Council appointed a committee on hospital care, with members chosen because of their familiarity with the issues and their ability to represent the broad public interest. After studying the extent of hospital service provided to the needy, how much it cost, and who was paying for it, the committee issued a report to the Board of Trustees of the hospital early in 1961 in the firm belief that its recommendations, if carefully studied and diligently applied, would lead to a solution to the problem. Failure to solve the issue of an increasing annual deficit, they claimed, would not only leave unsolved a serious community problem which involved hospital care of the needy, but because of its impact on the stability of the hospital it would also place in jeopardy hospital services to all citizens.

While these studies were being made, the hospital was in conflict with the city over the charges the hospital had made for welfare recipients cared for in the hospital. The city refused to pay for services to welfare patients cared for in the hospital's emergency and outpatient departments, disputing a charge of $5 a visit—a rate set by the Hospital Cost Commission and substantially below the cost to the hospital for providing the service. Adding an "Alice-in-Wonderland" perspective to this dispute was the fact that the city authorities refused to pay the hospital for drugs, X rays, or emergency service rendered to its own welfare patients over the same period of time even though the propriety of these charges was not in question and regular payments were made by the city for similar services rendered at a nearby Catholic hospital. The hospital finally resorted to court action for relief.

In 1961, the State Legislature revised the hospital reimbursement law to enable the city and town welfare departments to reimburse hospitals on a complete and current cost basis. As a result of this legislation the Hospital Cost Commission established rates of reimbursement for welfare patients in hospitals that reflected the actual current cost of care provided these patients. Along with the progress made with the State Legislature and the Hospital Cost Commission were equally significant developments in the resolution of the problems with the city. The suit against the city was negotiated on the basis of the city's acceptance of the Hospital Cost Commission rates for outpatients and the payment of all back bills.

The agreement of welfare agencies to pay complete and current costs for hospitalization was a major step forward, but a difficulty arose in the definition of patients falling within the category of welfare responsibility. If the definition of medical indigence was not developed realistically, the possibility existed that the welfare agency would pay complete and current costs for those patients for whom it assumed responsibility but it would assume responsibility for only a small proportion of those who could not pay. Two important facts about the hospital were incontrovertible: it had the highest charges to patients of any hospital in the state; it was providing free care to a large number of citizens and subsidizing this care partially through endowment funds, gifts, and grants, but substantially through the overcharging of private patients.

The financial problems of the hospital continued on into 1962. A report to the community was prepared but not published, partly because of the desire not to participate in a public battle if private understandings could be obtained. Late in 1963 the hospital's Board of Directors decided to make its dire financial distress known to the public. They released to the mayors and first selectmen of the cities and towns in the area, to the Community Council, and to the news media in the state the report on the problems of financing the hospital and medical care to the indigent and medically indigent. It was an able presentation of interrelations between the cost of medical care, indigence, and medical indigence among patients who came to the hospital. The release may have been read and heard about by persons who had not previously known of the deficits encountered by the hospital, but it did not stem the flow of debts. During the three fiscal years (1961, 1962, and 1963) that elapsed while we were collecting data, the hospital's deficits aggregated almost $2 million.

The inescapable fact is this—the hospital's primary source of support is the fee it charges to a patient for the services he receives from it. Not all patients are able to pay for the services the hospital is obliged to render; therefore, the hospital faces chronic, severe, financial crises.

Summary

The Medical Center combines the functions and activities of a community hospital, a university teaching hospital, a regional hospital, and a municipal hospital. It serves as a diagnostic, treatment, and referral center for physicians and hospitals throughout a large area of the state. Insofar as patient care is concerned, the physician is responsible for making decisions regarding the patient's illness and treatment and the hospital assumes the obligation of carrying out the physician's orders. The hospital is responsible for housing and all related services for patients as well as for general staff nursing and the provision of technical services directly associated with the medical treatment of patients—operating rooms, anesthesia, laboratories, X ray, instruments, and medicines prescribed by the patient's physician. In sum, although the physician determines what is to be done for the patient medically or surgically, the hospital is the place in which the care of the patient is carried out.

There are times when the educational goals of the multiple programs carried on in the Medical Center conflict with the patient-care goals of the hospital. The cleavage between the twin goals of education and research and that of the care of sick patients will be discussed further in the next chapter.

NOTE

1. Article IV, section 8 of the Medical Staff By-Laws, entitled "Care of Ward Patients," stated: "Only members of the active staff, the clinical assistant staff, the house staff, and clinical fellows shall care for ward patients in the hospital, and no physician shall charge or accept a professional fee for such service." This rule applied during the years we were collecting data. However, while the data were being processed and the manuscript being drafted, Article IV, section 8 of the By-Laws became Article IV, section 1, entitled "Care of Service Patients," and reads as follows: "Only members of the active staff, the consulting staff, the house staff, and clinical fellows shall care for service patients in the hospital. Professional fees may be charged to such patients under policies and procedures approved by the Board of Directors." This change was made to facilitate recovery of medical fees from insured patients.

CHAPTER 4 PROFESSORS, ADMINISTRATORS,

AND PRACTITIONERS

THE DIVISION OF THE HOSPITAL INTO TWO PARTS, COMMU-
nity and university, gives rise to a troika-like association of professors, administrators, and practitioners. The hospital administrator may be viewed as the
center of this three-horse "team," flanked on the one side by the professor and
on the other by the private practitioner. The three are expected by the community to work together at the common task of caring for persons who seek
help through the physical, technical, and human resources of the hospital's
facilities. However, the diversity of their interests complicates the delivery of
medical service to sick persons. Although the administration of the hospital is
centralized in a single office, the two divisions of the hospital are housed, in
large part, in separate buildings and, what is equally important, are characterized by differing interests: The University Division focuses its attention primarily upon research and teaching; the Community Division provides private
practitioners with a suitable place to which they may send persons when they
judge it to be in the best interest of the patients' medical needs.

We present in the first part of this chapter a sketch of the University Division as it is seen by faculty in the School of Medicine, hospital administrators,
and student physicians (house staff and students in the School of Medicine).
The second part focuses upon the Community Division. Then, we present observations on the ways administrators and physicians cope with the dilemmas
they face as they pursue their diverse goals in a complex and often confusing
institution—the hospital.

The materials presented here are derived in large part from personal, tape-
recorded, face-to-face interviews with hospital administrators, the department
chairmen (chiefs of service) in Medicine and Surgery on the University and
Community Divisions, the senior residents in Surgery and Medicine, and a
random sample of physicians and house staff on the two divisions who cared
for either medical or surgical patients in the study.

The University Division

The chairman of a clinical department in the School of Medicine is designated in the hospital as the chief of a service: Medicine, Surgery, Psychiatry, Obstetrics and Gynecology, and Pediatrics. Thus, the chairman-chief plays two roles in the Medical Center. In the School of Medicine he is an administrator, academic politician, teacher, recruiter, researcher, fund raiser, consultant to governments and foundations, and a resource for private practitioners, prominent citizens, and faculty members who turn to him for help on special problems believed to be within his area of competence. Within the hospital, the chief of a service oversees the specialized service he represents (Medicine or Surgery insofar as this study is concerned). He is a member of the Medical Board and, as such, he helps set and execute hospital policy. He is the dominant authority in the selection of interns, residents, and fellows who work on his service. He supervises the house staff and the medical students on his service. In addition, he sees and cares for a limited number of private patients.

The chairman-chief's simultaneous incumbency of high office in both the School of Medicine and the hospital gives him great power in the Medical Center. His authority and responsibilities are so great that he is sometimes referred to as "an emperor." The interests of the department chairmen are identified with the primary concerns of Eastern University's faculty, namely adding to man's store of knowledge through research and the transmission of old and new knowledge to students. His reference group is composed of professors in this and other schools of medicine. A latent issue in the relations of the School of Medicine with the hospital is this: the central concerns of the School of Medicine and the hospital are diverse if not antithetical and the hospital has little interest in the objectives of the university. As a consequence, the department chairman–chief of service is caught between the avowed objective of the hospital to care for sick people and the fundamental objectives of the university to teach and do research. In the hospital the chief bears responsibility for the care of patients on his service. He is *not* rewarded professionally for providing a splendid service to the community's sick poor. In the university the chairman has primary responsibility for teaching medical students and carrying out research. He *is* rewarded in generous measure with salary, honor, power, and professional prestige for research and publications from his own laboratory or from the laboratories of the younger faculty members in his department.

Below the level of department chairman, faculty members focus their efforts on research and teaching, in this order. Their rewards come for their research achievements rather than for the excellent care they may provide for ward patients in the hospital. They personally take a minimal part in the care of patients, and they supervise it only to a limited extent. The supervision provided by them for individual patients is a by-product of their teaching of house officers and medical students. The chairman-chief looks to the house officers for the provision of patient care and a great deal of the teaching of medical students. The emphasis placed on academic medicine by the faculty is not unrelated tc the fact that the career objectives of a substantial percentage of medical students and house officers in the Medical Center are in academic medicine rather than in private practice. This means that they become divorced, for the most part, from the direct care of patients as they assume the roles of junior faculty members with interests in teaching and research, rather than in the practice of medicine in a community setting.

For the School of Medicine to realize its teaching and research objectives, it must have access to persons who seek the services of the hospital for the alleviation of their medical problems. For generations, the hospital has been the place in which indigent members of the community have sought relief from their afflictions. The School of Medicine through its clinical faculty and its students has supplied the trained and in-training personnel to care for the medical needs of the sick poor. The hospital provides the physical facilities in which those who seek help may be seen; the School of Medicine provides physicians and student physicians to examine and treat the sick poor who come to them. Faculty and students are able to realize their research and teaching goals by caring for these "service patients." The medical students learn how to practice scientific medicine, and the faculty physicians test new drugs and procedures on this "clinical material." Within the hospital's ward accommodations and its clinics the research and teaching interests of the university are pervasive. One administrator described the power relationships of the chairman-chief, discussed earlier, in the following words:

> The most powerful people in the Medical Center are the chairman-chiefs. It is inconceivable that the university would try to carry out a policy contrary to the wishes of the department chairmen of the Medical School and damned difficult for the hospital to carry out a policy contrary to the wishes of the chiefs. Below the chiefs the most important people to us are the house officers. The care of all patients hinges on the house staff, particularly the outpatients and more than two thirds of the inpatients on the University Division.
>
> The house officers influence all aspects of the hospital's operation way beyond their direct concern with the care of individual patients. They have limited authority officially and great power unofficially. They control the admission of ward patients from a practical point of view. Technically, the admitting officer controls the utilization of beds, but, as a matter of fact, the admitting resident controls most of the admissions from his little black book. He knows what he wants because he knows what fits into his teaching pattern and work load for the junior

house officers and medical students. The avenue of control in the house staff is through the chairmen and chiefs. I'm not saying this is wrong or right. I'm saying this is the way it is.

The position of the medical student is an ambiguous one: He is a student in the School of Medicine but a "doctor" in the hospital. Medical students presumably have little authority and no responsibility in the diagnosis and treatment of patients. Yet, they do examine, diagnose, treat, and care for large numbers of clinic and ward patients. Often, both the patient and the hospital have difficulty identifying the physician who is actually responsible for a particular individual's care. This is a source of concern to the hospital administrators, who worry about legal action if patients are not properly cared for, and to the hospital's public relations officer, who fears malpractice possibilities and public reaction to substantiated complaints. They view with mixed feelings the faculty, the house staff, and the medical students who provide patient care in the ward accommodations. They look askance at the university faculty who exert vast authority in the hospital. The administrators feel relatively impotent to influence the ways patients are cared for on the wards. They view the uncontrolled and loosely supervised coming and going of the young, disease-oriented, experimental-minded student physicians as possessing authority far beyond what is justified by their experience and training. Because the hospital administrators have overall responsibility for patient care but little authority over the providers of that care, this is a matter of much concern for them. One administrator told us:

> The hospital administration has little control over the house staff. The chief is the most important person influencing the future career of the house officers. When the intern wants backing he goes ultimately to his department chairman. It's very difficult to know who is responsible medically for the patient and therefore, for many orders. An imposter could readily enter this hospital and start caring for patients and get away with it, for a time at least. It's a horrible thought and it gives me a chill, but this is the nature of the organization.

The administrators are keenly aware of inefficiencies entailed in the actions of those who are inexperienced clinically. They note that the presence of medical students requires the hospital to provide more space and to purchase more supplies and equipment, ranging from examining tools to syringes, needles, gowns, and masks, than would be required if this were not a teaching hospital. Administrators believe the academic environment prompts medical students and house officers to order additional laboratory, X-ray, and other examinations for which the ward patient cannot pay. Some house officers, realizing the bind they are in while they are students, confirm this opinion. One told us:

This is why we are in an academic center—to learn, although sometimes the patients don't benefit from this. Sometimes the patients have extensive procedures carried out on them that wouldn't be done elsewhere. Sometimes a man suffering with a terminal illness will be kept alive for months on various procedures which completely deplete the family fortune and keep this poor person alive for a long period of time. All of us learn something from this. Maybe a day will come when alterations can be made in this approach and the patient won't be kept alive just to suffer, but in our keeping some patients alive only to suffer and die in pain, we learn something more about keeping patients alive to live.

Medical students and house officers are exhorted not to miss the opportunity to see and examine selected patients who exhibit particular kinds of pathology that is of teaching value. They are here to learn about disease in the living body; their prime responsibility is to the faculty and only secondarily to the patients. Those students who do exhibit some concern for patients realize they are not encouraged in this direction and that singlehandedly or as a group they are impotent to make changes. Sometimes house officers and students from other units flock around the unusual case. The students gave us colorful descriptions of this process. One reported:

So there I was standing in line with a dozen other students. I had a glove on my hand like the rest, waiting to stick my finger in and feel that cancer on her rectal shelf. That's the way you learn.

The hospital administrators understand the cleavage between the interests of the hospital in patient care and the interests of the faculty of the School of Medicine in teaching and learning. One administrator said:

There is an emphasis on teaching and research on the University Division. From what I hear from house officers, practitioners, and, well, everybody, medicine in the University Division is scientific medicine at its worst. There is a great difference between the University and the Community Divisions. On the University Division the doctors and medical students are always making rounds. The house officers are dashing back and forth. The nurses are running about and so on. It's bedlam there.

The administrators know that medical students and house officers are the chief individuals providing care for patients in the University Division, especially in the ward accommodations. There also is agreement that the student physicians follow the dictates of the research and teaching interests of the faculty. A second administrator reported:

The house staff reflects what I consider to be one of the major problems of this whole technology- and pathology-oriented medical center. All of the interest is essentially in the disease rather than in the patient who has the disease. They get all excited about the focal pathology of the patient, for example, who has pneumonia and they forget about how the patient got the disease, what his precise diagnosis and prognosis are, and what kind of management and prophylaxis he will receive. This is a very narrow focus and is the result of the atmosphere created by the individuals who control it—the faculty. It's not the individual man; it's the institutional organization! As a result, these young doctors treat the patients as part of the woodwork, as part of the teaching equipment of the place.

A third administrator supported this critical position:

The house staff is too enthusiastic over the scientific and research value of their contacts with patients. They neglect the care of the patient and disregard his comfort, economic problems, and so forth. The house staff feel they can do a little more experimenting on the ward patients than on the private patients, and I think they do. The educational program is predominant. The clinics practically close in the summertime, but when the medical students are here, they are going full tilt. This forces the hospital to be less efficient in utilization of space, nurses, and the supporting departments.

In brief, the hospital administrators believe that as a result of the teaching and research interests of the School of Medicine the hospital incurs debts, runs less efficiently, and puts less emphasis on the care of patients than might otherwise be the case.

However, while the administrators take a critical view of the consequences of the research and teaching interests for the care of patients, they are elated at being an adjunct to a distinguished, nationally known university. They are proud of this association and realize that the faculty, house officers, and medical students are a vital part of the hospital. One administrator said:

We have problems with the university and they are great. We criticize the university, but when we go to meetings out of town we use its name, not the name of the hospital. Everybody knows where and what Eastern University is. Who knows what the hospital is? Practically nobody! This grates on us, but we can't do anything about it. Since we have to put up with the university we might as well take advantage of its prestige.

Senior faculty members in the medical and surgical services have frequent contacts with the hospital administration through formal and informal meetings. While they are sympathetic with the hospital's financial and organizational problems, their attitude is that the administrators are "never right," since they "do not understand the importance of teaching and research." Senior faculty blame the hospital for poor nursing morale and nursing shortages. However, their criticism of the hospital is moderated by the tacit realization that they are in the more powerful position, and at times they have misused their power in dealing with the administration of the hospital.

Some of the views of senior faculty are reflected in statements they made to us. One said:

> The hospital administrator is torn by two things that are pulling in opposite directions. The chiefs of service are asking for things which cost money. This man [the administrator] is in the position of having to balance his books and he has to choose which demands are reasonable, which he can meet, and which he cannot. As a consequence, his is one of the most thankless jobs in the whole world, and people rarely have a good thing to say for the administrators of the hospital. I admire them for being able to stand up to this constant beefing.

Another senior member of the faculty reported:

> The administrators make it easier for the professionals to work, but I find they are too occupied with their committees, conferences, and their own offices. I haven't seen an administrator on the wards for 10 to 15 years. They rely too much on reports and too little on first-hand observations. They also are biased against the educational objectives to which this institution is committed. This causes problems.

A perspective of the dilemmas between physicians and hospital administrators was offered by another senior professor:

> The administrators have the responsibility for running this institution as a business enterprise. They've been badly maligned by the medical profession, but if it weren't for them running a good hospital, there wouldn't be much to work with. I'm fully convinced that a hospital reflects its administration just as it reflects its professional care. I consider this administration good.

Junior faculty members think the hospital administration is obliged to put up with research-oriented doctors and to make the necessary adjustments so that advancements in the field of medicine and hospital care can be made. One young physician said:

> When you get right down to it the hospital administrator's job is to see that patient care is furnished without the hospital going into debt. It isn't easy for the administrator to avoid debts because most of the services are medical in nature and the medical people carry on their own billing systems independently. But the administrator has got to accept these prima donnas and irregularities in demands and services. The hospital administrator has the job of pulling together all of his hospital family. He must provide the proper atmosphere for research and teaching. It's an enormous job for the administrator.

Most junior faculty members are distant from administrators and are not sympathetic to the problems of the hospital. One who was concerned primarily with laboratory research said, "Hospital administrators are a long way from where I am. They have to do with financing the operation and providing equipment. I guess they do an adequate job generally."

House officers realize that as student physicians they are dependent upon the hospital for the provision of patient-care facilities and upon the School of Medicine for medical supervision and teaching. They are generally antagonistic and critical toward the hospital's problems; they are dismayed at the hospital administration's lack of concern about the care of the sick poor, and they often blame the community as well. They belittle the importance of hospital administration in the provision of patient care. A senior resident, discussing hospital administration, said:

> I have to preface my remarks by saying that I am on the opposite side of the fence from the hospital administrators. Some administrators attempt to take over the function of the physicians in decisions about admission policies although they are not qualified to make decisions. Also, they get bogged down in their paper work. They write a lot of memoranda, most of which are just a waste of time.

Another house officer reported:

> I'm sure that the vast majority of benefits of hospitalization are not attributable in any direct way to the work of the administrators. As far as their attitude toward the house staff is concerned, it's one of longstanding neglect and disinterest in us. The administration screws the house officer out of every nickel it can.

A third house officer was critical of the hospital in its attitude toward money and patients:

> We [the house staff] feel they have little or no feeling for the patient. Last week a patient was sent a bill by the hospital after the first week. The patient was so shocked by the amount that his family moved him out even though he actually needed more hospitalization. We feel the administration is after cold cash. Also, we feel that we should be paid a more decent wage.

This house officer then went on to add his version of a story which circulated widely while we were collecting data. The outlines of the story are briefly as follows: A house officer asked the administrator why an intern in the hospital administration program was paid $5,500 a year while the house officers were paid less. The administrator is said to have replied that it was necessary and reasonable to pay a college graduate this amount of money. The house officers were angered by this reply as all of them had completed four years of college plus four years in a school of medicine and many had completed one or more years of internship as well as some work on a residency. The house officers used this story to support their contention that the administration is disinterested in them, penurious, and obtuse.

A review of the opinions of house officers demonstrates that they are loyal to the School of Medicine and usually antagonistic to the hospital administration. When they think their education is being impaired by lack of optimal patient-care conditions and learning opportunities, their annoyance becomes more focused. One house officer told us:

I'm very sour on hospital administration. Hospital administrators here are most interested in running a solvent hospital. They have an intensive-care unit on the private service for very seriously ill patients. It's air-conditioned like the lobby of the hospital or the operating room. There are little cubicles around the nursing desk where the nurses can watch all the patients. There's probably one nurse per two patients. If something goes wrong it's found quickly because the nurses are looking at the patients all the time. They don't have a setup like that for ward patients because the intensive-care unit on the private side costs the patient $72 a day. It's a paying proposition. You can't get this down on the ward; the ward patients can't pay for it. The ward has to do as it is! The administration doesn't look at the number of deaths or how happy and pain-free the patient was or how good the medical care was. The only things they consider are what's included in the annual report of the hospital administrator.

The house officers are deterred from open conflict with the hospital primarily because of their concern about a recommendation for their future career choices. One reported:

This hospital doesn't have to beg for house staff because of its wonderful reputation. They don't have to pay much. They don't have to do anything except exist and they will always have enough house staff. Practically all of us feel that we would tell the administration off if we didn't need a letter of recommendation. There are so many things to complain about like money, housing, parking, food. We are treated like second-rate employees in this hospital.

The hospital is also at fault in pretending to be an educational institution but at the same time, according to my definition, providing no ward service. Patients have to make a large down payment in order to have an elective admission. They have to get deathly ill before they can be admitted as an emergency. And that isn't right. We are here to learn. Sometimes I have to lie, falsify a record, in order to bring a patient into the hospital. He needs good care; I need the training; but the hospital won't allow him to come in unless he can put up the money. Sometimes I see a patient in the clinic and am not able to admit him, but I tell him to come back to the Emergency Room where I will make a slightly different diagnosis and get him in that way. This hospital provides us with too few beds and too few operating times. Our patients are people who can't pay their bills, but the beds here are filled with people who can give the hospital a profit. That's why *we* don't have patients.

Provision of hospital space, equipment, and personnel on an expanding basis is demanded implicitly by the community and explicitly by the university. The community, on the one hand, wants adequate hospital service without offering the funds necessary to pay for that service, especially that intended for the welfare of the poor. The university, on the other hand, demands adequate facilities to carry out its teaching and research programs without providing funds for the costs of a human laboratory. Each assumes that its services justify its demands on the other. One hospital administrator expressed this dilemma:

> The hospital wants to see that the community's needy get care. At the same time, the hospital is committed to the teaching program of the university and offers these needy as teaching cases. But expanding is out of the question. Buying bananas at 12 cents a pound and selling at 6 cents a pound is losing money. Increasing sales volume will only make matters worse. The University Division's ward accommodations and outpatient facilities are a financial deficit. The care of poor patients for the community is believed to be inefficient and to cost more because of the prime position here of teaching and research.

These statements reveal clearly that there is a divergence between the interests of the hospital administrators and the interests of the faculty, house staff, and students on the University Division of the hospital.

The Community Division

The Community Division is administered by the same officers who are responsible for the University Division, except that there are assistant administrators who supervise the day-to-day activities of each division. Patients are housed in two types of accommodations on the Community Division—semiprivate and private. The semiprivate rooms have from two to four beds; the private rooms contain a single bed. Patients admitted to either accommodation are the responsibility of the private practitioner who sponsors their admission; they remain a part of his practice.

The Community Division and the private practitioners make reciprocal demands upon one another. The practitioners need the services the hospital provides if they are to carry on practices acceptable to their patients. The hospital is in sore need of the patients of the private practitioners because patients on the Community Division are charged more than the hospital's costs for their care to compensate for the deficits incurred in the University Division and the ambulatory services. The paying guest (patient) and his sponsor (the private practitioner) enable the hospital more or less to balance its books.

As a consequence, the administrators maintain a constant interest in satisfying the private practitioners who use the hospital and whose patients are able to pay the fees it charges. Thus, a major concern of the administrator is the retention of the good will of patients on the Community Division. This concern covers several areas: the staff, the tastes of the patients, and the facilities of the hospital. Whatever the administrator can do in the interest of the private practitioner he does willingly and gladly. One administrator told us:

> The patient with the private physician is more likely to be disdainful of others because he feels he's different. He may be conditioned to this by his physician

who believes that the hospital is to blame for almost everything and teaches his patients to believe it also. The higher the patient is [socioeconomically], the more demands he makes and the more likely he is to use the private doctor as a lever to scare the nurse and the little guy in the white jacket [the house staff].

Another administrator said, "Some of the ancillary staff are colored and the private patients tend to reject them because of their color or their coarseness. The doctors tell us about this."

The administrators know that the major interests of the private practitioner lie outside the hospital. One commented:

They are concerned primarily about the care of their patients, most of whom aren't in the hospital. This is the way they make their living and they are interested in satisfying their patients. This has a kind of snowball effect on patient-patient referral.

Some practitioners are pleased with the way the hospital is administered. An internist said:

The only experience I've had with the hospital administrators has been through the letters that Mr. [actually Dr.] —— sends us which keep us informed of what they do in the hospital. I can get my patients into the hospital, which is very important to me. When they get in they get excellent attention from both the nursing and the house staff. Naturally, when that goes along well we know that the administration is good. What more can I say?

Most private practitioners, however, are critical of the hospital administrators. One busy practitioner summed up his view of the administration in these terms:

We rarely get together because the administrators almost never get down to the level of the doctors and patients. I don't think the administrators are interested in the problems of doctors. No administrator has ever approached me concerning the problems of this hospital.

The private practitioners criticize the hospital administrators for siding with the interests of the School of Medicine and for ignoring private practitioners and their patients. A private physician told us:

The patient has a right, and I think this is a basic American right, to choose his physician and choose the type of accommodation he can afford. I think this right is being denied.

This physician is hinting at a widespread complaint among practitioners regarding the School of Medicine and the hospital, namely that the private patients are being drained from the Community Division to the University Division, where they become patients of the faculty or students. In this way the private practitioner loses the fee he might conceivably collect from a patient. A surgeon affirmed this position:

> Many private practitioners are worried about their loss of control of their hospitalized patients. There's a certain fear among the surgeons and I think among the internists that the bureaucracy of the hospital, along with its house staff, may gradually take them over. Years ago the hospital was run by the doctors. Now it's become a business and, therefore, they have businessmen running it.

Most private practitioners draw a sharp line between their interests and the interests of the hospital and the School of Medicine. One told us:

> I'm going to have to side with my own club, so to speak. I'm a private physician with a private practice and I feel that, by and large, the care that I and others like me in private practice provide to patients is superior to that which they receive in any other type of setup. This is our business. This is what my family lives on. It's capitalism versus socialism.
>
> When the university faculty make a mistake or have a bad complication, they don't have the patient's family hovering over them. It doesn't hit them quite the same way as it hits us. The faculty is always going off to meetings. They're busy because they have other things to do. A resident may do the follow-up care to a large extent; maybe the resident even talks to the family. The patients are better off in the hands of the private physicians, but the hospital administrators are more allied with the university than with the private physicians.

Another practitioner rationalized his relationships with the administrators in these terms:

> The biggest problem of the administrators is that this is a large institution and the personal needs of patients are ignored. This hospital should exist for patients and no one else.

The "no one else" referred to here is the School of Medicine. This physician did not understand that the private practitioners were using the hospital to meet their own needs. He, like most other practitioners, justifies the hospital's existence in terms of the welfare of the patient. Still another practitioner voiced his antagonism in these words:

> The patient is not impressed by the title Medical Center and all that it implies. All he knows is that he had to stay on a bedpan long after he was finished with it because he couldn't get anybody to help him off it.

As the practitioners stated, the administrators are far removed from patient care, and this fact is recognized by some of the administrators. One said, "I'm strictly a business person. A patient wouldn't know me from any other visitor." The individual patient occupies little of the administrators' time or attention as long as there is no open dissatisfaction or threats of law suits.

Without exception, the administrators delegate authority for the management of patient-care units to the nurses and house staff. They think the hospital cannot depend upon the private physicians to meet the immediate needs of patients because they are absentee individuals, busy elsewhere with their private practices. To be sure, private practitioners have only distant relationships with the administrators; their contacts with the hospital are through the house officers and the head nurses.

Private practitioners realize the house officers are vital to the care of their hospitalized patients. One told us:

> I can sum it up by saying that it would be extraordinarily difficult to take care of patients without having the house officers here. The very fact that they're here when we're not available is most important. In some instances, the house officers save the patient's life. They serve as a check on our examinations and offer additional interpretations for a given condition.

A prominent internist told us:

> In the absence of the attending physician, they [house officers] take over his duties, and, in general, they do this very well. Sometimes, however, they have deficiencies. They're too blunt with some individuals especially of the lower class. They also assume too much responsibility in telling patients things we don't want them to know or in doing some things in their scientific way which really do not need to be done, even though they are accustomed to doing this on the other side [University Division]. Sometimes this puts you in a bad position; it's embarrassing. The family will call and ask about something and we don't even know anything about it, but in general the work of the house staff is very good.

A surgeon frankly told us of the problems he faces when his patients are examined and cared for by the house staff:

> I tell my patients that I do the operation and I direct and participate in postoperative care. But I don't live here. I'm not at their beck and call day and night. Most patients understand this. They have to accept the house staff. If they do, it gives them a sense of security. I emphasize that the house staff is under *my* direction. The house officers confer with *me* and they're not going to do anything on their own unless they are *my* orders. You have to explain this to the patients because there's always a group that says, "Now look here doctor, I don't want any interns fooling around with me." That patient has to be spoken to at once and set straight. They then get over this foolish notion. I know where they get it from —the other side. It's an old wives' tale that they'll be experimented upon.

Aspersions about "the other side," meaning the University Division, are a repetitive theme in the statements of the private practitioners. Often, they are put bluntly:

Many of the physicians on the University Division are quite excellent scientists and quite knowledgeable regarding the rare disease but they are inexperienced in handling people as humans. They lack finesse, which patients need.

Practitioners are convinced this attitude is carried from the University Division to the Community Division by house staff, who rotate from one side to the other during their training. As a consequence, one physician told us the house staff "look to the academic man with awe and to the private man with disdain." This attitudinal set on the part of the practitioners and the house staff gives rise to tensions between attending physicians and house staff. A senior physician with long experience in the community told us:

> The house staff are more likely to take their vacations when they are working on the Community Division and many of them have the 40-hour-a-week psychology. They cherish their nights off and are less interested in patients here because they are not in charge. Their work habits are less effective than when they are performing for doctors on the University Division who determine their futures. There's a natural tendency for them to shine a little more when they're on that division. However, they do a good job and I know we couldn't function without them. If we didn't have the house staff, we'd have to make some arrangements with patients when they are suddenly taken ill in the daytime when we are in our offices, or in the operating room, or at night.

The practitioners look upon the house staff as their assistants, as the following statement shows:

> They take a lot of drudgery from us. They do the initial history and physical examination and a lot of paper work for us. They also do many procedures which would be physically impossible for us, since we are very active and busy in private practice. They're always here and I think this is probably the most important thing. If anything should happen, they can take care of it or at their discretion call us. They are there all day long. I can only be there once or twice a day. They are of incalculable aid to us.

The administrators know there are occasional conflicts between house officers and private physicians. They generally choose not to take sides in these quarrels because they see the strength of the argument on both sides. On the one hand, the house officers bring a fresh approach and moderate the tendencies of some physicians to treat their patients in individualized, parochial, or vintage fashions. On the other hand, the house officers are sometimes difficult to get along with because they are young, insecure, and eager to "try their wings." On the wards they are "the boss" but in the semiprivate and private accommodations their position is generally ambiguous. On the Community Division they may have responsibility for patient care in large part or not at all, depending upon the doctor and patient in question. While the administrators have ambivalent feelings toward the house staff, they are grateful and appreciative for their presence and their generally favorable impact upon patient care, hospital services, and relationships with community physicians. They know that the house officers exert influence over the community practitioners so their actions will conform to hospital policies. The administrators would like to have more support for the house staff from practitioners than they are able to obtain. A senior administrator related:

> The attending physicians in the Community Division do not appreciate the amount of work done by the house staff. For example, two or three years ago, the hospital proposed to tax the attending physicians to assist the hospital in supporting the house staff. The attending staff screamed like wounded eagles over this proposal and the matter was dropped. Some of the attending physicians could not believe that we were serious but we were. The private doctors felt there was something inherently wrong in this proposal. The hospital lost this battle almost as soon as it started. Some of the doctors reminded us that their private patients were bailing the hospital out of debt anyway. Taxing them, and therefore their patients even more, was inherently unfair when the house staff were here to learn. The private doctors think they should do the work just as has been the custom.

The house officers create some problems for the administrators, as the following statement reveals:

> The house officer acts as a liaison between the private doctor and his patient. Often the patients' questions are directed to the house officer—the little man in the white coat. He is a second physician. If the house staff is poor, we are in trouble because then we can't cope with our prima donnas and poor practitioners. If the house staff is good, we can cope with both. Our biggest problems with house officers arise when they lack technical skills and are rough or swear at patients, especially those of lower social backgrounds. They spend more time and are more gentle with higher-status patients.

Members of the house staff express definite views of their role on the Community Division. The first citation describes dilemmas with attending physicians:

> The availability of insurance places many ward patients in the private category. We're just running out of ward patients for training. The private attending physicians as a whole are sophisticated, but there are some who are damned poor. Some surgeons won't allow the house officers to do much surgery; others let you do the case because they're incapable. You get to do a lot of little cutting and yet you don't learn anything because the surgeon's not teaching you anything. You're just sort of blundering through because you can probably blunder a little better than he can.

A senior resident in Medicine and a senior resident in Surgery took part in a joint interview. The surgical resident said:

The contributions of the private practitioners can be very great. Some of them teach on occasion. The best of them give you operations to do. There are three or four surgeons who give the residents big cases when they think we can handle them. This is the greatest thing that can happen; it's better than doing a ward case by yourself with another resident teaching. You've got a guy with experience. The residents decide just when to operate and so on, but the surgeon guides you. You feel like you're taking care of the patient. I might add that, as far as the patient goes, I think these patients get the best care in Surgery on the Community side.

The patients with attendings that don't teach may not get bad care, but they'll get the minimum. Some of these private doctors don't even bother to see you and talk to you about their cases. They don't teach at all. You may learn from the cases just by seeing what's going on, but they don't give any cases away in the operating room. Some guys bring in a lot of junk—elective procedures such as hemorrhoids, and no one can learn too much from that. The house officers aren't interested in them. Patients of good teachers always get good care. Patients of poor teachers get variable care.

The senior resident in Medicine commented:

The attendings don't appreciate good medicine. An intern may be up all night with a patient and the private doctor will never even stop to ask how the patient is doing, see the patient, or write a note. He disappears and that's it. In many cases, there is no communication between the intern and the private doctor, and they certainly are not appreciative at all. There are a few who should show appreciation but they don't do it. I don't think they are able to evaluate good work. They just don't know how. This gripes me. Of course in Medicine, this makes an advantage because it means that the management of most of these patients is in the hands of an intern even though they're private patients. Fabulous numbers of patients each year are sent in by private men who know nothing about what's going on with that patient or his care. When the house staff says what things should be done, the doc will say, "whatever you say" and the house officer runs the case completely. If the intern wants the patient discharged, he'll tell Dr. Jones that his patient can go home now. The intern will discharge him and that's it. Then Dr. Jones sends a nice fat bill.

After this comment by the medical resident, the surgical resident then added:

The same thing applies with postoperative care in a lot of surgical cases. Sometimes the doctors don't know the first thing about taking care of some of these patients in the hospital. It's really a bad situation.

The house officers have the same educational interests regardless of their assignment on the two divisions. They believe generally that their best learning opportunities occur in the ward accommodations where they are "the boss" and where they have the "best" supervision by full-time faculty, but they have some praise to offer about the Community Division. They "enjoy the steady stream of pathology." They also comment upon the greater accessibility of the nurses:

> If you have a good set of nurses on the floor, you can find out a lot from them. These girls, if they have a chance and aren't rushed out of their minds, sit down and discuss how the patients are doing and all the problems. This is a good chance for you to learn something.

The house officers are most unhappy about the manner in which private surgeons decline to share operations with them when they do practically all of the preoperative and postoperative care of a patient. Certain "mass practice" physicians are designated as unfair in this regard. These "purists" are resented because of the deficiency this creates in the educational experience of the house officer. Such a problem was not pointed out on the medical service.

Senior house staff planning to enter private practice shortly are more likely to show an interest in the problems of the personal management of patients. A senior resident commented:

> I've been very disappointed in attending physicians on both sides. The full-time attending staff is not geared toward clinical problems. They're not geared toward patient care. The surgeons in this community enjoy an extraordinary position in that they operate on people day and night and almost never take care of them. The most preeminent surgeons in our community do just about no postoperative care at all. Many of these private attendings are not very competent and they leave most of their difficult problems such as the dying patient to the house staff.

While the house officer suffers from an ambiguous position regarding the responsibility for patients, he generally is given supervision by those physicians who assume more responsibility; at the same time he has the benefit of being "the boss" on the care of patients whose nominal physicians assume little responsibility for their care. A practitioner who turns patients over to the house staff for medical care and to nurses for nursing care corroborated some of the allegations. He told us:

> The house officers write most of the orders. They take care of the patient; they watch him; they're valuable for emergency calls. I've been satisfied with the work these young men do. Of course, they're young and have certain attitudes. They're not so humble. When they come on the private service we let them do a lot of things. And if there are certain things we want done and we don't find them handy to do, we just write a note and they take care of it. I have no problems.

While there are ambiguities and disagreements in the care of patients on the Community Division, there is an underlying attitude that these patients get better care than ward patients. One administrator summed up his position on this point:

Patients in the semiprivate and private accommodations get the better breaks all the way around. Technologically, the care is supposed to be better on the ward accommodations, but I don't believe that's true. I think it's just as good on the Community Division. Furthermore, the personal service is far better on the private side.

The Dilemma of Diverse Goals

We have drawn freely upon the tape-recorded interviews with hospital administrators, faculty physicians, private practitioners, and house staff regarding their views of the hospital, the services it provides, and the attitudes they express toward one another. Each person quoted has personal knowledge of the operation of the two divisions. The salient points the different groups make in their interviews enable us to draw some inferences of what we think they are saying about their relations with the hospital and the patients they care for here.

On the University Division the primary interests of the faculty and students and those of the hospital's administrators are divergent. To realize their objectives of adding and transmitting knowledge in medicine, the university physicians use selected patients as suitable subjects for their teaching and research. These patients are largely poor persons housed on the ward accommodations. The administrators enjoy the cosmopolitan nature of the institution, but they remain uneasy about the care provided by students and the poor public relations that may arise from inadequate supervision. The hospital administration's chief concern is to balance its budget. There is no easy solution to this issue because a deficit is a built-in condition of the use of the community's poor people as teaching and research materials for the School of Medicine.

On the Community Division the private practitioners expect the hospital to provide hotel accommodations—attractive, clean rooms, good food well served—special technical services, nursing care, and a substantial amount of medical manpower to assist them in the diagnosis, treatment, and inhospital care of *their* patients. They also expect the house staff to make a major effort to assist them in working up and caring for *their* patients. The hospital administration provides what the practitioners demand, but the practitioners feel threatened because they are sure the administrators are aligned with the scientific and intellectually more prestigious University Division. The faculty of the School of Medicine casts a disquieting shadow upon the field the practitioner wants for himself and wishes to cultivate and harvest in his own way.

One administrator commented on the economic and prestigious relationships between community practitioners and university faculty:

The community practitioners make an absolutely indispensable contribution to the Medical Center which is not appreciated by the full-time staff. On the other hand the community doctors have a tremendous sense of hostility and suspicion about the Medical Center which in many cases is unwarranted. They are hostile mostly about what they imagine to be economic competition for patients. On Medicine there's almost no competition in fact, but there's much fear of it. Competition is more keenly noticeable on the surgical service which requires patients to be operated upon.

There's also the prestige factor dividing the university and the community physicians. The community doctors think of almost everything in the long run in economic terms. They consider the economic consequences of their participation in teaching and patient-care activities here. There is relatively little altruism. After all, the prestige of the university connection is beneficial to them in their own private practices. They resent having to pay by working in the clinics because this work is thoroughly unpleasant to them, but it is from this work that they get the prestige of the university connection. They also recognize the importance of this as a kind of police action to be sure that the hospital does not become too competitive with them.

The private practitioner looks upon the house staff, as well as specialized personnel and equipment characteristic of the modern hospital, as aides to his practice. A smoothly functioning hospital is vital to the private physician with little time for the few of his many patients who may be in the hospital at a given time for several days or weeks. He wants the hospital to be operated so that complaints of patients are minor and the promotion of his practice is supported. The private practitioners praise the house officers for their superior performance, on the one hand, and blame them for their shoddy, amateurish ways and lack of loyalty to them, on the other. They listen to the complaints of their patients and reflect their views, whether these views are reasonable, representative, supported, or a symptom of the patient's emotional state. They complain vigorously, occasionally bitterly, about the inadequate nursing care and sometimes they find fault with the cleanliness of the rooms and the long delays in answering the calls of patients.

The hospital administrators are a long way from the rank-and-file private physician, his interests, and his patients. The house officers and the head nurses are his closest links with the hospital. When the private physician thinks the house staff is acting in the interests of the hospital rather than in the interests of his practice he calls attention to the failures of the administration to support his interests adequately. This position, to be sure, is justified as being primarily in the interests of his patients, but the private physician is quick to point to the research and teaching interests of the School of Medicine and the adherence of the house officers to these policies and practices.

Although the private physicians look with mixed feelings upon the house staff, they realize how dependent they are upon them to get much of their work done in the care of their patients. They admit reluctantly that their practices could not be carried on as they are now if the house officers were not present to take over much of the medical care that is provided for their patients within the hospital. Without house officers, their periods of relaxation, family life, and social life would be compromised to a greater degree than under current conditions. This is an important aspect of the relationship of the private physician to the hospital.

The private practitioners, nevertheless, do hold the trump cards in their relations with the hospital since they supply the hospital with its paying patients. However, they are not responsible for the service provided; they are not commonly found at the side of their hospitalized patients, and they identify with their patients, not the hospital. The physicians blame the hospital if their patients are not satisfied. The hospital has to function in terms of these realities whether the patients and the practitioners have legitimate complaints or are only carping. The reciprocating relationship between the hospital and the private practitioner is maintained by the needs of physicians for the services and facilities that are available to them only in the hospital, while the hospital, to remain a viable institution, is dependent upon the patients whom the private practitioners admit to its facilities.

In the relationships of private physicians with the hospital, we see the impact of obsolescence and of variations in training. Physicians who are less skilled in the treatment of diseases call consultations for some patients but use the house staff for others. They may turn over practically all of the care of their inpatients to the house staff and still maintain a nominal position of responsibility by admitting the patient, while allowing the house staff to have a "free hand." There is a built-in excuse for this kind of doctor-patient relationship: The house officer is here to learn, and delegation of the responsibility for working-up and looking after a patient is entirely appropriate. The administrators, accordingly, allow several kinds of practices of medicine within the hospital. Its doors are open to many patients and to many doctors—general practitioners as well as specialists. What the house staff does and what the private physician does may vary greatly, depending upon the interest and competence of the private physician. The house officer may take up the slack and perform his role, ensuring generally that the patient receives the requisite care, but he often thinks he gets too little credit for his efforts and his loyalty to the institution and to this system of medical care. Strains in the relationships between the house officers and private physicians, thus, are sometimes great not only because of different interests in education and research but also because of differences of opinion on the care of patients. In the words of one practitioner, "The house staff who come to the private service have a suspicion that everyone who works here is inept. That may be so in some instances, but generally it is the house staff who are inept in dealing with patients." Other physicians point out that there is little consistency in house officer–practitioner relations since house officers and private physicians "individualize" their working relationships just as they say they "individualize" patient care.

Summary

The hospital administration faces many dilemmas in its relationships with physicians on the two divisions. First, there is disagreement on the primary mission of the hospital among the physicians identified with the different divisions. Second, even though physicians associated with each division generally do not work for the hospital, they direct the hospital's medical services. Third, physicians within the respective divisions have different professional orientations and career objectives. Fourth, physicians in the two divisions are sometimes in conflict with one another and are in conflict even more frequently with the hospital administration. Fifth, the hospital has only limited authority over the physicians who work on the two divisions. Generally, physicians on both divisions have little interest in the hospital's chief problems: payment of bills, the hospital as a community institution, and public relations. This diversity of interests and objectives profoundly influences the relationships of physicians with the hospital administration, the administration with physicians, and both the administration and physicians with patients.

The operation of the hospital is determined in large part by the physicians. The administrators accede to what the physicians on the respective divisions demand; hospital practices are controlled largely in the interests of the physicians. The University Division meets the needs of the School of Medicine for students to learn how to practice medicine and for the faculty to pursue its research interests. The administrators are unhappy about the ward accommodations because of the financial deficits incurred and the impersonal human relationships which characterize the care of patients there. They are, on the other hand, generally pleased with the semiprivate and private accommodations because the patients pay their way and more, which enables the administrators to meet a major part of the deficit created by the care of medically indigent patients. The administrators show concern about obsolescent or less able physicians who admit patients to the Community Division, but they feel incapable of controlling these physicians. They attempt to correct practices of which the hospital does not approve although the economic need for paying patients is of such vital importance that one may wonder how serious their efforts are. If the administrators did not accommodate the practitioners the way they do, the financial position of the hospital could conceivably be worse.

The respective interests of the differing groups of physicians who practice on its two divisions make the hospital what it is. Interest in teaching and research dictates policies and practices in the ward accommodations and, to a lesser extent, throughout the institution. The effects of the ideological orientation characteristic of the University Division are transmitted to the Community Division by the house officers who rotate on all services from one division to the other. Physicians do not generally support the hospital directly unless the issue is of interest to them in solving their problems. The hospital's aims are different and many: The hospital must provide a favorable atmosphere for patient care, teaching, and research; if it is to remain open it must satisfy enough patients and practitioners to ensure continued use by them; but, in doing these things, the hospital is in constant conflict with physicians who are identified with nonhospital interests. The central interest of the faculty of the School of Medicine is an adequate supply of interesting "clinical material" upon which students can learn and faculty can carry out their research. The prime interest of the private practitioner is the support of his practice. Perhaps the most telling statement was made by a physician who thought that several of the "generals" (administrators) should be fired and more nurses hired. If this were done, he said, the private practitioners would have fewer competitors for power and more people to assist them with their work. In reality, the hospital probably needs more administrators, as the size and complexity of the bureaucracy grows rather than lessens, but this viewpoint is not accepted by physicians who view the administrators as a hindrance to the ways in which they desire to handle patients. The irony of this dilemma is that the hospital is not organized to diagnose and treat patients; diagnosis and treatment are the province of the physician. This creates problems for the hospital, the physicians, and, above all, for the care of patients.

The underlying issues of town versus gown—salaried physicians versus fee-for-service physicians, scientific medicine versus the art of medicine, service patient versus paying patient, and so on—create strains in the relationships of the administrators with physicians on the two divisions. The university-oriented physicians complain that the private practitioners are not interested in science and have little interest in patient care but a strong interest in money. The private practitioners respond that the university physicians are interested essentially in research and advancing their academic careers. They assert that interest in patient care is lacking in the superscientific world of the academician. Although these polar orientations exist, there is a substantial minority of individuals on both sides who recognize the importance of each orientation for the promotion of the more basic issue of better health for people in the community.

IN THIS CHAPTER WE SHALL EXAMINE THE INTERRELATIONS between nurses, hospital administrators, and physicians. Our focus will be upon the registered nurse as she functioned on the patient-care division.

At the time we collected our data the Department of Nursing was the largest administrative division in the hospital; its employees comprised 40 per cent of the work force and they received 27 per cent of the hospital's annual expenditures. Its personnel ranged from professionally trained registered nurses with graduate degrees to relatively unskilled aides who may have dropped out of high school. Traditionally, the Department of Nursing is charged with responsibility for the bedside care of patients; to meet this responsibility it developed a bureaucracy with a complicated assignment of functions.

The Department of Nursing was headed by an assistant director of the hospital—a registered nurse with a graduate degree, responsible to the hospital administrator. The Director of Nursing had accumulated in her experience on all levels of nursing over many years a vast knowledge of the intricate workings of the hospital. Four associate directors and four assistant directors, all registered nurses, were directly responsible to her for each section of the nursing department: the University Division, the Community Division, the Outpatient Department, and Special Services, which included central supply, operating and recovery rooms, delivery suites, and the hospital's school of nursing. The respective medical services—Medicine, Surgery, Pediatrics, Obstetrics and Gynecology, and so on—were in the charge of nursing supervisors who worked out of the associate and assistant directors' offices. The supervisory staff was organized so that persons of comparable training and experience were assigned to the two divisions of the hospital.

Each patient-care unit in each division was under the direct charge of a head nurse, who was the key figure in the functioning of a patient-care unit. Two lines of authority converged in her role. She was the hospital's representative on the floor, responsible for following policies, rules, and procedures laid down by the administration of the hospital—particularly the Medical Board and the Department of Nursing—and she was the physician's representative on the floor, responsible for carrying out his orders for individual patients. These lines of authority were not articulated, one with the other. Therefore, they presented the head nurse with a dilemma which she had to solve to the best of her ability. Often she sought a solution which might not satisfy any of the four groups of persons with whom she had to work: the nursing hierarchy, hospital departments other than nursing, private practitioners and house staff who cared for the patients on her floor, and, finally, the patients and their families.

The head nurse was responsible for the work force assigned to her patient-care unit: registered nurses, licensed practical nurses, student nurses, nurse's aides, and usually a secretary; in addition, she had some responsibility for the supervision of orderlies, volunteers, and others. The head nurse was scheduled to work 40 hours per week, but patient care had to continue throughout the 168 hours of each week. This means that three shifts of registered head nurses had to be available for each unit each day. The nurse "in charge" was supplemented by registered nurses, some of whom were temporarily assigned wherever they were needed, P.R.N. (*pro re nata*) in the language of the profession. If we assume that there was at least one registered nurse on a patient-care unit at all times and the head nurses were allowed time off the floor for meals and short rest periods, then some 5 hours of P.R.N. time needed to be available for each division each day.

The Department of Nursing keeps detailed records of personnel and the location, time, and duration of their assignments. These records were made available to us by the Director of Nursing so that we were able to determine the amount of time the hospital provided for nursing care on the divisions in which patients in this study were cared for during the time we were gathering data. We added the hours each type of nurse spent on each accommodation and divided the total by the number of patients cared for on that unit in order to answer the question *How much time did each type of nurse have available for the care of patients?* The quotient, as summarized in Table 2, is the mean amount of time each type of nurse had available to care for each patient each day on each accommodation. The data in Table 2 show that the registered nurses had the same amount of time available for the care of patients in each of the three accommodations. The same was true for the licensed practical nurses except that there was a slight gradient by accommodation: The wards had the most licensed practical nurse–hours assigned to them, with the semi-private accommodations midway between the wards and the private accommodations. Student nurses were assigned in large part to the wards and the semi-

TABLE 2. MEAN NURSE-HOURS PER PATIENT AVAILABLE DAILY,
BY TYPE OF HOSPITAL PERSONNEL

Type of Hospital Personnel	Nurse-hours by Accommodation		
	Private	Semiprivate	Ward
Registered nurse	1.1	1.1	1.1
Licensed practical nurse	.6	.7	.8
Student nurse	.7*	1.6	1.7
Nurse's aide	1.1	1.2	1.1
Total hours	3.5	4.6	4.7

Private compared with semiprivate and ward, p < .05.

* No student nurses are assigned to the private surgical divisions;
thus this figure is for the private medical divisions only.

private accommodations of both Medicine and Surgery. Nurse's aides worked in all units and spent about the same amount of time per patient in all accommodations. The amount of nursing time assigned for the care of each patient each day demonstrates a gradient by accommodation: The wards had the most and the private accommodations the least.

However, the personnel assigned to the patient-care units by the Department of Nursing and paid by the hospital were only part of the manpower involved in the care of patients. (Whether or not student nurses are paid is a moot point, but as an integral part of their training they do help in the care of patients.) Employees of the Department of Nursing were supplemented by a corps of private-duty nurses who did not work for the hospital. The private-duty nurse is registered and, like the private physician, she works in the hospital as a free professional. The private-duty nurse works when she chooses and for whom she chooses. She is paid by the patient who engaged her or by the patient's family. Private-duty nurses were concentrated on the private accommodations. Few were employed by semiprivate patients, and only in instances of unusual need did the hospital engage a private-duty nurse to "special" a ward patient. As a consequence, the amount of private-duty nurse-hours used by patients on the three types of accommodations forms a sharp gradient: ward, 0.2 hours per patient per day; semiprivate, 1 hour; private, 5.2 hours. When these figures are added to those of the nursing care provided by the hospital, the gradient at the bottom of Table 2 is reversed, as seen in Table 3. Of the total hours worked by registered nurses in the units on which we collected data, 67 per cent comprised private-duty nurse-hours. (Private-duty nurses were paid some $935,000 annually for the care of patients on these units.) However, they cared for only 25 per cent of the private surgical patients and less than 1 per cent of the ward medical patients. (It is interesting that the rate of hospital deaths per admission is less than 1 per cent on private Surgery but

TABLE 3.   MEAN NURSE-HOURS PER PATIENT AVAILABLE DAILY, BY
TYPE OF NURSING PERSONNEL

Type of Nursing Personnel	Nurse-hours by Accommodation		
	Private	Semiprivate	Ward
Hospital personnel	3.5	4.6	4.7
Private-duty nurses	5.2	1.0	.2
Total hours	8.7	5.6	4.9

Private compared with ward, $p < .05$; private compared with semiprivate, $p < .05$; semiprivate compared with ward, $p > .05$.

over 12 per cent on ward Medicine.) The registered nurses paid by the hospital, representing 33 per cent of the nurse-hours, met the minimum requirement of one registered nurse to a unit on each shift. The mean number of registered nurse-hours per 24-hour day on the private accommodations was 29; on the semiprivate 33; and on the wards 30. With this level of staffing the registered nurse was primarily a supervisor in the operation of her unit. Individual patients may be able to get along without registered nurses, but patient-care units cannot.

How did registered nurses view the roles they played on the patient-care division? How was the registered staff nurse on the floor viewed by hospital administrators, physicians, nursing administration, and private-duty nurses? To answer these questions we drew upon the tape-recorded background interviews we held with staff registered nurses, private-duty nurses, physicians, and hospital administrators. We asked each respondent the same questions about the contributions of the different groups in caring directly or indirectly for patients.

The registered nurses, whether they were administrators, supervisors, head, staff, or private-duty, were of central concern to hospital administrators and physicians. Hospital administrators, physicians, and registered nurses were in agreement that the head or charge nurse is the executive officer of the patient-care unit. The hospital administrators and the physicians realized that the administration of the hospital's policies and procedures, combined with the carrying out of physicians' orders, is of prime importance in the operation of the patient-care units. Although physicians desired personal care of patients by registered nurses, they hardly expected it under the circumstances. The head nurses most of all believed they could not be executive officers and care for patients at the same time. These nurses were more sensitive to this dilemma than either the physicians or the administrators because they were closer to it. They were frustrated in not being able to provide nursing care for the sick and in their inability to follow good nursing practices. They expressed feelings of guilt in failing to meet the expectations of patients. They were aware of demands, often conflicting, from the varied groups. Some of their comments on this dilemma were:

NURSE A:

The registered nurse is limited in how much she can do both physically and emotionally by the number of people she has working for her and just what she has to do during the day. If she's going to do all the medications and all the intravenous work and keep all the records besides, she just doesn't have time to see all the patients during the day. If she's going to carry this much of a work load it means she can't see the patients. It's impossible! You can just cut yourself into so many pieces, and that's all there is to it.

NURSE B:

There just isn't enough time to go around. You just have time to say a brief hello and run in and run out. I don't really get to know patients as well as I would like to. I think the head nurse should be more aware of her patients.

NURSE C:

I try to spend as little time as possible on administration, but there's a certain amount you know has to be done. Much of my day is spent with medications. I don't find myself becoming as familiar with the patients as I would like. I still think the nurse's place is at the bedside. I think those nurses who have had to be away from the bedside are limited by the lack of patient contact. I don't think they can possibly keep up with the new patient developments and symptoms and things of that sort unless they are there.

The problems with which head nurses had to cope daily were best understood by their supervisors. The supervisors were generally younger women who had been head nurses in the recent past. They realized the paucity of head nurses and registered nurses in general. One of the nursing supervisors illuminated some problems for us:

One of the greatest shortcomings is this business of relating to patients—the nurses are all taught this and are fundamentally aware of this, but due to pressure they don't carry through. The pressure of nursing with the great shortage we've had contributes to the feeling that people just don't want to give all of themselves. I think sometimes the nurses are under such pressure that they get to the point where they can't do anything else or they just don't care. They're so rushed that when they have a few spare moments they're inclined to flop and talk with each other rather than utilizing this time for patient contact. The terrific pressures of getting out medications and treatments and getting the things done on a busy 40-bed division where she's the only nurse keeps her away from the patients.

I never get around to see patients anymore, except the VIPs or someone like that. The head nurses are now junior executives, running big divisions. I am involved in so many things—staffing, committees, insuring minimal coverage, and so forth. This is not a matter of choice. Nurses are now, in all instances, junior administrators of some kind.

An assistant director of the Department of Nursing told us:

> The head nurse coordinates the patient and physician activity. The physician is the person who makes the overall plan of treatment for the individual patient: he develops the medical care plan for the nurse, and then the nurse takes this medical care plan and develops her nursing care plan which is separate from the medical care plan. She's also concerned about the safety of the patient, his comfort, hygiene factors, and all the rest.

The respondent could not be encouraged to elaborate more fully on her notion of the "nursing care plan."

The hospital administrators viewed the staff of the Department of Nursing as their agents in supervising the patient-care divisions. The administrators held the head nurses responsible for maintaining adequate supplies and equipment in their divisions. Like the senior officers in the Department of Nursing, the administrators were distant from the patient-care divisions. They recognized this and felt some uneasiness. Some of their responses to our questions follow:

ADMINISTRATOR A:

> The nurses have been telling us they get more and more administrative and paper work—everything but real bedside nursing care. This is probably true. They take patients' valuables, watch their diets and drugs, order supplies, send charge tickets. Sure, Dietary now delivers the trays to the patient's room instead of the nurse, but the nurses prefer to fix the patient for the food. If the tray carrier cranks the patient up or down, it might hurt the patient. Also the pharmacy now stocks the floors with drugs, but the nurse still sends the charge ticket and it has to be correct. In Accounting and the laboratories, the supervisors figure they can rely on the nurse. When the house officers make out the slips they're usually fouled up. The nurses know how to do it, but the house staff doesn't. Some of the house staff just doesn't give a damn.

ADMINISTRATOR B:

> The head nurse is everything to everybody except the patient. She has to tell the admitting officer when she can or can't take a patient. Having an empty bed does not necessarily mean you can take that patient because you've got a cranky patient or one with an infectious disease whom you can't move and free up that empty bed. She has to direct her staff and make out accident reports of patients falling out of bed, giving the wrong drugs, and that sort of thing to satisfy the insurance company. She has to worry about supplies, charge slips, medical records, narcotics, and God knows what else. To top it all off, she has to be sure that the doctors aren't stepping too far out of line. The head nurse has to take the initiative to report things that are out of line whether she wants to or not. It's a tricky thing for a nurse to do that because she's lower than the doctor and has to live and work with him, but sometimes it's the only way the hospital has of seeing to it that policies made by the Medical Board are carried out. Many doctors

don't give a rap about hospital policies and procedures. They only care about solving their individual problems with individual patients.

ADMINISTRATOR C:

Nurses are far removed from patients. They have to deal with administrative matters. In addition to keeping everyone on his toes, filling the slots, and so forth, they have the problem of dropped radios, poor liaison with the doctors, and patients who have lost various items such as teeth, rings, and so on. The nurse is very important to step in and calm a patient and settle the problem of the broken radio. This is a very important role. She commonly comes between the private doctor and the patient, especially if the house officer washes his hands [of the patient]. If a house officer drops the ball, the nurse has to pick it up. The nurse is far better at doing things like this than I am. She is seen as a bigwig. I am a business person in a business suit.

The administrators were troubled by nursing performances which they thought were less than ideal, and they were worried also about nursing morale. Administrator D offered some perspective on these matters:

ADMINISTRATOR D:

The nurse has more and more of a discontinuous contact in the care of the patient. We use nursing pools to cover the patient-care units and this breaks up the nurse-patient relationship. Since the nurses can't practice the way they might be motivated to practice, they are inclined to think "the hell with it—I'm doing the best I can." The dedicated ones say it later and more reluctantly, but they come to say it just the same. The registered nurse is being crowded by an ever increasing ancillary staff whom she must supervise. The growth and importance of other paramedical skills influence her power and authority.

The administrators generally expressed confidence in the head nurses' ability to perform well in giving medications to patients, assisting the physicians in emergencies, and managing the divisions, given the trying circumstances often found with patient care, teaching, and research activities competing for the time of all on the floor. The administrators were in agreement that the head nurses did not give personal bedside nursing care to the patients on their unit. They also stressed that the nurse is subordinate to the physician in relations with patients.

Physicians saw two roles for the head nurse: administrator of medical orders and assistant to the doctor. They believed the head nurse helps in emergencies, assists physicians in selected procedures, and gives medications but spends most of her time transcribing orders, relaying messages, and generally running the division. Some typical views of physicians are:

PHYSICIAN A:

Nurses give medications and provide some necessary physical care. They also inform physicians of special problems such as falling blood pressure. The nurse is absolutely essential to the functioning of the floor. Most of her work is administrative—keeping other personnel moving along proper lines, dishing out medications to patients, and sharing responsibility with the physician for patient care. They are not able to spend time with patients individually, but they do direct patient care to a large extent. Nurses have too little time to sit and talk with patients who need them.

PHYSICIAN B:

If you have a well-organized head nurse everything runs like clockwork. If she's absent for a week or is unable to administer properly, everything is absolute chaos. The registered nurse gives practically no nursing care. Her nursing care as far as I can see is limited to injections and directing somebody else to give the care. Medications now are so much more numerous than they used to be and they're given largely intravenously or intramuscularly. Of course the nurses don't give the intravenous medications, but they are reasonably responsible for getting them ready. That may comprise a larger part of the nurse's time now than before antibiotics were available. They are not nurses in the old-fashioned sense of taking care of the sick. They do administrative work on the floors, not nursing care. It's a rare registered nurse who knows all the patients and knows all about the patients on the floor. This is particularly true on units where they have private-duty nurses. She feels she should not be bothered with the care. As far as contact with doctors is concerned, it's mostly through the doctor's order book. There's no doctor-nurse relationship as such in this hospital.

The head nurse was accountable to two medical authorities—the house officer and the private physician. The house officer provided most of the medical manpower for the examination and treatment of all patients on his division. He was the most available physician much of the time, and he was available immediately for emergencies. He was viewed by the nurses as youthful, not always dependable, and, except in the ward accommodations, not "the real boss." The house officer's relations with the head nurses were complicated further by the fact that he was generally more interested in learning than in patient care, whereas the registered nurse was concerned about the care of patients in her charge. The private physician fed patients into the hospital, but he spent large segments of this time pursuing his office practice; hence he had to rely on the house officers and nurses to look after the patients for whom he was responsible. This problem was compounded for surgeons who divided their time among their offices, the operating room, and the floors on which their patients were housed. The private physician was, in reality, a small multitude of community physicians, each of whom had his own ways of dealing with patients both personally and technically. The nurses were forced to cope with the individualistic and often particularistic ways the different physicians carried on their hospital practices. One head nurse said:

Each one wants to get attention for his patients regardless of what the other patients need or what the problems of the nurses are at that time. They tend to blame the nurse too readily if patients complain about the care that's given to them. The nurse isn't always wrong.

Another nurse commented:

The intern and private doctor write contradictory orders. The house officer will ask you why something wasn't done and the attending will ask you who ordered it, and why some additional thing wasn't done. This leaves the poor nurse right in the middle. It's very frustrating to the nurse because she feels she's caught between the doctor and the patient or between a couple of doctors. The nurse spends a fair percentage of her time with these problems.

There's little rapport between the private doctor and the house officer in many situations. Also ninety-nine times out of one hundred, interns and attendings go into the isolation rooms not dressed properly. I don't see why it should be left up to the doctors to make the decision on isolation when the manual indicates that a certain patient should be isolated. That's procedure and, therefore, it should be followed. If they want it changed, they should go through channels of administration. This puts a nurse in a difficult position, especially in the eyes of the patient, because she is observing precautions but the doctors are not.

The head nurses have mixed feelings regarding physicians' demands. One said:

Frequently you just drop everything when they insist. This is something you come to expect. At times it may be very inconvenient, but you do it anyway. The doctor's purpose seems to be to have the nurse available when he wants to give orders.

Head nurses on the private accommodations were more subservient to the community practitioners than those on the semiprivate accommodations. One head nurse told us:

The private doctor does the ordering. He knows the illness of the patient and what has to be done. If there is any special care he tells the intern and the intern tells us or the doctor may tell us directly. Often the nurse has to request the house doctor to carry out the or ˙ ˙rs of the private doctor. Usually the house officers do this, but sometimes when work is not done the private physicians complain. I apologize for the error and go to work rectifying it.

The house officer showed the same interest in learning on the private accommodations as on the ward, and, though he was not truly responsible for the patient on the private accommodation, he often resisted the authority of the private physician. These strains operated to cause considerable confusion in nurse-physician relationships, especially those with house officers.

This type of situation was compounded further by the variation in responsibility assumed by private physicians. The private physician often did little or nothing for lower-status patients he admitted to the semiprivate or private accommodations, leaving their medical care largely to the house officers. (See Chapter 8, pp. 134–137.) When this occurred, the head nurse tried to avoid overt alignment with the house officer or the private physician, but she recognized the wisdom of siding covertly with the private doctor. The house officer was a temporary sojourner on her floor who would probably move on to another hospital and a different community in a few months; the private practitioner was a resident of the community with a stable practice, and the head nurse was likely to have to deal with him as long as she worked in the hospital. The house officers were aware of these problems and adapted to the covert alignment of the head nurses with the private physicians. One house officer who knew we were interviewing head nurses and private physicians asked, "What do the head nurses say these duckies [physicians] want of us?" Such feelings are understandable in the light of the following report by a head nurse on a private floor:

> Most of the private doctors are very careful with their patients. The house officers also should be careful of the person's background. Sometimes their approach toward the patient isn't very gentle. Then the patients don't want them near their rooms. We report this to the doctor in charge and the house officers are no longer allowed to go near that room. This makes the intern furious. Some interns just go in and give an I.V. [intravenous injection] and don't care how they turn it on. They don't go in a second time because the patients won't allow it. The private patient has his own doctor; he is of a different caliber and class and is used to having consideration on the outside. The poor patient on the ward has to accept these things.

The head nurse depended on the house staff and the attending physician. She realized that the organization of medical practice was largely responsible for the conflicts between the house staff and the private practitioners. When the house officer and the private physician clashed and an unsatisfactory relationship developed between the younger and the older man, the nurse was obliged to mediate between the doctors in order to solve problems of inconsistent or unclear direction for the care of the patient.

The house officers showed little concern for the role performance of the nurses as they tried to realize their ideals of giving tender loving care to distressed ward patients. The head nurses were particularly sensitive to the presence of medical students on the wards because they knew that medical students often disrupted nursing procedures. They were aware that some medical students offered remarkable help to troubled patients while others were rude, crude, and offensive to patients and nurses. Patients protested to the nurses but the house officers paid little heed to the complaints of the head nurses. Shortly after one head nurse had reported some complaints about medical students' behavior to an assistant resident instructing medical students, he said to them, "Go ahead. Examine the patients and ignore the nurses." This young physician told us afterward, "Medical students have to learn on clinical material so later on they will be able to practice on people."

The obligation to care for the down-and-out at a net loss to the hospital was a grim reality to the nurses who were forced to manage in ways acceptable to the community. The minimal staff had to provide for the physical needs of patients cared for on the medically indigent service. The desires of these patients were secondary to their physical care. The staff had to make choices concerning the priority of patients to be cared for and when and how they would be treated. For the most part, the staff was not disturbed with the choice they had to make between the realities of the situation and what they were taught unless they were reminded that other matters were being neglected; then, the system was not comfortable for anyone.

Nurses exhibited concern primarily when the ward was not running smoothly. They showed little concern about shoddy personal management of individual patients; evidently their impotence to make corrections prompted rationalized adjustments. The medical staff was little concerned about the nursing care of patients as long as their orders were carried out so that the patients' diseases were treated according to their prescriptions. Stated briefly, the primary tasks of the house officers and head nurses in the ward accommodation were to diagnose and treat physical diseases of patients. Both house officers and head nurses had responsibilities to teach the medical and nursing students at the same time they were caring for patients. Other than the points of tension concerning the immature professionals' roles and the occasional insecure or hostile nurse or intern, the nurses and physicians generally exhibited a good deal of respect for each other's performances; although they were quite distant from one another they worked together in reasonable harmony.

The head nurses had mixed feelings toward the house officers. On the positive side they saw the house officers as hard working young physicians of high caliber who cared for the illnesses of patients, and they realized the house officers supported them in their dealings with different patients. One nurse told us:

> The house officers save lives. They give us [the nurses] a lot of support and often follow our suggestions. The house officers are here much of the time. The interns certainly work very hard and I'm sure they don't get enough credit for what they do. The attendings are around daily but contact with them is limited.

Another reported:

> The house officers fulfill most of the requirements in caring for patients. I've become more sympathetic to their cause than I used to be. I used to be at odds with the doctors working on the floor, but now I help them out whenever I can.

Actually the total patient-care plan on this floor is the house officer's, with suggestions from the attending doctor. It's really a terrific learning floor. The interns enjoy it while they're here.

On the negative side, the house officers were viewed as novices who caused considerable upheaval in the operation of a patient-care unit. A surgical nurse reported:

The house officers lack maturity in dealing with patients, especially at the beginning. They get impatient quickly with a hesitant patient when they want to do a certain procedure. Some can be excessively demanding. Some of them fail to recognize exactly what the nursing staff does.

Another nurse reported:

In the beginning the young house officer usually makes a real production of both the technical and personal aspects of the care of his patients, but then he changes. Only a few retain their delight in patients. The new intern is particularistic and scared. He writes ten or twelve orders when two or three simple ones would do. This is extra work for the nurse. He wants to protect the patient and cover himself. He gives time to the patient which is good, but he is a greenhorn in writing orders. Later, he writes good, simple orders and ignores the patient. The nurse has to help solve the problems in both cases. No matter what, the nurse can't win.

Head nurses in the ward accommodation expressed their concern and sometimes alarm about the performance of house staff who bullied both nurses and patient alike, creating almost intolerable tensions. One said:

We have a lot of trouble with interns on this floor. Although they are reasonably conscientious workers they have no real concern about the patient. When the nurses can't get along with the house staff, the tension is felt by other staff on the floor, and this is indirectly taken out on the patients. When you have an inefficient intern the floor can't possibly be run smoothly because the nurse and the doctors are constantly pulling in different directions. The majority of interns and residents are reasonably good, but when you have a poor one you sure have a time.

Within the ward accommodations social status, work demands, and learning concerns operated to prevent a close relationship from developing between the doctors and patients or patients and nurses. This influenced the nurse-physician relationship.

In the semiprivate and private accommodations the relationship of the head nurse to physicians was changed by the fact that each patient was the direct responsibility of a particular physician. On the private accommodation, acceptable social status, privacy, and specialist supervision promoted harmony among physicians, nurses, and all others concerning the care of the patient. The rights of the patient usually prevailed and learning considerations were often set aside. The nurses were present more frequently and were more understanding. Although the private accommodations were the special preserve of the private-duty nurse, who constituted the most severely disruptive influence from the perspective of the head nurse, doctors and nurses worked together in greater harmony there than on the semiprivate floors.

In short, the roles of nurses were complex and fraught with internal and external contradictions. The head nurses expressed dissatisfaction with many of their duties. Their greatest claimed source of satisfaction lay in caring directly for patients. Nevertheless, the head nurses spent only a small percentage of their time in face-to-face contact with patients, and even then the contact was fleeting. (Data supporting this statement are presented in Chapter 11.) Although registered nurses realized that they contributed to patient care in other ways, few were able to reconcile their lack of patient contact with their ideals.

Supervisors, assistant directors, associate directors, and the Director of the Department of Nursing comprised the upper echelons of the nursing hierarchy. The head nurses had mixed feelings about their supervisors. The majority thought the supervisors failed to understand their problems. The head nurse often resorted to seeking support from the attending physicians when she couldn't get it from the nursing department. Many head nurses were dissatisfied with the nursing department's administration, but they felt powerless to do anything about changing the conditions under which they worked. Even nurses who were displeased with their social contacts with desirable bachelors in the School of Medicine often blamed the Department of Nursing and, incongruous as this may seem, the complaints were bitter ones.

The head nurses as well as the supervisors recognized the need to "cover" the hospital areas and, therefore, the need to be quite ruthless in the assignment and manipulation of the staff, but their recognition of the need did not lessen the discontent arising from reassignment of nurses to areas they disliked. The nursing department became the logical target for criticism. There were, however, some nurses who enjoyed the administrative role and the challenge of bringing order out of confusion, of being forced to deal with crises day after day. Several head nurses were using their current positions to prepare themselves for higher administrative posts or positions in nursing education.

There were nurses, especially in the Community Division, who thought their supervisors were helpful to them directly in the solution of their more difficult problems, but most head nurses were uneasy because they realized the administrators of the nursing department were distant from patient care and did not readily understand their problems. Nurse L reported:

I think about the problems we [the head nurses] have brought up again and again in meeting after meeting with the nursing administrators. When there is no indication that anything has been done about them, it's discouraging. No one takes the actual time to go over what may have taken place or see if there's any interest in the problem. Occasionally there are exceptions to this, but we become discouraged from bringing up anything that is a real problem to us. The meetings are a waste of time as far as most of us are concerned. A while ago we let our hair down and brought up some good ideas. Following the meeting we asked if anything had been done about them. We were told off cold that this would not be discussed in future head nurses' meetings. Everybody was pretty disgusted after that.

When questioned about the nursing administrators, most physicians expressed appreciation of the capabilities of the supervisors to provide staff, at least in an emergency, at a minimal level and to provide suitable equipment. They also found supervisors useful to them in recruiting private-duty nurses for their private patients. Some physicians recognized the capabilities of individual nurses as administrators, but the majority had sharp criticism of the more senior, directing authorities in the nursing department. Several physicians declined to discuss the nursing department because they chose not to "become embroiled in that old subject." This feeling was very strong and problems inherent in the department were viewed as unsolvable, at least at that time.

The majority of physicians indicated their contacts with the administration of the nursing department were indirect ones. They listened frequently to the complaints of head nurses who felt abused by the Department of Nursing and the hospital. The physicians' contacts with the nursing department usually came about when the head nurse brought issues involving doctors to the attention of the administrators in the Department of Nursing. The doctors, as self-directed professionals, did not welcome challenges from the nurses even though the policy to which the nurses adhered was set by the Medical Board of the hospital. From such experiences, physicians became biased and antagonistic toward the nursing department.

Physicians indicated they were distant from the nursing supervisors. In the words of one specialist:

I don't see the nursing supervisors. They work at another level and primarily with nurses. I have been aware of some nursing supervisors who are very good and some very bad. Frequently they are very disagreeable to the house officers who are vulnerable persons, but they have a lot of facility in getting things done, especially at night.

Another practitioner reported:

I have no experience with the nursing supervisors. It's not an area of my concern. I guess their duties are defined some place, but I don't have any knowledge to comment on them.

The hospital administrators were divided in their views of the Department of Nursing. The Executive Director believed the hospital was dependent upon the nursing department to manage its patient-care units. This officer gave full support to the nursing department and was prepared to defend the nurses against all others, whether practitioners, professors, or administrators. The Executive Director told us:

> Doctors complain to me about the poor performance of the nurses. Actually a good deal of this is poor performance by the doctors. Some doctors tell me we don't need the nursing supervisors. I don't see that at all. We need someone to evaluate the nursing staff on the floors and give them supervision.

All administrators viewed the nurses as responsible for administering patient care on the floor, but they thought the nurses were poor administrators, especially on the supervisory level and higher. They criticized the registered nurses for their inconsistencies in wanting and at the same time rejecting more patient contact. They viewed the nurse's cherished role of providing personal bedside care to patients as an outmoded romantic illusion in the modern hospital. Nevertheless, they agreed that the registered nurses on the patient-care divisions were capable of good technical performance in giving medications, assisting in emergencies, and directing the ancillary staff. They admired the individual nurse's abilities as a manager and a skilled worker but they were critical of the organization and administration of the nursing department and they were hostile to the nurses as a group. These hospital administrators viewed the nursing department as a rigid hierarchy, defensive of all that is nursing, obstructive, secretive, and ambiguous in their behavior. They reported that nursing administrators influenced the head nurses unfavorably. Administrator A said:

> The registered nurses complain about this administrative role of theirs, but the whole nursing hierarchy is inconsistent. They say they need more patient contact and that patients need them. I agree, but they will not give up their administrative responsibilities when they are given an opportunity to do so. I have a strong feeling that nurses are scared to be with patients. For some reason they're going away from the patients rather than going towards them. Basically I see their role as being with the patient, but I think this is not being carried out.

A second administrator carried this line of thinking further:

> The registered nurse doesn't know how to meet the emotional needs of patients. She does not help the patient psychologically to adjust to the hospital environment. She is actually fearful of getting into personal relationships with ordinary patients, although she definitely enters into personal relationships with the VIP's.

A third administrator said:

The nurses are involved in record-keeping, ordering, and that sort of thing. They maintain that they have to copy the doctors' orders, but I don't know just how legitimate that is. They're tied up in paper work and administrative details. The nurses complain that they're not able to do things for patients. I have the feeling that they really don't want to do anything for the patients anyway.

Some hospital administrators were irritated by the complicated bureaucracy that regulated internal communications within and between the various levels. One stated:

The head nurses believe they are not heard. Their only recourse is through their supervisor; she gets to an assistant director and then to an associate director, and finally to the Director of Nursing. By that time the damn problem is so watered down that the Director of Nursing doesn't know what's happened. Everybody is fighting for her own survival.

When I start an investigation of a complaint by a patient, I usually hear an overwhelming counter-complaint about the patient from the nurses. They are extremely defensive. They tell me the trouble is with the patient. They tell me they couldn't do anything to satisfy him. They aren't really interested in trying to satisfy or even understand the patient.

Another administrator said:

In the University Division the supervisors are chiefly a buffer for the house staff. In the Community Division, they assist the head nurses and do a pretty good job. They're afraid as hell but they're pretty sure of the support of the administrator. It irritates me that I can't talk with the nursing administrator. I can't get past her secretary. I've learned one thing. If I ever administer a hospital, I'll never make a director of nursing an assistant director of the hospital. I think this is a bad mistake in organization.

Still another administrator indicated his irritation with the nursing department:

The nurses feel that an administrator can't direct the nursing department but they see nothing wrong with a nurse becoming a hospital administrator. Nurses are a very tight profession in which they jealously guard their status from people outside. Communications break down and everyone beats on the nurse. Instead of patting her on the back and giving her a little credit, they kick her in the butt. Nursing morale is low. I try to interest the nurses into looking at their morale which I feel is a problem, but I get blank looks and lifted eyebrows. "What do you mean morale?" Well, I didn't know that was a new thing!

I think supervisors could be eliminated, probably to the advantage of both the head nurse and the persons higher up. The head nurse is the most important person in the whole nursing department. Patient care, liaison with physicians, and communications with hospital administration all depend upon her. When the supervisors fail to perceive and communicate, the head nurse fails. The nursing department attributes this to the shortage of nurses and to the difficulty they have in getting along with doctors. This is a stock answer. I believe the low morale is the result of problems between the nursing department and hospital administrators rather than in patient care or the relationships with doctors. Some of us have told the nursing administration that the doctors are often wrong, but they aren't wrong often enough to account for all these problems.

The hospital's administration relied heavily upon the powerful, long-established matriarchal nursing department for the direction of its patient-care units. The inconsistencies reported in the nursing department were, in part, a projection of the inconsistencies built into the organization of the patient-care units. The diversity of opinion among the administrators caused conflict within the administration over the direction of the nursing department, but it was held in check because the senior authority's decision was clear. It may be suggested that support for the nursing hierarchy was support for the status quo in which the nurse was largely an administrator; therefore, she could not offer personal care of a compassionate nature to the deeply troubled sick.

In the social structure of the hospital, private-duty nurses were a peripheral group; nevertheless, they were present in large numbers, particularly in the private accommodations. All private-duty nurses were registered. Each provided personal care for a single patient who was not necessarily critically ill. Each private-duty nurse was an individual entrepreneur, not a salaried member of the hospital's staff. A private-duty nurse sketched her position for us in these words:

The private-duty nurse is an independent contractor. It's a financial, contractual relationship between the private-duty nurse and the patient or the patient's family. A good many private-duty nurses are, shall I say, rugged individuals.

Except in instances when the hospital arranged special care for a ward patient, the private-duty nurse was paid directly by the patient or by his family, as was the private attending physician. The private-duty nurse was in charge of her patient; she guarded what she believed to be his interests with jealous solicitude. Another private-duty nurse told us:

We represent the old-fashioned idea of nursing, where a nurse has intimate contact with the patient. She does everything for the patient. She is a buffer between the patient, the medical staff, the dietary staff, head nurse, and so on.

By acting in this manner, the private-duty nurse indulged in more or less covert warfare with the staff nurses for supremacy and resented all interfer-

ence in what she felt were her prerogatives. The private-duty ı
manipulated patients, families, and even doctors through selective
cation and judicious advice that were perhaps more in her intereş
that of the patient she was nursing. (This point is discussed in Ch.
pp. 240–241.)

The attitudes of the private-duty nurses toward their work and the
were markedly different from those held by the head nurses. The reg
nurses, who were hospital employees, directed their strongest criticisms ι
patients and families, and, to some extent, toward the private attending
sicians. The private-duty nurses were most favorable to precisely these gr
they aimed their sharpest criticisms at the staff registered nurses, the anci
staff, the administration, and to a lesser degree the house officers. The
tern is clear: Staff nurses criticized nonhospital people, while private-c
nurses criticized hospital personnel.

Private-duty nurses saw themselves as the true nurses; they viewed he
nurses as administrators who have left nursing and the licensed practic
nurses as upstarts. They accused the staff nurses of neglecting patients so th
work had to be done by private-duty nurses. One private-duty nurse told us

> I think the floor nurses should be prepared to give us an adequate report on a sick
> patient and not leave all the work for us to do like cleaning up the room, but
> this happens all the time. Particularly when a patient has only one shift of private-
> duty nurses, you know he has not been touched from the time you leave until you
> return 16 hours later. I know this is so because I mark the sheets like the other
> private-duty nurses do. We see those little crosses we leave all the time, and we
> find that the patient has been in a soiled bed possibly without any care, waiting
> for us to come back.

The private-duty nurses felt that the staff nurses were hostile and unappreciative of them. Nurse K told us:

> I came on the floor not too long ago and my greeting from the charge nurse during
> report was, "Ha, so now he's [the patient] got a special nurse! We weren't
> good enough to take care of him." Do you realize this attitude was absorbed by
> everyone because that one nurse set the example. For the time I was on that floor,
> that attitude remained.

The private-duty nurses were critical of the nurses chosen by the nursing
administration for promotion to the head positions. One private-duty nurse
commented, "I feel the worst possible nurse condoning anything would be a
tremendous success here, and a good nurse would be let go. I have seen it
happen time and time again." The private-duty nurses believed the house
officers were unappreciative and unfriendly, if not insulting, in their deroga-
tory references to them. One said:

tagious disease, was considered a poor credit risk, or was of low social class. The administrators were annoyed with private-duty nurses who behaved in such ways.

Physicians were generally as critical of private-duty nurses as were others in the institution. One physician reported:

> Okay, sometimes the patients are deathly ill, but sometimes they're not. These nurses, for the most part, have little feeling of obligation to patients because they can, and do, sign off whenever they want to. "Sorry, I can only work three days because the weekend is coming up." So they leave. They feel no obligation to be on at all times. If you're operating on a patient on Saturday—a big operation— you can't get a special-duty nurse. You call the Nursing Registry—"I'm sorry, we have nobody on." The Nursing Registry doesn't take it upon themselves to have somebody for you if you need her. The private-duty nurse business is a crime, I think. It hits a patient for $84 a day to have nurses around the clock. That's a lot of money.

Some private physicians used selected private-duty nurses especially for their high-status patients and were satisfied with them, but the majority of physicians were critical of private-duty nurses because of their unwillingness to work with patients they considered undesirable and their freedom to abandon patients unfortunate enough to be ill on the weekend or to have a contagious disease which frightened away private-duty nurses. Many physicians were insulting in their remarks concerning private-duty nurses, whom they viewed more as chambermaids and companions than as competent nurses. Several of the senior physicians were relieved that the hospital had begun to make adjustments in the patterns of patient care so that selected, acutely ill patients could be cared for in a suitable fashion in the intensive-care units where well-trained personnel were brought together with special equipment to perform the necessary diagnostic and treatment procedures. These physicians believed that private-duty nurses were not only often unavailable when needed but were incompetent. One senior specialist who usually had several patients in the hospital reported, "We [physicians] don't trust the private-duty nurses with the very sick any more. We find the intensive-care unit far more suitable."

As a group, the private-duty nurses were deeply troubled concerning their contributions to patient care, their relationships within the hospital, and what they feared, quite realistically, might be their progressive displacement by licensed practical nurses and intensive-care units. They recognized that their employment was by high-status patients and that they were being used often as companions and chambermaids rather than as nurses in the professional sense of the term. They were humiliated by this, and some showed a sense of guilt because they did not care for sicker patients. However problematic the situation may be, it is evident that the services of private-duty nurses will be in demand as long as the services provided by the hospital are viewed as insufficient. Private-duty nurses were promoting this feeling of insufficiency in their own defense, and the sick were prey to their manipulations.

It is probable that the private-duty nurse, in selected instances, was the most effective of all the registered nurses in providing a superior technical and personal service to patients. Despite the neutrality or even antagonism of most groups, the power these nurses derived was considerable, but some adjustment will be necessary for their continued effectiveness in the hospital setting.

The ancillary staff consisted of licensed practical nurses and aides. A discerning patient told us, "The registered nurse runs the show, the LPNs take care of patients, and the aides do the chores." The licensed practical nurse was viewed by others and by herself as a person who gave patients bedside care. A number of licensed practical nurses realized they were doing more and more things formerly done by registered nurses. They recognized that they were developing favorable status from their advantageous proximity to the patients. The licensed practical nurses were the most stable group of employees in the nursing department. Many had already had their families and possessed a good deal of common sense in the care of sick persons. Sometimes difficult situations arose, however, when a younger registered nurse had to supervise an older, more mature licensed practical nurse or when a licensed practical nurse, who was sometimes left in charge of a patient-care division, had to supervise a registered nurse on private duty with a given patient on that division.

Licensed practical nurses viewed themselves as being much above the aides in ability, social status on the floor, and responsibility in the bedside care of patients. Although physicians and administrators were somewhat anxious about the technical competence of licensed practical nurses to carry out the duties assigned to them, they knew these women were filling a vital role in the work of the hospital. Some licensed practical nurses recognized their dependency upon the registered nurse and accepted it with appreciation, but there was rivalry between licensed practical nurses and registered nurses. One registered nurse told us:

> The LPNs are beginning to feel their oats. They are doing more and more of the things that we should be doing but can't with all these administrative chores. The registered nurse must still supervise and direct the LPNs.

The licensed practical nurse faced the same dilemma as the registered nurse regarding promotion in the hospital. Those providing the most direct care were not rewarded highly for their efforts nor given opportunities for advancement except by abandoning their direct care of patients.

The lowest rung on the ladder of patient care was occupied by the nurse's aides. Most aides were far removed from the physicians and administrators. The physicians were aware, for example, that the more stable aides were assigned to the private accommodations in which they, along with others of the nursing staff, carried out the care of higher-status patients. Some aides were recognized to be superior individuals who were more competent than the less able licensed practical nurses. To the Department of Nursing the aides were an important source of recruitment of licensed practical nurse students. There was a constant effort to screen out the less able aides, keep the better ones, and encourage selected ones to take licensed practical-nurse training so they could become even more useful to the hospital.

There was a high turnover in this group, some of whom were described to us as disinterested, poorly educated, and ineffective. Most administrators believed the turnover would have been higher if the hospital discharged the mediocre aides. However, the salary level was so low that the hospital had difficulty recruiting enough aides, and the Department of Nursing was reluctant to discharge an aide unless she was really incompetent.

Summary

The Department of Nursing employed more personnel than any other department in the hospital. Its employees ranged from highly trained women with graduate professional degrees in nursing to high school dropouts who functioned as nurse's aides. A complicated bureaucratic structure—the nursing hierarchy—developed to administer the activities assigned to the nursing department. Although the head nurse on a patient-care division was a key person in the nursing hierarchy, she was in an unenviable position. She carried responsibility for the conduct of other people; she had to perform an array of tasks requiring a number of different skills; her rewards were not high; and she could not advance in the nursing hierarchy without leaving active nursing to become more of an administrator than she was. Two lines of authority converged in her position. The head nurse, or her alternate the "charge nurse," was usually the only registered nurse on the floor who was responsible to the hospital. At all times she had to be conscious of her position as the chief agent of the hospital in delivering its services to patients on the division under her direction, but she was also the personal representative of the physician caring for a particular patient on her floor. She had to follow orders of the medical staff, and in so doing she was "caught in the middle" when the attending physician and the house officer held different views of the patient's problems and issued different orders for his care. At the same time, the head nurse also had to supervise her ancillary staff, administer medications, comfort patients and deal with distraught families, keep an extensive set of records, and report to her supervisors in nursing administration. In addition, she frequently had teaching responsibility for nursing students.

We drew freely upon the tape-recorded interviews for the answers to questions about interrelations between nurses, administrators, and physicians. We found that head nurses realized their dilemma. They knew they could not at the same time be administrators and care for patients in a personal way. The nursing supervisors understood the conflicts of the head nurse better than the higher-ranking nursing department administrators, hospital administrators, or physicians. The hospital administrators pointed out that the efficient use of the head nurse's time precluded close nurse-patient relationships, and attending physicians generally expressed appreciation for the skill head nurses exhibited in their administration of the patient-care divisions.

Private-duty nurses were a special group of registered nurses who worked in the hospital but were not hospital employees. They guarded with jealous solicitude what they considered to be their particular patient's interests, which incidentally were often their own. Private-duty nurses were engaged primarily in caring for patients on private accommodations. There was mutual hostility between registered nurses employed by the hospital and private-duty nurses caring for a patient on the same division.

Licensed practical nurses and nurse's aides worked in all the accommodations and patient-care divisions. As a group, the licensed practical nurses were the most stable employees in the Department of Nursing. Head nurses, hospital administrators, and physicians were in agreement with the licensed practical nurses, themselves, on the importance of the licensed practical nurse in the personal care of patients.

Nurse's aides occupied the lowest position in the nursing hierarchy. Their function was primarily oriented toward chores integral to the care of patients. They were poorly paid and there was a high rate of turnover in the group.

I N OUR DESIGN OF THE STUDY WE VISUALIZED THE FAMILY as of central importance to an understanding of the care each patient received during his illness. The sick person lived in a family before he came to the hospital, and the family was the social group to which he, hopefully, returned after his discharge from the hospital. Our definition of the *effective social environment* (see Chapter 1, p. 3) is focused on the family. The family has a social structure and a position in the community. Historically, the family is much older than the hospital and of more importance to the general welfare of its members. Viewed theoretically, the family is a key unit in society. Each person is born into a family legitimately, or he is born illegitimately, outside of a family. In the course of a normal life cycle each person is a member of two nuclear family groups—the family of orientation into which he is born and the family of procreation which he creates when he marries. Our research design specified that each patient would be a *principal member* of a family of procreation. We define *principal member* as either the husband or wife of a spouse pair who live in the same household. Each family, brought into our sample by selection of one spouse who was admitted to the hospital, shared a series of sociobiographical characteristics comparable to those of all other families in the study. One of our objectives was to learn whether the families who utilized the different facilities provided by the hospital were similar to or different from one another when viewed from the perspective of their bio-social characteristics. Therefore, in the first half of this chapter we focus attention upon sociobiographic characteristics common to all families and show how they were or were not related to the accommodations and services the hospital provided for persons who were admitted as inpatients. In the second part of this chapter we examine the inner structure of families from the perspective of the adjustment the several members exhibited in their behavior toward one another. In later chapters we will refer to these data to help us answer questions around which this research is focused.

The age range for the selection of the patient is a sample specification. Our primary interest is the age of the patient, rather than the age of the spouse. Therefore, we established forty and sixty-four years of age as the lower and upper limits for patients included in the study, but we did not specify any age range for the spouses of patients. (The age of a patient and the age of his spouse could conceivably be similar or quite different.) In the following discussion, we present first the data for the patients by sex for each five-year group; then we present and discuss the ages of the patients' spouses.

TABLE 4. DISTRIBUTION OF PATIENTS BY SEX, AGE GROUP, AND ACCOMMODATION

Age Groups	Patients by Accommodation		
	Private	Semiprivate	Ward
A. Females			
40–44 years	26%	32%	18%
45–49 years	18	24	9
50–54 years	32	20	9
55–59 years	18	8	32
60–64 years	6	16	32
N =	(34)	(25)	(22)
p > .05 for each accommodation in comparison with other accommodations.			
B. Males			
40–44 years	13%	14%	20%
45–49 years	23	17	25
50–54 years	23	27	15
55–59 years	22	15	15
60–64 years	19	28	25
N =	(31)	(29)	(20)
p > .05 for each accommodation in comparison with other accommodations.			

The figures in Table 4 show that age was not linked to accommodation in either sex. We stress this point because particular forms of disease are associated in significant ways with both sex and age. The distribution of ages within the patient groups shows some variation from one type of accommodation to another and from one five-year age group to another, but these differences are not significant for either sex. Other tabulations and tests of significance revealed no association between age and sex and the service on which the patients were treated.

When we examine the data on age from the perspective of the spouse pair, we find the husbands were approximately the same age whether they were patients or the spouses of patients in the three accommodations. The mean age of the husbands of families represented in each accommodation is: private, 54 years; semiprivate, 53 years; and ward, 54 years. The same finding holds for the wives whether they were patients or the wives of patients; there is no significant difference from one accommodation to another. The mean age of the wives by accommodation is: private, 50 years; semiprivate, 50 years; and ward, 52 years. The same general finding holds when the data on age and sex are examined by service of treatment. The differences in the mean ages of the husbands in comparison with the wives is attributable to the marked tendency in our society for men to marry women of their own age or younger than themselves.

The religious affiliation of husbands and wives was similar within each type of accommodation and service. Catholics predominated in the ward and semiprivate accommodations, whereas Protestants were about equally divided in the three accommodations. Jewish patients, singularly absent from the wards, were concentrated in the private divisions of the hospital: Only one Jewish patient was found on the ward service. By denominational affiliation, the private patients were significantly different from the ward and semiprivate patients, but the religious identifications of the families who used the semiprivate accommodations did not differ from those who used the wards.

All of the patients and their spouses were Caucasian and predominantly native-born; fewer than 20 per cent of each sex were from a foreign country. Two out of three of the husbands represented in the ward and semiprivate groups and three out of four of the wives were native to New England. The private group revealed a higher percentage of husbands and wives who came from other parts of the United States. From the perspective of nativity, there are no meaningful differences among the three types of accommodation and the two services under study.

The families exhibited a high percentage of first marriages for both spouses; only 18 per cent of the husbands or wives had been married at least once before. There are no significant differences from one accommodation or service to the others. There were children in 91 per cent of the families. The number of children in the family does not differ from one accommodation or service to another. This generalization holds for families whether the present husband and wife were the parents of the children, the husband was the father of all or some of the children, or the wife was the mother of all or some of the children. Generally, parents in their forties and early fifties had children still living in the parental home; parents in their later fifties and sixties did not usually have children at home.

The proportion of families who shared their homes with persons other than the members of the nuclear family did not differ significantly from one accommodation or service to another. The private patients tended to live in homes in which there was no sharing, but the figures are too small to be meaningful. The specific percentages of families who shared their homes are: private, 8 per cent; semiprivate, 16 per cent; and ward, 18 per cent.

The socioeconomic status of each family was calculated by the use of Hollingshead's *Two Factor Index of Social Position*.[1] This index relies upon the occupation and the years of school completed by the household head to estimate the socioeconomic status of a family. Each component is ordered on a 7-step scale and weighted by a statistically determined value. The weighing factor for occupation is 7, for educational achievement 4. The scale score of each factor is multiplied by the factor weight to obtain a partial score. The partial scores for occupation and education are summed to give the total score for the household. The Two Factor Index scores for socioemonomic status range from a high of 11 to a low of 77.

Socioeconomic scores are linked to the accommodations families utilized when either the husband or the wife was hospitalized. Families of higher socioeconomic status used the private accommodations; the mean Index of Social Position score of families who selected the private accommodations is 33. Families represented in the semiprivate accommodations were of medium socioeconomic status with a mean score of 53, while those on the ward accommodations had a mean score of 63. These scores are significantly different from one another. Stated otherwise, there is a direct relationship between socioeconomic status in the community and the accommodation used in the hospital. The Index of Social Position scores for patients on the medical and surgical services do not differ significantly from one another in any accommodation; that is, when we control for accommodation the Index of Social Position scores are similar for each of the two services and both sexes.

From the viewpoint of occupation only, the private patients were significantly different from the semiprivate patients and from the ward patients. Two private patients out of three came from families headed by a professional, executive, or managerial worker. Among the ward patients, only one in 20 came from families headed by a worker who could possibly be considered a managerial employee; one husband in the ward group, so categorized, managed a small custodial service; the other was a distributor of pornographic motion pictures shown at men's parties. Although there was a higher percentage of managerial workers among those in the semiprivate accommodations, both the ward and the semiprivate accommodations were used in large part by manual workers. The occupational differences between the husbands in families whose members were housed on ward accommodations and those in semiprivate accommodations are not significant.

We gathered data also on the occupation of the wives. More than one half were housewives. There was a slight tendency for fewer wives to be gainfully employed among the families who used the private accommodations whether they were treated on the medical or the surgical services, in comparison with those who used the other accommodations. Among the wives who were gainfully employed, there were significant differences between the private and semiprivate groups and the private and ward groups. The largest differences between occupations followed by the wives in a family with a hospitalized member occurred among the women in the private accommodations who were professional, executive, or managerial workers. The opposite trend was in manual employment; few families with wives who did manual work occupied private rooms; such work was concentrated among the wives of those families utilizing semiprivate and ward services.

The level of educational achievement of the husbands in the three accommodations traced a similar pattern to that of the level of occupation. The husbands in the private group completed significantly more years of formal schooling than those in the other two groups. There were slight differences between the husbands of families using the ward and those who used the semiprivate accommodations but they are attributable to chance factors. (See Table 5.) Among the wives, educational achievement traced a pattern similar to occupation: There were significant differences between the levels of education reported by the wives in the private group and those in the semiprivate and the ward groups, but there was no meaningful difference between the ward and the semiprivate groups.

The dollar income is another measure of socioeconomic status. We asked

TABLE 5. LEVEL OF EDUCATION OF PATIENTS AND SPOUSES, BY ACCOMMODATION

Level of Education	Patients and Spouses by Accommodation		
	Private	Semiprivate	Ward
A. Males (Patients and husbands of patients)			
One year of college and more	45%	9%	6%
High school graduate	26	13	20
Less than high school graduation	29	78	74
N =	(65)	(54)	(42)

Private compared with semiprivate, p < .05; private compared with ward, p < .05; semiprivate compared with ward, p > .05.

B. Females (Patients and wives of patients)			
One year of college and more	30%	9%	7%
High school graduate	38	32	30
Less than high school graduation	32	59	63
N =	(65)	(54)	(42)

Private compared with semiprivate, p < .05; private compared with ward, p < .05; semiprivate compared with ward, p > .05.

each family about its income during the year preceding the hospitalization. The amounts ranged from less than $1,000 to more than $100,000. The family with the lowest income was on "town relief"; the sick member was an indigent patient in the ward accommodation. The family with the largest reported income lived on an exclusive estate and had national business and social connections; the sick member was housed in a deluxe private suite in the hospital. While these two examples are extremes, the median figures for annual income reveal a distinct association between income and accommodation: private, $12,691; semiprivate, $6,228; and ward, $4,254. Although the figures reported here are medians, we tested for significance of differences between the means and found each mean to be significantly different from the other two. No meaningful differences were found between the mean annual incomes of medical and surgical patients within each of the three accommodations.

The median and mean income figures are a reflection of the socioeconomic differences between the families indicated by the *Two Factor Index of Social Position*. Families with high numerical scores on the Index of Social Position tend to have low incomes; families with relatively high incomes usually have low scores on the Index of Social Position. The figures on median family income also mirror the sharp differences among the persons who were found in the different accommodations. Between the private and semiprivate patients there were $6,463 in income and 20 points on the Index of Social Position scale. The differences were not so great between those in the semiprivate and those in the ward accommodations. Persons who utilized the semiprivate accommodations were much closer in socioeconomic status to families dependent upon the ward service than they were to families who chose private accommodations.

From the beginning of the study of each family until the conclusion of the fieldwork on it, we were concerned with behavior—of the spouses to one another, of the parents to the children, and of the children to the parents—and the actions of family members in their relationships with nurses, physicians, and other hospital personnel. The stories family members told us about themselves and other persons in the family and in the community also were of interest in helping us understand the family. These stories, observations, and identifications the different family members made to the patient, to one another, and to persons involved in their care became the basis of our evaluation of family adjustment. *Adjustment* of persons to one another and to their social situations, as used here, is a judgment of the behavior of indivduals as they interact within the family and in the social space encompassing them. The adjustment of family members to one another, to the neighborhod, and to the larger community is a discernible dimension of the social situation in which families are enmeshed. Adjustment of one person to another is a subtle quality. Although it is hard to define, it is an important factor in the interpersonal relations of family members and it may be a meaningful component in what happens to a sick person before he reaches the hospital, during the hospitalization, and subsequently.

We do not have a measure of family adjustment such as we have of socioeconomic status. Nevertheless, we made a global judgment of the functioning of indviduals as members of the family and within the larger community. We grouped our judgments of family adjustment into three categories: *adjusted, moderately maladjusted,* and *severely maladjusted.* The placement of a family into one of these three categories is based upon our assessment of all the evidence we gathered on the family. The judgment was made by each author independently. When their judgments differed, re-examination was made of the detailed materials gathered on the family from all the persons who were interviewed or observed while the family was being studied. After restudying the data, a collaborative judgment of the family's adjustment was reached. Within each of the three categories there are broad limits of specific behavior which varied from family to family. Rather than attempt to define precisely what we mean by each category, we present brief statements of particular family situations and tell the story of a family in each category to give the reader an understanding of what we mean by adjusted, moderately maladjusted, and severely maladjusted. Each family story is one of a number of such family stories that might have been used to indicate the types of behavior associated with the category. There are differences in specific details of behavior and interaction within the family from one family to another in each category, but there were no differences in our judgment of how to classify a family.

Mr. and Mrs. Ash represent an adjusted family. We saw them for the first time in the hospital room to which Mr. Ash had been taken on a stretcher a few hours before. Mrs. Ash was sitting beside the bed holding one of his hands in hers and stroking it. Mr. Ash greeted us with a weak smile on his pallid face. Mrs. Ash, who was carefully groomed and neatly dressed, was cordial but guarded in her behavior. We told the Ashes their private physician had given his consent for us to approach them to take part in a study we were making, and they readily agreed to cooperate.

Mr. Ash is the foreman of a crew of some thirty men working on outdoor projects. He has been employed continuously by the state for almost twenty-five years and is within a few months of retirement on a pension. Six years ago they built a five-room Cape Cod house located in one of the suburban towns. Almost every evening and on weekends Mr. Ash works around the house. He has a workshop in the basement where he repairs household appliances for his wife and other family members and toys for the children in the area. He is known in the neighborhood as the man to go to when you want something done. He has always been an ardent do-it-yourself person. He looks forward, with only a certain measure of anxiety, to his retirement, when he plans to spend all his time refinishing furniture and following his other hobbies.

Mr. and Mrs. Ash are practicing Roman Catholics. Both were widowed when they married some fifteen years ago. Mrs. Ash lost her first husband about twenty years ago; she had no children. Mr. Ash and his first wife had two sons and two daughters and two adopted sons. After his first wife died Mr. Ash lived alone with his children. Upon remarriage to his present wife, he and the six children moved into her fourteen-room home, inherited from her parents. The second Mrs. Ash completed the rearing of the children. She saw that they all finished high school, obtained jobs, and as time passed were married and began to raise families of their own. Her ancestral home was sold, and the couple built their present smaller home.

Mr. Ash has been an active participant in community affairs since he was a young man. As a youth he played on the town's baseball team. Later, he helped promote amateur athletics among the young men of the town. He has been a member of the town's vounteer fire department for over thirty years. Mrs. Ash has been a member of women's groups in the church and the community. She is particularly interested in aid to crippled children, as she suffered from a severe malady of unknown origin when she was about 16 years of age.

The six families of procreation stemming from this family all live in the community and all have children of their own. The different families visit one another almost every week; in addition, there is lively telephone communication between them. Both Mr. and Mrs. Ash look forward to the time when one or another of the older grandchildren will marry and have children. They anticipate with pleasure becoming great-grandparents.

Mr. Ash reports that this is his first hospitalization and that he has never been sick "a day in my whole life." The onset of his illness was sudden, unexpected, and dramatic. After returning together from Mass, the Ashes sat down to have breakfast. Mrs. Ash noted that Mr. Ash was pale and his hands and arms were shaking. Although he insisted that he was all right, she went into another room and called their oldest son on the telephone; she also telephoned their physician to ask him to come right over. When she returned to the living room she found Mr. Ash stretched out on the floor. She hurriedly telephoned the fire department for the emergency ambulance and the church for their priest. Within a few minutes the physician, the oldest son and his wife, the priest, and the ambulance all converged on their home.

While Mr. Ash was in the hospital, Mrs. Ash visited him daily. Every evening she telephoned the oldest son's wife to tell her of "Pappa's" progress. There was close communication among the several family members. When Mr. Ash was able to have visitors the family members came in rotation. Before he left the hospital all of his children, their spouses, and his fourteen grandchildren had come to see him. After his return home, Mrs. Ash each day made a report about his condition to one of the children in a system of unified reports decided upon by the family so that Mr. Ash would not be annoyed by telephone calls.

Mrs. Ash is unquestionably the social and business manager of the family, a point of pride with Mr. Ash. He has handed her his paycheck on payday ever since they were married. He told us, "She never wasted a nickel and she gets a nickel-and-a-half's worth out of every nickel." He never worried about the hospital bill as the family had insurance; he said, "Mother has the money. When I walk out of this hospital every penny of that bill will be paid." Throughout the hospitalization and during the home visits, we heard or observed nothing that would lead us to believe that there is any disruptive tension in this family. Mr. and Mrs. Ash are emotionally very close. They live for one another, for the children, and for the grandchildren. Their adjustment within the family, to the neighborhood, and to the community is wholesome. Mr. Ash's physician characterized him as "John Q. Citizen, U.S.A."

The Beech family represents those judged to be moderately maladjusted. Mr. and Mrs. Beech and their teen-age son and daughter live in a six-room house in one of the suburban towns. Mr. Beech is a minor official in a small construction company. The family moved to this community from a nearby state at the end of World War II when Mr. Beech took the job with his present company. The two parental families had lived in the same town and the same neighborhood. Mr. and Mrs. Beech had played together when they were small children, gone to school together, courted, and eventually married. Their removal to this area occurred when their elder child, the daughter, was a baby, and it was their first effort to become independent from their parental families. However, some time after they moved to this city, Mrs. Beech's mother moved here so she could be near her daughter. Before long, Mr. Beech's parents moved here also so that the elder Mrs. Beech could visit with her son every day.

When the young couple first moved to the community, they rented an upstairs flat. The man who owned the property lived downstairs. For amusement, this man locked Mrs. Beech out of her apartment while her small daughter was inside. On several occasions he locked Mrs. Beech in the basement. Before they could find adequate housing in the tight market following

World War II, Mr. Beech developed a stomach ulcer and Mrs. Beech became a "nervous wreck." Mr. Beech, periodically, has suffered from intestinal difficulties which his physician attributes to nerves. Mrs. Beech realizes her husband is susceptible to emotional upsets when things do not go well for him, when his mother fills him with "her goodies," or when the children make demands on the family.

For several months before Mr. Beech's admission to the hospital, their life situation had been growing worse. Mr. Beech made a series of mistakes in estimating the cost of jobs his firm was bidding on; in one two-week period the firm lost five jobs upon which he made estimates. The year before the firm had not given him a bonus, and to make matters worse the teen-age son and daughter had talked their parents into buying an English sportscar for them. As Mr. Beech became more tense and worried, he made more mistakes on his job. Mrs. Beech claimed she had to act like "a policewoman" to keep him away from his mother and the food she insisted he eat when he visited her.

The day before the hospital admission Mrs. Beech had taken the family car and gone on a shopping trip with her mother. According to Mr. Beech, the two women had gone all over town spending money. Mrs. Beech arrived home just in time to prepare supper for her husband. He came home tired and worried over an estimate he had made on a prospective job. A family argument developed at the table. Although Mr. Beech had an uneasy stomach after dinner, he visited his parents. His mother, in her accustomed manner, gave him lemonade, popcorn, and peanuts. About 10 P.M. he returned home and retired but awoke in the middle of the night with a "terrible gut ache." This was followed by uncontrollable bowel movements. As the hours wore on, the diarrhea and the "gut ache" continued and anal bleeding was observed; at this point the family physician was called.

Our first view of this family was in the hospital. Mr. Beech was lying in bed in apparent discomfort. His wife was sitting on one side of him holding one hand and mopping his brow with a handkerchief; his mother was sitting on the other side of the bed holding the other hand; she, too, was mopping his brow with a handkerchief.

While he was in the hospital Mrs. Beech's mother did not come to visit, but his mother came at the beginning of visiting hours each day and stayed until the hospital personnel forced her to leave. She was a trial to both spouses. The senior Mrs. Beech always referred to her son as "my baby." On one occasion, Mr. Beech turned to the data collector and said, in embarrassment, "Yeah, some baby!" Mr. Beech told us privately he wished his mother would stay at home but he could not say that to her; he told us, "If she's nice enough to come, I have to let her."

The Beeches are nominal Protestants, but they do not go to church. Mrs. Beech is a member of several women's organizations. Mr. Beech belongs to a lodge and occasionally attends meetings. The children appear to get along well with their parents and grandparents. The daughter has a "steady boyfriend" who came with her to the hospital to visit Mr. Beech. The maladjustment in this family revolves around intergenerational relationships. The two older women compete with one another for the attention of their children and grand-children, and there are strained relations between the younger and the older Mrs. Beech, as well as between Mr. Beech and his mother-in-law. The emotional involvement of Mr. and Mrs. Beech with one another, with their mothers, and mothers-in-law as well as the demands of the children for status symbols the family cannot afford and Mr. Beech's difficulties on the job are evidences of moderate maladjustment.

The Catalpa family is judged to be severely maladjusted. We first encountered Mrs. Catalpa sitting up in bed in the hospital. She was under an oxygen tent, but she had pulled the edges loose so she could talk with greater ease and have more freedom in bed. We soon learned that she was hard of hearing; when she desired to talk or hear she put on her hearing aid; when she did not want to communicate with us, her family, or hospital personnel she removed it. Before we could understand what she was saying we had to wait until she took from under her pillow a complete set of false teeth and inserted them in her mouth.

Admission to the hospital culminated a long sequence of events in Mrs. Catalpa's life. The immediate antecedent events started about three weeks earlier when Mrs. Catalpa had pain in her chest, difficulty in breathing, feelings of faintness, and "no energy." She was alone in her rural home when her husband came home tired and irritable. A quarrel ensued because she did not have the housework done and his supper ready. Mr. Catalpa claims he tried to get her to go to the public health officer in their town—the only physician they knew about or had contacted during some thirty years of residence in the community. However, she did not want to see a doctor and he did not insist. Mrs. Catalpa told us, "I have always been in good health." She continued to have trouble breathing, coughed violently, and felt weak. Her condition worsened as the days passed. On the Saturday night before she was brought to the hospital Mr. Catalpa came home drunk; they quarreled again, he continued to drink, and sometime during the evening Mrs. Catalpa "fell asleep" again in her chair. When the oldest son and his wife happened to call at the rural slum shack, they found Mr. Catalpa stretched out on the floor in a drunken stupor and the mother very ill. The son drove to the house of the public health physician of the town and asked him to come to see his mother immediately. Although the physician was given directions to the house and promised to come that night, he did not arrive until midmorning on Sunday. He examined Mrs. Catalpa and told the son and his wife that the old woman had to be hospitalized. According to the family, the physician collected $10 and called an ambulance. When the ambulance arrived Mr. Catalpa was still drunk. Mrs. Catalpa was brought to the hospital alone in the ambulance. No member of her family came until several hours after she was admitted from the emergency service to the ward accommodation. Then her son and his wife arrived.

Mr. and Mrs. Catalpa's ancestral families have lived in New England for several generations. They were born in the same community in another state and attended the same elementary school. As a teen-ager Mr. Catalpa joined the army. When he was discharged he returned to the rural community of his childhood and married the 15-year-old neighbor girl. Some seven months later the first child was born and in rapid succession fourteen more children followed. Early in their marriage they decided to come to this community because "there was plenty of work here." Mr. Catalpa found a job as a laborer in a coal yard. The little family settled down in a cold-water flat in the slums near the waterfront. Every year a new baby arrived. The family moved often as they did not pay the rent; during one three-year period they moved eight times. When things became too difficult Mr. Catalpa left home for several months at a time. During one of these interludes Mrs. Catalpa and eight of their children lived in one room. (There is some evidence that a male friend shared the room with her and the children.) In time, Mr. Catalpa returned and removed his family to an adjacent town where they lived in a shack while he did catch-as-catch-can labor on farms. A few years later the family went on "town charity." They remained on it for ten years, during which time two children died. One, a patient in this hospital for several weeks, was returned to the family supposedly well but died during the night of his first day at home. Mr. Catalpa wrapped him in a blanket and came to the hospital. He attacked the intern in the Emergency Room, accusing the hospital of killing the child. However, as he told us, "Two bulls got to me first and knocked me unconscious."

A year or two later a visiting nurse came to their home to talk to them about their oldest daughter. According to the Catalpas, the nurse had a paper that said the girl was to be sent to a school in Boston. Several weeks later they heard from the girl who had been admitted to the state mental institution. She has remained there throughout the intervening years. The Catalpas are very bitter at what they consider their poor treatment by medical and welfare agencies.

The twelve living children of the Catalpas have given them "no end of trouble." The oldest son "ran away from home" to join the army. Since his return he has beaten his father on several occasions for drinking. A younger brother became a juvenile offender with a long record of arrests and sentences; he has been in every male correctional institution in the state. While Mrs. Catalpa was in the hospital he was in "safekeeping" in the state prison for 10 to 13 years. Another brother and sister became intimate, and the girl gave birth to an illegitimate child; this child was taken from the family by the Welfare Department. The girl had a second child whose paternity we could not ascertain. This child she took with her when she married and left the family home. Mrs. Catalpa complained bitterly that all her children married "foreigners." The oldest son married a "Pole"; others married "Germans," "Italians," "Irish," and so on; according to Mrs. Catalpa, one daughter even married a "half-Irish, half-Indian boy." One son married a girl who bore him two children; she divorced him, married him again, divorced him a second time, and married another Catalpa son; she divorced this son and married a third son. "Now," said Mrs. Catalpa, "she's having a try at Dad." (This latter may be a fantasy, but the earlier multiple marriages and divorces did occur.) Another son accused his wife of having affairs with other men. One night he followed her and caught her in a car having intercourse with a strange man. One daughter, separated from her husband, was "taken back again," and then "got kicked out again" when he learned she had become pregnant while they were separated.

The Catalpas demonstrated such gross social pathology that there was no other alternative but to rate them as severely maladjusted. Although they exhibited the severest forms of maladjustment, there were other families in the study who were as miserably disorganized and could have been substituted for them to describe this category. All of the families in this extreme group were isolated from the community; the members identified with no community institutions; there were one or more members who were severe alcoholics; there was poor communication between the family and the larger society; often there was little communication between family members; and finally members of these families refused to share joint responsibilities. The majority of families in the severely maladjusted category were not as openly disorganized and asocial as the Catalpas and some other families who were comparable to them, but they all exhibited behavior in their relations to one another, and often toward their neighbors and the community at large, which convinced us that they should be categorized as severely maladjusted.

This point will be made again and again, without our mentioning it each time, in the details we present about the inner life of families. As we discuss diverse facets of patients' illnesses and present specific examples to illustrate them, the reader will have many opportunities in reading about the behavior of a patient, a spouse, or some other family member to judge a family's adjustment for himself.

Viewed statistically, there was no association between family adjustment or maladjustment and the accommodation on which the husband or wife was housed in the hospital. Adjusted families were found on all accommodations, just as the moderately and severely maladjusted families were distributed in similar proportions from one accommodation to another. The same conclusion is reached in regard to the service on which treatment occurred. Overall, 11 per cent of the families were judged to be adjusted, 34 per cent were viewed as moderately maladjusted, and 55 per cent were assessed as being severely maladjusted.

The small proportion of families who received ratings of adjusted in comparison with the large percentage who were judged to be severely maladjusted may be startling to the reader. However, in this connection it must be remembered that although we saw these families in crisis we interviewed each spouse repeatedly. In addition, we gathered information from all the salient figures who surrounded them during the hospitalization. We visited them in their homes and we tape-recorded conversations. In sum, we moved behind the scenes and observed family functioning. Another point to keep in mind is that these husbands and wives were mature individuals; they had been married long enough for the romantic illusions of courtship and early marriage to wear off. They had been coping with life and its problems for a long term of years. Living with their problems— emotional, financial, personal, physical, and medical—had left scars. In spite of their disillusionments and personal problems, they had learned to live together. Severely maladjusted or not, they were able to cope with one another. Often the raw edges of interpersonal conflicts were reflected in the symptoms of the sick person's illness.

Summary

The 161 families are characterized by a series of sociobiographical items that are very similar from one accommodation to another—sex and age, religious affiliation, stability of marriage, number of children, area of birth—but significantly different on other items—occupation, education, income, and social position. When we controlled for accommodation we found no significant differences on any item in the comparison of the medical and surgical services.

The quality of interpersonal interactions and behavior of the members of each family are evaluated on a three-point scale—adjusted, moderately maladjusted, and severely maladjusted. The authors assigned each family to a position on this scale on the basis of what the members of the family told us about themselves and other members of the family, as well as their interactions in the larger community. We were startled to learn that over one half of the families were rated as severely maladjusted. This finding is particularly interesting when we realize that 82 per cent of all the spouses were married to their original partner. All of the husbands and wives were middle-aged or approaching senior-citizen status. As such, they had been married to their present spouses for most of their adult years. In the process of living together, each had developed techniques and behaviors which enabled him or her to handle his spouse. These techniques may not be healthy from the viewpoint of either spouse, but they did not result in the break-up of the family. Even in families as chaotic as the Catalpas, the spouses remained in a common household. The opposite partners developed a symbiotic relationship viable enough to overbalance the divisive factors which encapsulated them in their relations with one another. The pertinency of these interpersonal relations to the illness which brought the spouse into the hospital will become clear as we move through successive chapters.

NOTE

1. August B. Hollingshead, *Two Factor Index of Social Position* (copyrighted 1957), privately printed, 1965 Yale Station, New Haven, Connecticut.

PART **III** THE PATIENT

Oᴜʀ ꜰɪʀꜱᴛ ᴄᴏɴᴛᴀᴄᴛ ᴡɪᴛʜ ᴛʜᴇ ꜱɪᴄᴋ ᴘᴇʀꜱᴏɴ, ʜɪꜱ ᴘʜʏꜱɪᴄɪᴀɴ, and one or more family members occurred a few hours after the patient was admitted to the hospital. Prior to admission the immediate family had usually become involved in the illness. Viewed retrospectively, the involvement of the family in the patient's illness followed a sequence of steps: First, the sick person became aware of unusual body feelings and functions. Second, he decided to consult someone about his feelings—the spouse most frequently, but sometimes someone with assumed medical knowledge. Third, the spouse or someone else, possibly the sick person himself, decided that a professional opinion should be sought. In due course the patient consulted a physician who identified the symptoms as pathological. Eventually, a decision was reached to hospitalize the sick person. For the vast majority of patients admission to the hospital marked a personal crisis in their lives; for all concerned it was a turning point in their efforts to cope with the illness.

To understand the sick person's behavior when he became aware of his symptoms, we considered his previous experience with illness, practitioners, and hospitals. Chronicity of the condition was a crucial factor in the ways the person and his family coped with the illness prior to this hospitalization. Among the patients we studied, two out of five hospitalizations were for a disease or illness condition which had been treated at some prior time. There were no meaningful differences on this point among the three accommodation groups, two sexes, or two services of treatment. These patients used previously established contacts with physicians and the hospital for their continuing care. The remaining 60 per cent who claimed that this was the first experience with this disease reacted in different ways to the recognized onset of their symptoms: most (75 per cent) first attempted to treat themselves: others (25 per cent) saw a physician and asked for an evaluation of their condition before using any remedy; 80 per cent of these new cases combined self-treatment at home with the professional advice and prescriptions they received from a physician.

In approximately nine instances out of ten, the troubled individual discussed his problem with his spouse before he sought the advice of a physician. The remainder waited until after consulting a physician before discussing their health problem with their spouses. There were no differences regarding this mode of behavior among the accommodation groups, the two sexes, or the two hospital services—Medicine and Surgery. However, advice reported to have been given by the spouse shows two distinctly different patterns: Persons who later became semiprivate or private patients in the hospital were advised to see a physician or were given no specific advice, whereas persons who became ward patients were directed by their spouse either to a physician or to seek help at this hospital. Persons who, in due course, were admitted to the private and semiprivate accommodations sought out private practitioners for an evaluation of their symptoms. Only 5 per cent of the private patients and 10 per cent of the semiprivate group did not first seek professional help from a private practitioner; these few patients either went to a physician at their places of employment or were brought to this hospital as emergency cases but were admitted upon the recommendation of their private physicians. Persons who became ward patients were divided unequally between those who sought help from private practitioners (38 per cent) and those who came directly to the Emergency Room of this hospital (62 per cent).

Forty-six per cent of the private, 33 per cent of the semiprivate, but only 19 per cent of the ward patients were "fully satisfied" with the first physician they consulted for this illness. In spite of these reported proportions of full satisfaction with the first physician consulted, the percentages are reversed when the data are examined to learn if more than one physician was consulted about this illness. Among the private patients 65 per cent consulted a second or third physician, while only 35 per cent of the ward patients consulted more than one physician; the semiprivate patients were evenly divided on this point. These proportions are significantly different when the private and semiprivate groups are compared with the ward patients.

The length of the illness in the prehospital phase was calculated from the date on which the sick person believed he perceived the onset of his symptoms. (We realize, of course, that the person's illness may have been developing for days, months, possibly years before he became aware of it.) The amount of time which elapsed between the perception of symptoms by the ailing person and the first visit to a physician or admission to the hospital did not differ significantly from one accommodation to another. If we accept what the patients told us as accurate, we may infer that some four out of five who became seriously ill were hospitalized within six months of the appearance of their symptoms.

We also made an assessment of the danger of the delay that occurred between the onset of symptoms and hospitalization, based on each person's statement regarding the date he thought his symptoms began, combined with the nature of the disease. The consequences that could be anticipated for the person if he procrastinated in seeking medical help was the criterion for making the evaluation rather than the mere passage of time. For example, a middle-aged person who experienced severe chest pain and did not seek medical advice as soon as possible for a threatening physical condition is considered to have delayed in a major way; similarly, persons who discovered bleeding from a body orifice or a growth on the body and did nothing about it for weeks or months were delaying treatment in an outstanding way. On the other hand, a patient with a recurring hernia might have delayed seeking medical advice for several months without the delay constituting a major threat to his health. The same might be true of minor conditions like hemorrhoids or skin tumors. The estimates we made on the question of delay in seeking medical advice showed *no delay* in 83 per cent of the private, 69 per cent of the semiprivate, and 55 per cent of the ward patients. What we categorized as *outstanding delay* showed the opposite gradient: 11 per cent for private, 20 per cent for semiprivate, and 36 per cent for ward patients. The figures are significantly different when the private are compared with the ward patients.

Delay in seeking medical attention may be attributed to the failure of the patient to act or, in a few instances, a failure of the physician consulted to act appropriately after the patient sought his advice. Delay occurred in 48 of the 97 persons afflicted for the first time with the illness for which they were hospitalized. In 83 per cent of these cases delay is attributable to personal or family characteristics; in 17 per cent the delay is traceable to the performance of physicians who were either less complete in their examinations or misled the patient. Mrs. Rose illustrates an example of outstanding delay attributable to the advice she received from her physician. She discovered a lump in her breast and went to see a general practitioner who, like her, had been born and reared in a European country. He decided to do nothing and encouraged her to ignore the developing mass. Partly out of fear, she followed his advice, hoping he was right. She kept the information to herself and came to seek competent medical care only after metastases had become widespread. The cause of delay in this instance resulted from the actions of the patient following the advice of the first doctor who saw her. Another case of outstanding delay is that of a professional man who knew a good deal about heart disease but who chose to continue working for three days with severe chest pain before he agreed to see a physician. Others did not perceive that their symptoms required any special attention until they were so miserable they could not follow their daily routine.

For all patients, sponsorship by a physician was linked clearly with the accommodation on which the patient was housed upon admission to the hospital. (See Table 6.) Among persons who used the private accommodation, general practitioners attracted only about one in three. Most of those who went to a general practitioner were referred to a specialist, then on to the hospital. Some two out of three private patients sought out a specialist first for the evaluation of their symptoms; then about one half of these were referred by the first specialist to a second specialist before they were sent to the hospital.

TABLE 6. TYPE OF MEDICAL CONSULTATION PRIOR TO HOSPITALIZATION

Type of Medical Consultation	Patients by Accommodation		
	Private	Semiprivate	Ward
General practitioner–to specialist–to hospital	29%	46%	—%
General practitioner–to hospital	6	7	14
Specialist–to hospital	34	31	7
Specialist–to specialist–to hospital	30	16	—
Clinic physician, this hospital	—	—	17
This hospital	—	—	62
N =	(65)	(54)	(42)

All comparisons are p < .05.

Sick persons who, in due course, reached the semiprivate accommodations went to private practitioners when their symptoms developed; none came directly to the hospital for help. About one half (53 per cent) went first to a general practitioner, and 46 per cent were then referred to a specialist; only 7 per cent came directly from the general practitioner to the hospital. In no instance did a person go from a specialist to a general practitioner.

Some eight out of ten persons admitted to ward accommodations did not have any physician contact in this illness before they came to the hospital; these persons sought help from either the ambulatory clinics or the emergency service of this hospital on their own initiative. Seventy per cent of these patients named a private practitioner they had contacted in a previous illness, but when the need for this hospitalization was recognized they bypassed this private practitioner. Twenty-one per cent of the ward patients had sought help from a private practitioner before they were hospitalized for this illness.

These patients usually went to private practitioners who sent them to this hospital for help but did not arrange for admission. We encountered only three private practitioners who directed patients to the hospital and telephoned the admitting officers about the case. The physicians called the hospital's attention to the need of these patients for admission, but the responsibility for admitting the patient rested with the hospital. In every instance the physicians of persons who used semiprivate or private accommodations arranged to have them admitted as their patients. These persons were sponsored by their physicians *to* and *in* the hospital. No ward patient was sponsored *to* and *in* the hospital by a private practitioner.

To determine prior utilization of the hospital we examined the medical records of each sick person with great care and we interviewed the patient and the spouse regarding the use of this and other hospitals in earlier episodes of illness. The hospital was well known to these families. For the most part they were residents of the community or the nearby area towns; some two husbands and wives out of three were reared in the immediate area. Utilization of this hospital was measured by three types of data: visits to clinics, use of the emergency service in the year preceding the hospitalization, and all prior admissions regardless of the year involved.

Persons who were admitted to the wards in the present hospitalization were the heaviest users of the clinics during the year prior to their present admission: 56 per cent of them had been to the clinics one or more times, whereas only 7 per cent of the semiprivate patients and 9 per cent of the private patients had been treated in the clinics during the year under scrutiny. For those who had used the clinics, the mean number of visits by the ward patients was 7.7, for the semiprivate patients, 2.1, and for the private patients, 1.5. The use of clinics by persons who entered the wards was significantly different from that of the semiprivate and private patients.

Visits to the emergency service revealed a similar pattern: 69 per cent of the ward, 20 per cent of the semiprivate patients, and only 14 per cent of the private patients came to the emergency service for medical aid during the year preceding this hospitalization. The proportion of ward patients who used the emergency service is significantly greater than that of either the semiprivate or private patients. In sum, the utilization of the clinics and the emergency service by the ward patients far exceeded that of the semiprivate or private patients—both in number of patients using the services and the average number of visits made to the respective ambulatory services.

The length of time since the last admission to this hospital was analyzed in relation to accommodation. The semiprivate group had the highest number of patients with no previous admissions; they differed from both the ward and private patients. The ward patients tended to have more hospitalizations

TABLE 7. PREVIOUS ADMISSION TO THIS HOSPITAL, BY ACCOMMODATION

Time of Previous Admission	Patients by Accommodation		
	Private	Semiprivate	Ward
Less than 1 year ago	23%	11%	36%
1 year to 8 years ago	31	28	19
More than 8 years ago	17	7	17
Never	29	54	28
N =	(65)	(54)	(42)

Private compared with semiprivate, $p < .05$; private compared with ward, $p > .05$; semiprivate compared with ward, $p < .05$.

than the semiprivate patients and more recent hospitalizations than the private patients, as shown in Table 7.

Each person was asked about his use of other hospitals. The responses indicated that more semiprivate patients had been admitted to other hospitals than private or ward patients. This is significant when the semiprivate patients are compared with ward patients.

The reasons given by patients for coming to this hospital, rather than to the other general hospital in the community, are summarized into three categories: *patient assumption that this is the only hospital available to him; recommendation of a private practitioner;* and *contrivance by patient* to come here. (Actually, for ward patients this *is* the only hospital available to them, but those who claim contrivance did have to show motivation and a measure of determination to be admitted.) Evidence from the private and semiprivate patients revealed that about one half came to this hospital despite the recommendation of their physicians to go elsewhere. In some instances these patients threatened to go to another physician unless they were admitted to this hospital, and a few individuals postponed entering the hospital until their diseases had advanced dangerously rather than go to another hospital. The distribution of the answers to our questions on reasons for selection of this hospital is given in Table 8.

TABLE 8. ATTRIBUTION OF FACTORS IN SELECTION OF THIS HOSPITAL
BY ACCOMMODATION

Selective Factor	Patients by Accommodation		
	Private	Semiprivate	Ward
Advice of physician	46%	59%	26%
Limited availability	—	—	38
Patient contrivance	54	41	35
N =	(65)	(54)	(42)

Private compared with semiprivate, $p > .05$; private compared with ward, $p < .05$; semiprivate compared with ward, $p < .05$.

Among the private and semiprivate patients, private practitioners made the decision about hospitalization in some nine out of ten instances. Semi-private and private patients looked to the private practitioner for leadership in the decision for a change from office-patient to hospitalized-patient status. Among the ward patients only 10 per cent believed a private physician made the decision that they should enter the hospital. The person who became a ward patient was a long way socially from private physicians, but he did have access to the clinics and the emergency service of the hospital. When he came to the hospital for help he did not perceive himself as being sponsored medically; clearly he took the credit for his admission to the hospital, and he probably deserved it.

Whether the decision to enter the hospital was made by a physician or the sick person, the patient, his spouse, and other family members usually made efforts to implement the decision: 89 per cent of all sick persons accepted the decision with the active support of their families, 9 per cent were neutral, and only 2 per cent resisted professional advice. We conclude that once families were committed to a course of action, they followed it whether it was their own choice or that of a professional decision-maker. Each seeker for help probably made his decision before he saw the physician; possibly the state of his health was such that he had no other choice. The specific figures for those who were reported to have made the decision for hospital entrance are presented in Table 9.

The last step on the route to the hospital occurred at the time of admission. Admission marked the transition from illness-at-home to illness-in-the-hospital, but before a person was admitted to the hospital he had to pass two gatekeepers—an examining physician and an admissions officer. The examining physician was required by the rules of the hospital to certify the need for hospitalization. The certification of need could be made by a licensed practitioner in the community or by a member of the house staff. A medical

TABLE 9. PRINCIPAL DECISION-MAKERS ON HOSPITAL ENTRANCE, BY ACCOMMODATION

Decision-maker	Patients by Accommodation		
	Private	Semiprivate	Ward
Patient	8%	6%	19%
Private physician	85	90	10
Hospital physician	2	2	57
Spouse and family	5	2	14
N =	(65)	(54)	(42)

Private compared with semiprivate, $p > .05$; private compared with ward, $p < .05$; semiprivate compared with ward, $p. < .05$.

doctor could not admit a patient to the hospital unless he had staff privileges. However, if he did not have an affiliation in this hospital he could examine a patient and make a recommendation to the patient and to the hospital.

Persons who came directly to the hospital to seek medical care were subject to very careful scrutiny by both the financial officer and the house officer responsible for admissions on a given service. Although the house officer was an employee of the hospital he often personally identified his interests with the School of Medicine rather than with the hospital. (See Chapter 4, pp. 48–52.) If he admitted patients to ward beds when it was not absolutely necessary or when the person did not have teaching value, he might be admonished in unpleasant ways by his colleagues. To admit a turkey (uninteresting patient) scored against one in the medical game. The residents evaluated one another regarding the ease or difficulty with which they admitted patients to the wards. A resident who gained a reputation for admitting too many patients to the ward accommodations was known as a "sieve." A resident who was known to be a stern gatekeeper for the hospital was a "rock." On some services the resident who admitted the most patients was acclaimed "the sieve of the year." A truly "hard rock" went down into "the pit" (the Emergency Room) to evaluate each prospective admission very carefully. To be known as "a sieve" was embarrassing to the resident, but the decisions of "the rock" were probably more hazardous for the patient.

From the viewpoint of the hospital, particular circumstances mediated between the desires of the house officer to admit patients and the financial needs of the hospital to minimize the annual deficit. If a person was very ill and admission was judged to be an emergency measure, the person was admitted and financial arrangements were discussed later. If the admission was not an emergency, the house physician might not admit the patient until clearance was obtained from the admitting office. The financial officer secured from the physician a statement about the nature of the illness, the expected length of hospitalization, and the type of laboratory and other procedures anticipated. Then the financial officer made a determination of expected costs. He discussed with the prospective patient, and/or a responsible member of his family, insurance, savings, and so on, having to do with payment of the costs of the hospitalization. The patient might be asked to make provision for payment prior to admission. Additional third parties, such as social service or local welfare officers, were often brought into the discussion.

The financial officer usually assumed that a person coming to the hospital as the sponsored patient of a private practitioner could and would pay the hospital at the time of discharge. Questions of finance were not discussed unless the financial officer discovered that the prospective patient, for some reason, desired an accommodation judged to be unsuitable for his socioeconomic status; then his ability to pay came into question. Occasionally, patients raised this question themselves. If so, the financial officer was instructed to explore the situation and counsel the patient accordingly. This could involve further transactions between the financial officer, on the one hand, and the patient and physician, on the other. The admitting physician and the financial officer in consultation with the patient and/or the responsible family member then settled upon the accommodation in which the patient would be housed. At times, the hospital insisted that a patient be placed in the ward accommodations to minimize the hospital charges and eliminate the competing fees of the private practitioner. The patient was then removed from the responsibility of his physician and cared for by the committee. (See Chapter 8.)

Semiprivate and private accommodations were reserved for patients who gave promise of paying both their hospital and their medical bills. If a private practitioner or faculty member of the School of Medicine sponsored an indigent person as his patient, the hospital was displeased when the meager funds available from the family were diverted, in part, for his fees. At the same time the hospital promoted the practice by the School of Medicine of charging ward patients a professional fee when these patients had an insurance policy which would pay a physician for his services to a hospitalized patient. Funds from this source were used for house staff support, a problem which concerned both the hospital and the School of Medicine. This system of billing maximized income with minimum distortion of the patterns of patient care. It also placed the private practitioner, the hospital, and the School of Medicine variously in competition with one another in the "scramble for the little guy's dollar."·

If a private practitioner believed that a patient should be hospitalized on the wards and the admitting resident did not agree, the private practitioner could request that the patient be admitted at least overnight, if not longer, for further evaluation. Usually it was possible for the community practitioner and the admitting resident to agree upon a plan acceptable to them and to the patient. However, this very seldom happened because few sick persons who were admitted to the ward accommodations had any sponsorship from private physicians.

Ways of dealing with medically indigent families were understood by the practitioners in the community and the hospital. The admitting officers, medical and financial, had keen eyes for dress, verbal performance, residence, occupation, and other indices of socioeconomic status. The house physician and the financial officer usually viewed as economic liabilities families who sought unsponsored medical attention. The hospital and local practitioners were in agreement about these families: their sick members belonged on the wards; to provide a more extensive sponsorship medically or a more expensive accommodation within the hospital would only add greater burdens to the family and higher uncollectable bills for the physician and the hospital.

When a semiprivate patient sponsored by a private physician was to be admitted, the sponsor usually called the admitting office to alert the financial office to the admission. The elective admission was dealt with by sending the patient in advance the forms to be filled in and returned to the admissions office so that, once the patient arrived, admission to the hospital could be carried out without delay. These forms dealt with insurance, identifying information, and so on. A statement of rates was sent along with them. When a bed became available, the admitting officer notified the patient's physician and the patient. The patient usually came to the hospital with a member of his family, most often the spouse, and the admitting officer then queried the family members. However, this issue was usually handled with tact; at the very least, the economics of the family were explored.

Private patients, especially those of high-status physicians, had a streamlined admission to the hospital. They entered the hospital with the sponsorship of a prestigeful specialist who was generally viewed with respect by the financial officer. These patients were almost never told that the bill was due and payable at the time of discharge. They were simply asked to sign as a matter of routine. The admitting officer did not want to risk offense in her contacts with these patients.

We asked the admissions officer her judgment of the social status of each patient within twenty-four hours of admission. Comparing our calculations of the family's Index of Social Position scores with the judgments of the admitting officer, we found that the admitting officers were able to place in the appropriate accommodation people who sought admission to the hospital. Patients and families were characterized in such terms as: "Oh, she's the wife of a VIP; she belongs on the west side." "He's a very important executive; definitely private." Families of less prominence were not placed with such precision but the general judgments were accurate in two families out of three. "Her husband is a businessman; she's the private type." "He has a good job with the telephone company; he belongs on the private side." On occasion, the admitting officer made a correct assessment of the social status of a family but the patient demanded an accommodation the officer judged not to be suitable. Then we heard such comments as, "She's not the private type, but the family insisted on a private room. Well, it's their money."

The admissions officers were less secure in their evaluation of social status among the families who entered on the semiprivate divisions. Because these families were able to pay for a private physician *and* the hospital bill, the admissions officer tended to rate them higher in social status than was indicated by their scores on the Index of Social Position. Nevertheless, the admissions officers were correct when they made such comments as: "He's not the private type, but he's not the ward type either." "Her husband's the solid citizen type; he's worked at the electric company for years; they'll be happy on the semiprivate side." An insecure response to our inquiry regarding social status is illustrated by: "I'm not sure. I do know that they pay their bills. We checked with the credit bureau on that."

Persons admitted to the wards were placed with the greatest precision by the admission officers. Their judgments were in accord with the Index of Social Position scores in five families out of six. The admitting officers viewed persons who were admitted to ward accommodations as being "on the bottom of the pile"; "ward types"; "a welfare case—nowhere else to go." Candidates for the ward accommodations were largely residents of the city or one of the adjacent suburban towns. The admissions officers became well acquainted with the kinds of multiple problems with which these families coped year after year. Typical comments were: "Oh God, he's the third generation on the wards"; "I was here when she came in with her first illegitimate child." The admissions officers were able to make remarkably accurate assessments of the social standing of ward patients in the community as well as the kinds of financial problems they had. Above all, the admissions officers were concerned with the hazards the admission might have for the financial office.

The status value assigned to each type of accommodation provided by the hospital was understood widely in the community. Favorable status was attached to the private rooms on the west side of the new building. One floor of the old building—the most sumptuously furnished division in the entire hospital—was set aside especially for private patients and was acceptable to knowledgeable persons who were concerned with excellent care rather than the location in the Medical Center complex. No stigma was attached to the semiprivate accommodations by most people, but a large percentage of those who used them would prefer private accommodations if they could afford them. The wards carried an aura of dishonor among self-respecting people: to be a ward patient implied that one could not pay his way in society. Persons who were medically indigent usually knew they would be investigated by the financial officer on the admitting service; they realized if they were admitted they would have no choice of who cared for them, and they realized that they would be billed for the services the hospital performed for them. Admission to the wards was not easy and it was not accepted willingly by those who could avoid it. The vast majority of poor people resented the stigma they had to assume in order to be admitted to the hospital as a ward patient, but when they were desperately ill they had no other choice but to accept what was available to them. If they had enough money to command the services of a private physician they enjoyed considerable personal satisfaction in entering the hospital on the semiprivate accommodations. If a person entered the hospital as a semiprivate patient and was forced by circumstances to be transferred to a ward, he had a deep feeling of resentment.

Mrs. Figaro represents a family that was forced to cross the social cleavage separating the semiprivate from the ward patient. About four years before her hospitalization her husband had become disabled in an industrial accident. Simultaneously she began to have aches and pains of increasing intensity; as her husband got worse, her symptoms mounted. Eventually, her husband won a lawsuit claiming payment for his injury, but most of the money was paid to lawyers and doctors for the services they had rendered. With the dwindling of the family's resources Mrs. Figaro became progressively worse. Her family physician evaluated her symptoms and decided to admit her to the hospital as his semiprivate patient for a diagnostic evaluation. Mrs. Figaro enjoyed her new role as a hospitalized patient. She told us she found it gratifying to get some attention instead of having her husband get it all.

The diagnostic evaluation indicated that Mrs. Figaro should be considered for surgery. However, the family could not afford a private surgeon; if an operation were to be performed Mrs. Figaro would have to be transferred from the semiprivate accommodations in the new building to ward accommodations in the old building. Transfer to the ward was viewed with alarm; it meant she had to accept a "hospital doctor" and "the wards." She had to face the grim fact that she was poor. The enforced transfer humiliated her and was a severe blow to her self-esteem. She was furious about the peeling paint on the walls of the old building and the cluttered, unclean hallways, but above all she felt the social distance from her cherished private practitioner. In place of his personal attention, she had a disinterested committee of house officers and medical students. She became sullen and resigned. The "hospital doctor" and "the wards" symbolized to Mrs. Figaro her failure as a self-respecting American housewife.

Persons who were housed on the ward accommodations seldom realized initially that they had to endure the indignities of ward treatment in order to benefit from the advances of medical technology which were probably developed in the first place on some hospital ward. They resented being passed over by powerful professors in the School of Medicine who moved around them on the wards, treated them as clinical material, and "talked their Latin" as they discussed the case with the medical students and the house staff in front of the patients. These patients and their families knew that a gulf of social distance separated them from the important figures inside and outside the hospital. They did not fully understand what went on around them, but they had an awareness of their ignorance and they were humiliated at the treatment they had to endure to get medical attention.

Mature persons who had heard tales of conditions that existed on the wards in past years had definite attitudinal sets toward the hospital. Experiences of some member of a family in the hospital's wards were told and retold in family circles; through the process of oral transmission in the family and among friends, unpleasant experiences became legendary realities. On the one hand, many persons believed that professors in the School of Medicine brought about dramatic, almost miraculous cures. One woman was convinced that young physicians in the ward saved her husband's life years ago. A husband of a ward patient had implicit faith that his wife would be saved by the young doctors who were assigned to her care by the "professors" in the School of Medicine. On the other hand, some ward patients and their families looked upon the physician's search for the causes and cures of disease as "probing" or "making guinea pigs of the patients." Thus, admiration for the technical knowledge and skills of the physicians was mixed with resentment toward the hospital.

Some of the social processes enmeshed in the lives of low-status people and the way they felt about them are illustrated by the story of Mrs. Toski. As a child Mrs. Toski was reared in a foster home. She gained her first impression of the hospital while living with her foster family who referred to it as "the butcher shop." Stories were told about the wrong people being taken to the operating room and experimentation by young physicians on poor people unfortunate enough to be there. Although Mrs. Toski's introduction to the Medical Center was a vicarious one, it gave her a set of attitudes toward the hospital, the ward accommodations, and the School of Medicine.

When she was about 16 years of age she married a laborer nine years her senior. A few months later she was admitted to the wards of this hospital for childbirth. She was very fearful about coming to "the butcher shop," and she was ignorant about conception and delivery. She asked the doctors on the ward how the baby would get out but received no satisfactory answer. She described to us how four to six medical students and interns stood around her bed and poked at her belly. She remembers vividly a high forceps delivery. It was traumatic, physically and emotionally, and although she resolved at that time never to have another baby she became pregnant again. She chose to abort herself and succeeded. This experience was repeated twice more.

Mrs. Toski managed to stay away from doctors and out of hospitals until three years before her current admission. During a vacation in Florida with her second husband, she had an acute abdominal pain. A doctor was called and when she refused to go to a hospital he gave her some medicine which she took until it was finished some four days later. By this time she was in desperate physical condition, and she was taken to a hospital where it was found she had a ruptured gall bladder and acute peritonitis. She was told that she might have complications from the advanced abdominal inflammation and she should obtain medical care in case of need. When she returned home she gathered from friends the names of five physicians, but she was too frightened of doctors to call any of them. She had come to think of doctors as "stuffy" persons who "keep their business a deep, dark secret." She did not trust them to tell her the truth.

When violent stomach pains developed Mrs. Toski came to the emergency service of this hospital. Overwhelmed with pain and fear, she was admitted as a ward medical patient. She said the room to which she was taken was dirty, there were used bedpans remaining about for hours, and she was brought food when she had been told to take nothing by mouth. She told us she was "not rich or royalty" but neither was she "trash" and she would not be treated "like trash." Arguments soon developed between Mrs. Toski, the interns, and the nurses. When she threatened to leave the hospital because she thought she would get better treatment at home, an intern who viewed her as "nasty" removed the intravenous needle and called her husband to take her home. The intern told us later that this maneuver was contrived to frighten Mrs. Toski into submission, but she was undaunted and signed out of the hospital against advice. With alarm, the intern counseled her and Mr. Toski to get immediate medical attention if she would not remain in the hospital.

Mrs. Toski then turned to her list of physicians and proceeded to telephone each one, telling him that before she would become his patient he would have to inform her of the nature of her illness and explain to her exactly what he was doing and why. Four of these physicians declined on the grounds that her demands were unreasonable or that to spend as much time as would be required to meet these conditions would not allow them to make enough money on the case. The fifth physician accepted her terms and two days later admitted her to the hospital as a semiprivate patient under his care. This physician is a general practitioner who has practiced medicine in this city for several years. He is familiar with the patterns of medical care and the attitudes of many people toward the various hospital accommodations. When he gave his approval for the inclusion of Mrs. Toski in the study he said, "I think you'll find her rather hostile from her other experiences. You know what the wards can be."

There is ample evidence to support the conclusion that the social and psychological problems of Mrs. Toski contributed to the confusion concerning her care as a ward patient. Speaking figuratively, she had come to the hospital like a bomb awaiting detonation, and conditions on the ward ignited the fuse. There was enough reality in her suspicion and enough prejudice in her views so that she could see only the worst in her experiences. When the interns and nurses showed annoyance with her complaints, she felt they were treating her "like trash."

To Mrs. Toski, to the foster family who reared her as a child, to her present friends, and even to her current physician, there was a stigma attached to the ward accommodations. Although conditions on the wards changed a great deal over the years, Mrs. Toski believed the horrible tales she had heard. Her friends agreed that she did the right thing in leaving the ward accommodations. She found the new building cleaner and people there more kindly in their manner toward her; above all, she was successful in her efforts to avoid "the poking of medical students and interns," and she had one doctor who would answer her questions.

The conviction that ward patients were treated as guinea pigs was held by a number of persons who were forced by circumstances to accept ward accommodations. Another patient, Mr. Mundy, was familiar with the hospital, having worked here as a maintenance man at an earlier time. He came to the clinic because he believed the physicians in the hospital clinics could help his arthritis. A young physician in the clinic found a disease of interest for him to study, and an assistant resident chose to admit him to the ward for investigation. The medical students gave Mr. Mundy a very thorough work-up. He resented the pain, discomfort, and the long series of indignities to which he was submitted by the eager young men who were interested in his disease, not in him. (We might point out in passing that Mr. Mundy was found personally unattractive by the nurses, aides, medical students, and house staff. He refused to take a bath or allow anyone to bathe him while he was a patient.) The physicians communicated very little to him about his infirmities and disorders; he told us they talked to one another in "their Latin." He concluded that he was their "guinea pig." He helped to pass on the belief of poor people that the wards were for the training of medical students rather than for the treatment of patients.

Members of the community who had been able to avoid the ward service for a term of years but, through one circumstance or another, were identified by hospital personnel as a "ward type" resented the application of the hated status. A family in our study—the Albergs—who had been upwardly mobile to the extent that they were able to command the services of a private physician are cited to illustrate this point. Mr. Alberg had been treated years earlier in the clinics of this hospital for various diseases: skin infections, malnutrition, dental caries, and syphilis. In recent years he had become a salesman and had gone to a general practitioner for his health needs. On the occasion that led to this hospitalization he went to this physician, who referred him to an internist. The internist sent him to the hospital for immediate admission. No private beds were available that day so he was admitted to the older section of the hospital. Although he was given a private room it was on a floor of predominantly ward beds. Mr. Alberg was upset emotionally by this arrangement. Mrs. Alberg protested vigorously to the admitting officer, the nurses on the floor, and the house staff. Mr. Alberg had worked hard to become a successful, regularly employed salesman; he was prepared to pay his bills. His success had enabled him to change his pattern of life and he was no longer dependent upon charity, especially medical charity. To the Albergs the room was an insult, a challenge to their new social status. When they asked the internist to move Mr. Alberg, the request was denied. The physician, exhibiting a discriminating sense of social position, could not see that they were out of place. Although the hospital was prepared to move him to another division—a wholly private one—the physician ruled that the transfer was unnecessary. This was a severe blow to the Albergs' self-esteem. To be seen as persons who would not be uncomfortable on a mixed floor, even in a private room, was a painful and humiliating reminder of their earlier dependent status.

Summary

The route to the hospital is found to consist, in general, of five steps: recognition of abnormal bodily feelings, decision to have such feelings evaluated, identification of the feelings as pathological by a physician, decision on the part of the physician or the sick person to seek hospitalization, and admission to the hospital. For persons of lower socioeconomic status each step was taken in a different and more difficult manner than for those of higher socioeconomic status.

In the higher socioeconomic groups, persons usually saw their private physician when they discovered some unusual body function or symptom. A feeling of fatigue often resulted in consultation with an internist. Laboratory studies might disclose abnormalities requiring further investigation and treatment which were then pursued.

Disease and poverty are incompatible associates, yet they were frequently hosts to one another. To persons of low socioeconomic status, the hospital was a place to come in desperation—it was the last resort in a painful situation. This was unpleasant for the hospital also. An indigent patient could not be admitted if he did not require urgent care because the hospital would be forced to close its doors unless it was paid for its services by the patient, the family, or some third party. A complex of relationships, therefore, existed for ward patients. They were sick and usually had to be sicker before they were admitted to the hospital. Their sponsors were institutional physicians who were practicing inside the hospital rather than in the community. These physicians used, for the most part, the single criterion of threat to life and well-being as justification for admission to the hospital; the only exception was the occasional patient with a special disease a young physician might want to study for educational purposes. Before a bed was made available the poor person had to convince an intern or resident of his pain and he had to convince a financial officer of his dire need.

Persons in the lower segments of the socioeconomic structure of the community who entered ward accommodations of the hospital had few choices available to them when illness struck. They tried to carry on their usual activities at home or on the job. They "played out" before going to the doctor. On the other hand, persons in the higher socioeconomic groups who were admitted to private and semiprivate accommodations were more likely to be able to seek and pay for professional help. Moreover, such persons had a better knowledge about disease and interpretation of symptoms. In addition, they had the ability to manipulate their environment and to have a private physician sponsor their entrance into the hospital. Accordingly, perception of illness and what was done in response to it were different among persons who entered the three kinds of accommodations.

WHEN AN INDIVIDUAL BECOMES A PATIENT HE IS confronted with the necessity of dealing with a physician or physicians. The association brought into existence by the mutual interest of the patient and his physician in the illness—the doctor-patient relationship—is symbolized by *sponsorship,* the method through which the physician assumes responsibility and discharges obligations to care for the patient. Sponsorship is believed to have its roots in the mutual images and expectations of patients and physicians. Ideally, the doctor-patient relationship revolves around only the sick or troubled person who is a client (patient) and the professional person (physician) whom he consults. Crucial decisions regarding diagnosis and treatment of disease should not be influenced by extraneous matters. However, physicians and patients are inextricably parts of the society to which both belong. The broader social contexts of the patient and his family, the physician and his family, the hospital, insurance companies, the institutions of government, religion, education, and so on are related in one way or another with the interactions that take place between physicians and patients. The sick person looks to the physician for advice and help. The physician, in performing his professional role, is concerned directly with the problem the patient brings to him and indirectly with his own interests: his practice, possibly learning or research, or some combination of these pursuits. To a certain extent, therefore, each partner in this relationship must look after his own interests. The patient has an illness; the physician has a career. Each partner must make tentative judgments about the other. The patient accepts the competence of the physician to diagnose and treat his problem, and the physician accepts the sponsorship of the patient.

Reciprocal expectations between patient and physician were based upon the respective images which patients and physicians had of each other. Ward patients recognized their low status and expected to be used as teaching subjects and, to some extent, as research material. The doctors reciprocated these expectations and offered little apology since these patients, though being charged for their hospital services, were not being billed for their medical care. The semiprivate and private patients did not expect to be used as research subjects. Furthermore, the semiprivate and private patients were fully aware that they had physician sponsors who were responsible to them for the diagnosis and treatment of, and information about their diseases. They expected to pay their physicians directly for the personal services they had received from them.

In this chapter we focus attention upon the relationship between physician sponsorship and the social status of the patient as measured by the *Two Factor Index of Social Position*. (For a more detailed discussion, see Chapter 6, pp. 92–94.) Few professional or occupational groups outranked the medical specialist in prestige. Patients were obliged to cope with this fact, just as they coped with the authority of a lawyer, businessman, or foreman in other situations. While a patient's consciousness of social status may have been latent prior to hospitalization, once hospitalized his status vis-à-vis that of the physician became a crucial element in the doctor-patient relationship. Our data show that the assessment made by the patients of their own social standing generally agreed with that made by doctors, nurses, admitting officers, and the researchers. Not only did patients place themselves socially, but also had corresponding social placements for physicians: lower-status patients placed physicians on a very high level while very high-status patients placed them on, or below, their own level. High-status private patients often made subordinates of their physicians and were cool to house officers whom they usually viewed as students. Semiprivate patients realized they were "not in the top league," but they realized also that they were not at the bottom —the ward accommodation. In the ward accommodation, patients understood they were being used for teaching and research purposes. Low-status patients, recognizing their position, were often embarrassed in contacts with physicians.

An example of keen social awareness, which we observed frequently among our patients, was displayed by Mr. Jetson, a chicken farmer of limited education from a town outside the immediate metropolitan area. He was a semiprivate patient, placed on a division of mixed accommodations. When we invited him to participate in this project, he asked if we were "spies" for the hospital. After relieving his anxieties about this we learned that he suspected hospitals of charging all that people could pay. He had underreported his income to the admitting officer and, for this reason, felt that he was "getting away" with lower charges than would otherwise have been the case. He feared the loss of his meager savings if the hospital discovered them or the fact that he had just purchased a new automobile. He was sensitive for another reason: His family had migrated from Europe when he was a small boy. He viewed himself as a "simple person" and realized the limits of his education. He told us he had not had "the right contacts" and the fortitude within himself to "take the necessary chances" which others had taken and profited from. He had not done as well as many of the farmers in his area during World War II, and consequently he was very anxious to encourage his sons to take chances to improve their own standing.

In the hospital Mr. Jetson eyed both the impoverished and the well-to-do with an intense curiosity. In his room there was a man who had a telephone and used it to carry on some of his business affairs from his hospital bed. Mr. Jetson observed also a man in a private room nearby using a telephone constantly. He was aware of his lower status in relation to these men, and, as he observed other people in multiple-bed rooms being visited by poorly dressed family members, he commented to us that he knew the businessmen could pay their bills easily but that the impoverished patients certainly could not. He was embarrassed when we asked about his education, occupation, and residence but proud to report that he had his own doctor and could pay his bills. He realized he was "in between."

When we talked with physicians about including their patients in this study and asked about family relationships, they volunteered many remarks indicative of their perception of social status. Typical comments about high-status patients (usually in private accommodations) were: "He's the private type." "She belongs on the private side; she's demanding and expects a lot, so the nurses there will please her." "He's the executive type." "She comes from a cultivated family." Comments about middle-class families found predominantly in the semiprivate, but to some extent also in the private, accommodations were: "He's a deserving skilled workman." "She's a nice lady, well-intended, modest background, you know." "They have limited but adequate means." Comments about lower-status patients, usually in the ward accommodations, were more critical but nonetheless precise: "He can't give a good history." "She has little or no education." "He's the ward type." "You can have her with my compliments. I'll give you a stretcher to take her and some Gillette Blue Blades—she needs a shave."

The intent of some of the comments volunteered to us was to alert us to what we might expect in the way of a social type and, therefore, to assist us in our dealings with the patient during the data collection. This would allow us to proceed without offending the patients and protect ourselves as well as the doctor from embarrassment. Although we were grateful for these cues, we did not specifically ask for them. What surprised us was the frequency with which they were volunteered, the strength of the doctor's feelings, and the accuracy of the inferred social placement: 93 per cent of the physicians had a good working knowledge of the approximate class status of the patients they sponsored in the hospital.

When we began this study we knew that the hospital provided three kinds of accommodations for patients: private, semiprivate, and ward. We knew also that admission to the wards was controlled, in large part, by house staff and admissions officers in the hospital and that the patients who were admitted to the wards were cared for by medical students and house officers under the supervision of members of the faculty of the School of Medicine. We were aware of the fact that ward patients were mainly medically indigent persons. Therefore, we anticipated that the patients would be divided into two groups—those sponsored by private practitioners and those sponsored by the hospital. We expected to find that patients sponsored by the hospital would be placed on the wards and those sponsored by private practitioners would be placed on the semiprivate or private accommodations.

After we collected our data and began the systematic study of interrelations between physicians and patients, we came to the conclusion that the presumed dichotomy into institutional and private sponsorship was too simple. Private sponsorship of patients by physicians needed to be subdivided into three categories. We thus arrived at a fourfold categorization of sponsorship: one type that was unique to the wards, and three that were divided unequally between the semiprivate and private accommodations. We called these four types of physician sponsorship of patients in the hospital *committee sponsorship, semicommittee sponsorship, casual sponsorship,* and *committed sponsorship.* Each type of sponsorship was associated significantly with the social status of the patient. It was not related to his illness or his sex. Each of these types of sponsorship is defined and illustrated below.

Committee Sponsorship

One of the resident physicians used the term "committee doctor" when describing the physician-patient relationship in the ward accommodations. This gave us our cue for the label used here. *Committee sponsorship* was found to apply to all ward patients and to no others. The mean Index of Social Position score for the ward patient in committee sponsorship was 63; that is, the average ward patient came from the lower end of the socioeconomic structure. The patient in committee sponsorship had no single continuing doctor on whom he could depend. Care of the patient was vested in the always-present and ever-changing committee whose members—doctors at the house-staff and medical-student levels—rotated within the institution during their training years and then, in most instances, left it. These physicians and students identified professionally with the School of Medicine and looked to it primarily for aid in the development of their careers. They were most impressed and influenced by teachers and researchers who necessarily had little time for patient care and whose major interest was new knowledge through research. Learning was the overriding consideration.

In the School of Medicine, diseases were the necessary "clinical material" for the teaching and research program. In a conference room in the Medical Center, used for teaching students and house officers, a sign posted above a blackboard admonishes: "Think Pathology!" The hospital was the place in which the students and house officers saw patients. The patient was the vehicle for the study of disease. To be sure, these young physicians realized that the problems of patients were great; they realized the chief task of a physician is to treat disease, but they were students who had to learn how to become physicians before they could treat people. When we asked them about the patients, they usually knew the nature of the patient's disease and something about his ongoing treatment but they knew little about the patients as human beings; thus, our questions embarrassed them. Some told us we were choosing the less ill patients who required less time to care for or that they had been assigned to the patient in question for only a few days and had had little contact with him. One intern was more precise in his views; he ended a rather nonproductive interview with this comment: "I cannot answer your questions. You're interested in patients. I'm interested in the disease in the body in the bed."

There was a wide educational, financial, and social gulf between persons admitted for treatment to the ward accommodations and their committee doctors. The patients in the ward accommodations were usually poor, if not destitute. They understood that the wards were for poor people; they believed that semiprivate or private care was more desirable, but it was beyond their reach. In the ward accommodations the status differences between physicians and patients were felt in all interpersonal relationships.

Mrs. O'Pell, a 56-year-old woman of Irish birth, was selected to illustrate some facets of committee sponsorship. Mrs. O'Pell had been in reasonably good health most of her life except for her nervousness and hypochondriacal tendencies. She did not trust the general practitioners, whom she saw for these complaints, to deal with her more complicated problems. For these she went to the clinic. She considered the clinic and ward accommodations as places where poor people get care. She viewed the doctors as being much above and distant from her, and she communicated poorly with them; they responded in general by ignoring her as a person.

One week prior to her admission she had some teeth extracted under general anesthesia in this hospital. The day following the procedure, she developed pains in her chest and a sore throat. She visited the Emergency

Room where some X rays were taken and "pain killers" prescribed. Still feeling ill the next day, she came again to the Emergency Room and was sent to the medical clinic for further examinations. She was sent home again although the chest pain was not alleviated. She returned the following day to the medical clinic and decided to "sit them out." She told us, "I don't have a private doctor. I came through the medical clinic and the emergency service, but I was in no condition to sit around." When the doctors in the medical clinic could not see her for several hours she spoke to the nurse about the delay, emphasizing the severity of her pain. The nurse suggested that she get some lunch and see the doctor afterwards. However, Mrs. O'Pell declined to do this because she was afraid if she lost her place in line she might not be seen at all that day. She told the nurse, "I don't care whether I get lunch or even supper; I'm in pain and I'm going to sit here until the doctor sees me." (Mrs. O'Pell accepted waiting as a necessity in the clinics, but as she related this story to us she shook with anger.) Finally, a doctor did see her and decided to admit her to the hospital.

Up to this point, Mrs. O'Pell had been seen by two dentists, four medical students, two interns, and one assistant resident, all of whom she viewed as inexperienced students. She attributed her illness to improper anesthesia and poor dental technique of a "young student, that Puerto Rican dentist." When she was admitted to the hospital she was seen by three more members of the committee—a medical student, an intern, and an assistant resident. The medical student spent more time with her than the others so she felt that he was her physician more than anyone else. When he left for the weekend she was worried, but she assumed that he had left orders to be carried out in his absence. The student, however, spent little time with her, knew nothing about her family, and felt he did not understand her situation well. The family, while visiting and through telephone calls to the hospital, tried to get information by seeking a doctor to answer their questions. They never succeeded in finding a doctor who would listen to them.

Mrs. O'Pell realized the doctors were teaching one another and learning on her. In her opinion the pelvic examination was "quite a production." The doctors talked to one another but not to her. Three thoracenteses were done in just this way—one doctor teaching another. She said that one doctor seemed to be especially knowledgeable about "needles," while the other one seemed to know more about examining her. She told us:

> They examine me and examine me and try to figure out what the illness is. One seems to be more of an authority than the other. One is much older than the other. I don't know if they are medical students or not—they probably are, though. They look so young, like my own son. Two very brilliant-looking men came in yesterday and went over everything with the students. Everything had to agree.

Shortly after her admission to the hospital, the resident in radiology concluded from his study of the X ray that the problem was a pulmonary embolus. The intern reported this diagnosis to Mrs. O'Pell explaining that a clot which had probably formed in her leg had broken off and lodged in her lungs. Although she did not tell the doctors, she was extremely frightened by this diagnosis because a close friend had died suddenly and unexpectedly of this condition.

After Mrs. O'Pell was in the hospital two days, the attending physician (a faculty member in the School of Medicine), who was introduced to her as an outstanding international authority on diseases of her kind, visited her. He examined her briefly, listened to her history, and informed her that the doctors were doing the "right things" for her. He left before Mrs. O'Pell could ask him any questions. When she asked the medical students and the intern again what her diagnosis really was, they said she had an embolus and that the attending physician concurred with their diagnosis and treatment. In reality, the attending physician thought the cause of the illness was not embolus but aspiration during the dental extraction while under general anesthesia.

Mrs. O'Pell began to think about family members and friends who had died of heart disease, emboli, strokes, cancer, and tuberculosis. All her fears of these diseases became greatly heightened, and she wanted reassurance that she did not have any of them. The fact that the doctors seemed less than fully informative and honest led her to doubt everything they told her. Her doubts and suspicions were increased by the intern's elusive manner in answering her questions, but she felt she was basically an ignorant, unimportant person and she thought she could not question him more forcefully. Although they were distant and less than completely honest, the doctors were kind to her. She could see and feel with much gratitude the therapeutic results, and she gave the doctors credit for knowing what they were doing.

After discharge from the hospital, Mrs. O'Pell consulted a general practitioner for his interpretation of the cause of her illness. He examined her legs carefully, found no evidence of phlebitis, and said that embolization probably did not account for the illness. This was not reassuring to Mrs. O'Pell because, although she appreciated his interest in her, she discounted his competence. She then saw another physician who told her that she was very lucky that the clot had struck her lungs instead of her heart or her brain because then she would not have survived. Thinking of illness and death, Mrs. O'Pell decided to visit Ireland, the land of her birth, while she was still able to travel. In Ireland, she consulted some physicians about her illness and other problems including headaches and abdominal pains. One year after discharge, she was still anxious and very curious about the diagnosis of pulmonary embolism. She wondered if the attending physician's diagnosis had been reported to her correctly, but she knew of no way to find out.

From the viewpoint of the doctors, Mrs. O'Pell was a model patient, cooperative and forbearing. She made no demands and seemed to accept without any major challenge their explanation of her illness. She responded dramatically to treatment which was most gratifying to all, and finally she was discharged as "cured" from the medical clinic. The doctors felt that they had learned much while practicing splendid medicine. They knew nothing of Mrs. O'Pell's doubts and fears about her illness. Although the pulmonary disease was treated successfully, regardless of its nature, the management of this patient did involve some risks of treatment (anticoagulant therapy) which she almost certainly did not require and which was costly to her and her family. The management by the physicians had the effect of increasing the severity of her hypochondriasis; she went to more doctors, incurring higher costs, and her fears were never successfully relieved.

The story of Mr. Pagus, a man born and reared in Greece, reveals other features of the committee sponsorship. In a previous hospitalization for chronic pulmonary disease, Mr. Pagus found an intern who was much attracted by his stories of old Greece. This intern took a special interest in Mr. Pagus and followed him for a considerable period of time in the clinics after his discharge. When Mr. Pagus returned to the hospital with another complication of his chronic pulmonary condition, both he and his wife attempted to locate the friendly intern, but, as he had completed his year and left the hospital, they were unsuccessful. Mr. Pagus was told that the doctors now on the service had all his records and would care for him properly.

Mrs. Pagus, who had worked as a waitress in a restaurant near the Medical Center, had served some of the professors of the School of Medicine; she considered them her friends. At this point, she turned to them. One visited briefly and said that the interns and residents were treating her husband properly. Although she made further attempts to get their attention and to reach the cherished and trusted intern, no further responses were forthcoming. Mr. and Mrs. Pagus were left to face the chronic, recurring illness with physicians whom they didn't know and hardly trusted. They found that the new physicians were brusque and unable or unwilling to spend time with them, and there was no one to whom Mr. Pagus could talk about ancient Greece.

It was early in July and the new interns, who were starting their year of training, failed to see what was quite evident to Mrs. Pagus and to the data collectors—that Mr. Pagus was deteriorating. Finding the chemistries much improved, the interns announced optimistically that Mr. Pagus could go home in a day or two, but within 36 hours they had to change their prognosis.

He was placed in a respirator, and a tracheotomy was performed. Mrs. Pagus opposed the tracheotomy, believing it was of no use and would cause unnecessary suffering and additional expense. The procedure was also contrary to the opinion of the attending physician (a faculty member) who explained to us that he could do no more than state his view. He told us: "The tenor of this service is to provide the best scientific medicine." One week later, Mr. Pagus died.

During the earlier hospitalization, Mr. Pagus had enjoyed temporarily a physician sponsorship more like the *committed* type which will be described later. Its development was by chance and exceptional. The physician in the current hospitalization displayed a typical committee sponsorship relationship; he had no knowledge of the meaning of the previous physician and his sponsorship to Mr. Pagus and the family. Mrs. Pagus attributed the death of her husband to physician neglect. She felt the first intern had saved her husband's life during a similar illness and could have done so again. She blamed the doctors, was bitter toward them and the hospital, and refused permission for a postmortem examination.

We found many handicaps to a cooperative relationship between doctors and patients in the committee sponsorship. The patients viewed themselves as uneducated and incapable of understanding the explanations of the professionals; patients often referred to the doctors "talking among themselves" and using "their Latin" or "their Greek." Most patients believed the doctors withheld information from them. Several patients told us: "Doctors have their secrets." The patients were embarrassed by their ignorance and remained silent to avoid exposure. Thus, they failed to put their questions to the doctors although they asked such questions of family members, our data collectors, and sometimes the nurses if the latter would listen. (They did not often question the nurses, however, because they thought the nurses gave them little encouragement and were probably incapable of answering them.)

These patients lacked the standing to make demands upon their physicians. They expected to be cared for by interns and medical students, yet they were resentful of being "pushed around" and ignored as individuals. Some realized that inconvenience, discomfort, and at times higher costs for decisions made in the interest of teaching and research, rather than in the interest of the patient, were necessary in order for them to get the benefits of service within the ward accommodations.

The attitudes of ward patients were reinforced by those of the house officers who, characteristically, thought they worked long and hard for the patients while receiving little pay from the hospital. They thought that the public should support the hospital and physicians should not have to be concerned over the costs of caring for ward patients. They offered these views to justify their lack of concern when their decisions created economic hardships for the patients or the hospital. The patients represented diseases, not persons, to the members of the committee. They believed any inconvenience their learning might cause was amply repaid in the services the patients received.

The illness itself created another cleavage between the patient and the committee of physicians. The illness was more severe (see Chapter 9), and the gulf between patients and student physicians was correspondingly greater on the wards than in other accommodations. For the most part, the physicians were not able to identify with these patients. To be well, young, and vigorous was to be in a very different position from that of an older, sick, or dying patient. The future of ward patients was usually dismal; that of their sponsors offered an extreme contrast. The young physicians looked with anticipation toward a career in medicine. They hoped for the time when they would not have to do such work and associate with "crocks" and "crud." Meanwhile, they learned in the ward accommodations but indicated their awareness of the patients' situation in various ways such as naming these wards "the zoo."

Although the ward patients were silent about their treatment, they were often seething with anger. When they told us their stories, we had to cope with the resentment of persons who were often depressed and suspicious. They asked us why we didn't "do something" about their situation instead of "wasting time asking questions and doing studies." We could only answer that we hoped this was a beginning. (It was not a satisfactory answer to the patients, and the researchers often felt acute embarrassment.)

The unsatisfactory interpersonal relationships between sick patients and student physicians in committee sponsorship had pervasive consequences. Sometimes diagnoses were less than adequate. Patients were poorly informed and often confused. Even if the treatment was successful, the patients resented the attitudes of the hospital staff: student physicians, nurses, nursing students, aides, and so on. When the treatment was not successful, as was often the case among these very sick persons, their suspicions increased sharply. Weakened and frightened, they had to accept what was offered to them; there was almost no alternative choice. Both sponsor and patient recognized the distance between them; neither was comfortable with it, but only the patient had to endure it without hope for ameliorative change.

In summary, interest in the patient as a human being, though present occasionally in exemplary ways, could not be sustained when there was so little in common between the providers and recipients of service and when the patient was in no position to pay for the physician's time and hence make demands upon him. Interest in the disease, lack of interest in the patient, and difficulty in communication characterized the ward accommodation in which the formal learning of medical students, house officers, and senior physicians took place. The impact of these influences was noted for all ward patients.

Semicommittee Sponsorship

Semicommittee sponsorship involved a private physician nominally, but a large segment of responsibility for the diagnosis and treatment of the disease, as well as communication with the patient, was assumed by house officers. The private physician admitted the patient to the hospital and may have influenced the diagnostic and treatment choices or the timing of discharge, but he was not close to the patient or his care. The patients, the house staff, and the private physicians recognized this pattern of sponsorship. Private physicians in semicommittee sponsorship were often general practitioners, very busy internists, or surgeons who spent little time with their patients. These physicians often exhibited a lesser competence in diagnosis and treatment procedures, particularly on the medical service, than others described in the casual and committed sponsorships. In the semiprivate accommodation twenty-four patients and in the private accommodation seven patients had semicommittee sponsorships. Two-thirds of these were on the medical service and one-third on the surgical. The patients who were cared for by a semi-committee in the semiprivate accommodations had a mean Index of Social Position score of 58; the patients in the private accommodations who were cared for by this type of sponsorship had a mean Index of Social Position score of 40.

Interviews with the house staff and attending physicians on both the medical and surgical services revealed an awareness that the care of patients within Medicine took a different form from that within Surgery. These physicians realized that general practitioners and indeed many internists, shortly after their training ends, become less capable than house staff in diagnosing and treating patients. The house officers had frequent contacts within the School of Medicine where they could ask for consultation. They were in the hospital and available to care for all the patients, while the private physicians were obliged to deal with their private practices which were based outside the hospital. Only a small part of the average internist's practice was within the hospital.

This was not true for the surgeon, who is most truly a surgeon when operating on patients within the hospital. While minor surgical procedures were carried out in the surgeon's office, his lofty status was derived from his position in the operating room. On the surgical service, private surgeons were always the primary operator for their own patients, with only a few unspoken-of exceptions where the patient was "given" to the house staff. When this occurred the patient was most likely to be a semiskilled worker, or the wife of one, supervised by semicommittee sponsorship.

Mr. Barts, a 61-year-old warehouse worker, provides an illustration of semicommittee sponsorship on the medical service. This man had developed visual disturbances about one year before admission to the hospital. The optician he consulted referred him to an ophthalmologist. The first visit to the ophthalmologist resulted in no specific diagnosis although some retinal disorders were discovered. No treatment was recommended. In the month prior to hospital admission, Mr. Barts' visual disturbance became worse. He returned to the ophthalmologist who then referred him to a general practitioner. The general practitioner discovered hypertension and a trace of albumin and sugar in the urine. Although the only symptom was occasional blurred vision, the doctor became acutely anxious about the advanced complications of diabetes and referred Mr. Barts immediately for admission to the hospital. This doctor told us: "He's a very sick man. Much sicker than he realizes. He probably has advanced Kimmelstiel-Wilson disease and may not live very long. He may also have heart disease and brain problems."

Shortly after Mr. Barts' admission to the hospital his doctor invited two consultants to see him—an ophthalmologist and a specialist in kidney diseases. Neither consultant was much interested in Mr. Barts as a person or in his illness. Another consultant, a specialist in diabetic diseases, was invited to see the patient but he found the diabetes to be mild and easily controlled so he also had little interest in Mr. Barts. All the consultants and the house staff viewed this admission to the hospital as unnecessary; they had other patients to care for, they told us, who were "really" sick. However, as Mr. Barts' physician was distant and unavailable, the house staff gave him the required care with casual concern.

Mr. Barts had been in good health most of his life. He had known the general practitioner for only a short time before his admission to the hospital. Although this physician had cared for many patients with diseases of this kind and worse, he admitted Mr. Barts to the hospital on the grounds that his case was a special one, best treated by a specialist in diabetes. Mr. Barts noticed the physician's lack of concern for him, once he had been admitted to the hospital, but he reported to us that the general practitioner was "still my man." The physician, however, decided he would not continue to care for him. Confusion concerning the medication for diabetes, diet instruction, and treatment of his eye difficulty continued for several weeks as the house officers moved into the picture to replace the abdicating practitioner. Mr. Barts felt the lack of interest in the semicommittee sponsorship fostered on him, but he thought that he had no choice in the matter since his own doctor had referred him to the hospital and told him that the house officer was a "pretty big cog around here."

Before his hospitalization Mr. Barts had been looking forward to the day of his retirement from his warehouse job, but he had not expected it to take place for several years. The fear of his illness, instilled in him by the private physician, was a major influence in his decision to retire immediately, but no physician took any notice of his fears concerning his illness or his decision to retire. Although the details of his illness were eventually clarified, Mr. Barts never returned to work after leaving the hospital. In retirement he exercised less while eating at the usual rate. When he came back to the clinic the doctors were alarmed at his gain of between 40 and 50 pounds in one year. They warned him about this, and one doctor said to him bluntly, "When you get hungry live on your fat; you've got enough of it." In this case, the medical management of the patient under semicommittee sponsorship contributed to his premature retirement and unfortunate eating habits which were probably unfavorable to his health.

Mr. Lecase was another patient who had semicommitte sponsorship. He developed pain in his feet, which his internist attributed to vascular insufficiency and for which he was referred to a surgeon for further diagnosis and treatment. Evaluation by the surgeon revealed occlusive arterial disease of the lower extremities and, even more serious, far-advanced occlusive disease of both carotid arteries. Mr. Lecase and his family reacted with intense anxiety to this diagnosis, as he had young children still dependent upon him. The family feared not so much the loss of his feet as the loss of his "brain" or his life. His wife expressed her anxieties vividly to us but not to the doctors.

Mr. Lecase recovered from separate operations on both carotid arteries, but he faced invalidism, greatly aggravated fears for his life, and worries about the support of his family. His private doctor, the surgeon, saw him only briefly and intermittently. Although Mr. Lecase was depressed and weepy at times, he did not reveal his fears to the surgeon who assumed he was bearing up very well and was a model patient. The surgeon told us:

> He seems like a very well-adjusted fellow in terms of his approach to his problem. He appreciates the seriousness of the disease and he got along very well with the hospital staff.

When asked about the family, the surgeon replied, "I really didn't meet his family except one or two times." He could offer no more illuminating comments about either the patient or the family.

Mr. Lecase viewed the doctors as military leaders, superior to him: "They have their secrets. Medical and military secrets are much alike." He felt obliged to go through with the diagnostic and treatment program recommended just as a soldier would be forced to follow all orders in line of duty including the sacrifice of his life, if so ordered.

Mr. Lecase and his wife often sought to talk with the surgeon, but he was generally unavailable. Their closest relationship was with the house officers and even this was a cool and casual one. The house officer who was available to them understood that this was not really his patient but he, more than any other physician, was exposed to the anxieties of the Lecases. He reported to us:

> Mrs. Lecase was extremely labile during and after both operative procedures, but the patient himself, at least in front of the doctors, seemed to maintain a relatively stable general condition.

The house officer then went on to tell us that a patch had been put on one eye because of a corneal abrasion sustained during anesthesia. The family was told that the patch would be removed at 6 P.M. When it was not removed promptly at 6, Mrs. Lecase became extremely anxious. She and Mr. Lecase were fearful that parts of his body were going to fall off and they wondered if one of his eyes had been damaged seriously. No physician understood this aspect of the situation. The house officer, ignoring the real problems faced by Mrs. Lecase, attributed her behavior to an anxious and labile personality.

While the private surgeon was in the background and making the major decisions, the *real* sponsorship to Mr. Lecase and the family was that of the surgeon's agent—the house officer—while he, in turn, saw his relationship to Mr. Lecase as one which should be casual and uncommitted. The house officer told us that Mr. Lecase was treated by the surgeon "with less interest" than if he were "a patient of higher status."

In brief, the semicommittee sponsorship offered the patient little more than the committee sponsorship although he paid for the services of one or more private physicians. Sometimes the private physician offered some specific and helpful services or information but, more often, he simply became another member of the committee, not necessarily a very effective one. The patient, as in committee sponsorship, was pushed around a great deal. For the most part these patients and their family members had to find solutions for their own problems without benefit of expert medical leadership and counsel.

Casual Sponsorship

The focus of interaction between the patient and his physician in a casual sponsorship was upon the symptoms of the disease and the diagnostic and treatment procedures. Most of these patients expected little else, and the doctors were not prompted to offer more. The house staff functioned more as technicians than as physicians. Casual sponsorship was found in 54 per cent of the semiprivate and in 54 per cent of the private patients. The mean Index of Social Position scores for casual sponsorship was *51* in the semiprivate accommodation and *35* in the private accommodation.

Mr. Wither's case was typical of casual sponsorship relationships in which both patients and their doctors were pleased and neither party intruded upon the time of the other. Mr. Wither was a skilled workman and, according to his wife, a "loner." He had delayed surgery as long as possible until his wife, recognizing his increased disability, insisted on an operation. He went to a surgeon, complaining about a hernia. He did not mention his peptic ulcers or recurring headaches. The surgeon examined him briefly and "booked" admission to the hospital.

Once hospitalized, Mr. Wither said he had no questions. He told us his surgeon was "a very busy man," and he did not feel his questions about his ulcers or headaches were important enough to take up the surgeon's time. He asked for no medication for postoperative pain. The surgeon arranged Mr. Wither's care with dispatch, visited for a minute or two daily, and said he had a "very satisfied stoic" on his hands. Neither the patient nor the surgeon gave evidence of wanting a different relationship.

A different quality of casual sponsorship is illustrated by Mr. Jetson, mentioned earlier in our discussion of social perception. He was referred to an internist because of rectal pain and bleeding. The internist delegated principal responsibility for his care to a junior partner. The partner-physician carried out elaborate studies of the gastrointestinal system but learned little about Mr. Jetson personally. As the symptoms continued the doctors thought prostatitis might be causing part of the problem, so a urologist was consulted. The urologist felt he could not explain the symptoms and referred Mr. Jetson back to the internist. After three days in the hospital, the patient was sent home without any specific answer.

The rectal bleeding caused Mr. Jetson intense anxiety. A sister was dying of cancer and he was very fearful that he had cancer. To complicate matters further, a positive serology (lues) was discovered in the hospital, but Mr. Jetson was not informed of it until after his discharge. In the mailed report of the positive reaction, instructions were included for him to return in two weeks to the doctor's office for a repeat blood test. Mrs. Jetson opened the letter and learned of the positive reaction, which to her meant her husband was suffering from syphilis. Mr. Jetson followed the instructions, but the fear of syphilis, now added to his worries, caused considerable tension between him and his wife. Finally, it was demonstrated that he did not have syphilis but his symptoms of rectal pain were never explained. He was dismayed that the doctors were so ambiguous and had subjected him to the expensive tests and unnecessary worry about syphilis. On our last visit, Mr. Jetson told us he was planning to consult a well-known private clinic in another city, hoping to have his questions answered.

A third example of casual sponsorship is the case of Mrs. Coe, a lower-middle-class housewife from a suburban town who had suffered from neurotic symptoms of the gastrointestinal tract for many years. Her daughter had recently graduated from a nursing school in a local hospital and had learned enough about doctors and diseases so that she believed referral of her mother to an internist was desirable. The daughter selected a doctor, and the family general practitioner made the referral. The internist recognized that Mrs. Coe was fearful and anxious about her intestinal symptoms. He felt that a different approach was in order for purposes of "balancing" her treatment. He, therefore, deliberately treated her, as he said, "in a mechanistic manner." Although he attributed most of her symptoms to her anxieties he dwelt primarily upon a hiatus hernia for the explanation of her gastro-intestinal symptoms. He neither listened to Mrs. Coe's problems nor paid much heed to the findings and treatment of the general practitioner. He spent little time with the patient, explaining only briefly his diagnostic studies and findings. He outlined specific plans concerning medications, diet, and positioning so as to minimize her condition, and then promptly referred her back to her family doctor. Mrs. Coe's symptoms were only slightly and temporarily improved.

In summary, the physician was casual in his relationships with the patient and his family. Casual sponsorship was characterized by three attributes: (1) The physician looked upon the patient as his own and he remained in the forefront of the doctor-patient relationship; the house staff were not allowed to dominate the care and treatment situation in the hospital. (2) The physician focused his attention upon the presenting symptom or symptoms of the patient and treated the symptoms by recourse to the technical knowledge he had about the real or assumed disease of the patient; when the patient's symptoms were puzzling to the physician he sometimes asked for consultations from other physicians, but, in the end, decisions were left to his judgment; in the most casual of sponsorships the patient might be treated "mechanistically." (3) The physician allowed little time for the patient to question him about the illness; patients were told that the best of scientific medicine was being applied and, in some instances, that there was no substitute for the "tincture of time."

Committed Sponsorship

Committed sponsorship involved a determined assumption of responsibility for the patient by the physician. The physician's interest in the patient extended beyond his interest in the disease. These patients were of higher social status and some of them treated their physicians as subordinates. The physicians showed their interest and assumed responsibility accordingly. Twenty-four patients experienced committed sponsorship, nineteen on the surgical services and five on the medical service. Twenty-three of the twenty-four were housed in private accommodations; the only patient with a committed sponsorship in a semiprivate accommodation had the highest Index of Social Position score of all patients in semiprivate accommodations. The mean Index of Social Position score for patients with committed sponsorship is 24.

Dr. Sail, a successful practitioner of medicine, is an example of the optimal complex of medical and social relations characteristic of committed sponsorship. He developed a hernia and was admitted by a surgeon for treatment. These two physicians had dealt with each other professionally about patients of mutual interest and had met frequently on social occasions, but they were not close friends. Dr. Sail was admitted at his convenience and placed on the operating schedule so he would get fresh staff and the first choice of anesthesiologists. The surgeon saw to it that the admissions office, the floor nurses, the house staff, the operating room staff, and the anesthesiologists were informed of the admission of his special patient. Subsequent to the operation, the surgeon visited him frequently in his room, explained all treatments that were given, and supervised them diligently. Dr. Sail was given more attention than he wanted or needed by the nurses on the floor as well as by private-duty nurses caring for other patients. (These nurses either had been his patients or had cared for his patients at another time.) Mrs. Sail was kept informed of the progress of the surgery and the course of her husband's treatment. Dr. Sail's recovery was rapid and uneventful.

An exceptional performance of a committed sponsor is illustrated by the case of Mrs. Koster. Her internist, also her neighbor, understood Mrs. Koster's peculiar attraction to surgical treatment for symptoms of abdominal pain and some minor upper-gastrointestinal problems. As she approached her mid-forties, she developed some menstrual disorders and lower-abdominal discomfort. At the same time, her upper-gastrointestinal complaints increased. Her internist understood her wish for surgical treatment and was sympathetic but, nonetheless, firm in advising her against this course. A year before admission, her lower-abdominal symptoms became more severe. Consultation with a gynecologist was recommended. This decision pleased Mrs. Koster who felt that finally her internist would realize the need for surgery. The internist, however, understanding her state of mind, recognized that the surgical experience was neither pleasant nor likely to bring the kind of relief which Mrs. Koster hoped for. He cautioned her and specifically told her to expect a rather extended convalescence and not to expect too much from the surgery. The surgery was done by a gynecologist who was more a technician than her sponsor. The house officer, to Mrs. Koster, was secondary to the gynecologist and internist, but he spent more time with her than he did with his other patients. He reported personal satisfaction and enjoyment in talking with her and treating her, knowing that she was an intelligent woman who fitted comfortably into the private accommodation. Mrs. Koster was capable of attracting attention or commanding it if necessary. She could, therefore, secure a committed sponsorship which appeared to be satisfying to all and therapeutic to her.

Mrs. Koster also had the attentions of a private-duty nurse. This illustrates another aspect of committed sponsorship. Eleven of the twenty-four patients with committed sponsorship had private-duty nurses. The physicians for these patients knew them well and indicated specifically what nursing care their patients wanted or required. Committed sponsorship, therefore, not only involved a committed physician but also often promoted the development of a "private team" for the treatment of the patient.

Although committed sponsorship was almost always dictated and enjoyed by the patients, it was not always an enlightened relationship which served the patients' best health interests. For example, Mrs. Leadon was an anxious, emotionally unstable individual who had sought out the services of many physicians. In the year prior to her admission she managed to persuade the physicians to do a gastrointestinal series, two breast biopsies, and several examinations. One physician who saw her reported that her cysts were benign and, although they should be checked occasionally for any suspicious changes, they should be left alone. She was dissatisfied with his evaluation and went to see a doctor who had removed a breast cancer for a friend of hers in the recent past. She cultivated the doctor and he seemed to enjoy her company. He admitted her to the hospital for still another biopsy.

In her shopping for physicians, Mrs. Leadon revealed enough about herself to indicate that she needed medical care but never enough so that the physicians became aware that her behavior was a manifestation of an emotional disturbance. She enjoyed the physicians' examinations and discussed them freely. She told us one physician was a friend who "lives near by and does not examine me internally because he knows me too well and gets embarrassed." Mrs. Leadon enjoyed being seductive with her friends and particularly with her physicians. She not only demanded examinations but further operations. In the hospital her performance was childlike, exhibitionistic, and seductive. Although she made the most of her opportunity to perform, she was frightened of the anesthesia and surgery. She felt, however, that it was a necessary price she had to pay to be relieved, even temporarily, from the continuous adversities of her troubled life at home. The physician, in admitting her to the hospital, provided removal from the troubled home atmosphere, interest as a physician and a male, and dramatic validation of the sickness as evidenced by further surgery.

The surgical resident who saw Mrs. Leadon at admission was unaware of any of this background. He casually commented that he did not think another breast biopsy was really necessary at that time. Mrs. Leadon was infuriated; she told him to leave her room and not return. Meanwhile, her surgeon, a private practitioner, came in daily, held hands with her for a few minutes, and listened to her chat. She exhibited herself in varying ways to him, which he seemed to enjoy. Near the end of the hospitalization when she discovered the breast scar was longer than she had expected and when she was feeling very depressed at having to leave the hospital to return home, her surgeon visited and discovered her weepy mood. He put his arm around her shoulder and she immediately began to smile. He said, "You're happy; you're cheerful; you're content. We should do this more often." He joked with her for a few minutes and then left. Mrs. Leadon concluded that her surgeon was "very nice."

In talking to us Mrs. Leadon described herself as being "kind of nutty" or "mental." She discussed her favorite movie actors, all of whom were paragons of masculinity, and also she described her attraction to "powerful movies like those with miracles and the fantastic." She was extremely anxious about instruction for her children in sexual matters, courtship, and so on. She indicated her pleasure with her surgeon because she felt he had agreed to admit her for further breast biopsies at her desire. She thought this was what he meant when he said, "We should do this more often."

Mrs. Leadon's committed sponsorship was a continuing and close one, but we have to ask *to what it was committed.* The physician failed to perceive the main problem, or he chose to ignore it. He appeared to be concerned primarily with pleasing and enjoying his appealing, seductive patient and perhaps, in part, with the promotion of his practice of surgery.

Physician-patient relationships for six of the twenty-three private patients involved in committed sponsorships were similar to the interactions that prevailed between Mrs. Leadon and her physicians. The physicians were drawn into these sponsorships by powerful patients who communicated selectively and in some instances dictated diagnosis or therapy or both. Committed sponsorship, though very favorable for some patients, was not favorable for others. It may have promoted the practices of physicians and led to at least superficial satisfaction of patients but, as we have indicated in the example of Mrs. Leadon, the relationships were often less than therapeutic.

We found examples of unsatisfactory relationships among the casual and semicommittee sponsorships also, but the influence of those relationships was not nearly as profound since there was less time for the sponsorship to advance the relationship, pathologic or otherwise, between the patient and the physician. In some of these less than therapeutic sponsorships, group disturbances arose in which physicians were set against each other and against nurses who, in turn, were set against one another; that is, the patients allied themselves with some members of the staff against others; sometimes they rapidly changed allies. Commonly, the patient was in conflict with a house officer or a nurse over some procedure or recommendation which was basically sound and in the patient's best interest but which the patient feared. He was usually able to twist the situation and convince or command the sponsoring physician to take his side. The physician then censured, redirected, or banished from the side of the patient the offensive member of the staff. Needless to say, this did not improve staff relationships. Patients who created such disturbances were severely disturbed themselves in their prehospital mental status ratings. (See Chapter 10.) In the hospital the disturbance was much more severe, but the patient and physician did not recognize this as such or, if so, were in tacit agreement that they should not act upon that recognition. Instead, they dealt with the external situation even though the cause of this disturbance came from within the patient.

The final example of a committed sponsorship represents a special problem for the medical service, particularly among female patients. Mrs. McCaine was admitted to the hospital for one of a continuing series of hospitalizations arranged for diagnostic studies, all aimed at discovering the cause of abdominal pains. Mrs. McCaine had a phobia of cancer which she kept to herself. She had seen many doctors and was sponsored in this hospitalization by an internist who did repeat X-ray and other laboratory studies. She was viewed by him and the house staff as well as the nurses as "a well-bred, upper-class lady." Since her physicians, including the house staff, felt that "such a lady" could not conceivably be a "crock," they approached her with a sympathetic attitude. She confided to us that she approached them and their diagnostic efforts with an "open mind," while revealing only a limited amount about herself. She had witnessed physicians' performances before and had come to understand that they were not likely to find the answers to her problems. At the time of her admission to this hospital she predicted their failure: "They have to find out what the cause of the pain is, but I don't think they will."

Her internist made special efforts to secure a private room. He was pleasant with her and attempted to make her hospitalization as comfortable as possible. He informed her of the studies being made and the reasons for them, but he was quite close to Mrs. McCaine socially and the thought of a frank discussion of the turmoils of her life seemed most distasteful. No cause of the symptoms could be found. Further hospitalizations occurred after the one we studied; these were arranged by the same physician and with the same results. Meanwhile, the fact of admission to the hospital had convinced Mrs. McCaine that the doctors really were worried about cancer and, as the fear mounted, the symptoms became considerably worse. There was no frank discussion of this fear or of the fact that the findings indicated no disease.

Some of Mrs. McCaine's friends suggested she go to a well-known clinic in a city elsewhere. Mrs. McCaine mentioned this to her internist, who encouraged her to make the visit. When he offered to send her records, it convinced her all the more that he was worried about cancer. By this time Mrs. McCaine had learned to recite a reasonable, accurate, and quite convincing history of pancreatic cancer. The new doctors were perplexed by the long history of severe symptoms and the nearly normal examination. They felt they should clarify the matter by a surgical exploration of the abdomen. Following that hospitalization and return to her home, Mrs. McCaine explained her experience to us:

> The doctor asked me if I thought I had cancer. I told him I didn't know. He kept thinking I thought I had it. I think that's what he was looking for. The doctor told me that 50 per cent of such cases come out negative. I said it seemed like a waste to do the surgery if 50 per cent come out negative, but he said it's better to come out negative than positive.
>
> The doctors there thought cancer was a possibility. I don't think they would have opened me up if they didn't suspect it, but they didn't put it in so many words. I knew there was a possibility, and my husband thought I had it. I felt there was only one way to find out, and I did it only as a last resort to make it definite. I don't think they fooled me. I thought this would be the last thing. They decided by a process of elimination that it was in my mind. If it had been cancer they would have treated me or something. My doctor was right. He didn't want to operate. I think he suspected it was cancer, but he didn't object when the doctors wanted to operate. I think people are too cancer conscious. The doctors there told me they found everything normal. I know they weren't trying to fool me because I didn't need private-duty nurses. I go by that a lot.

Mrs. McCaine was the kind of person who habitually reveals little of herself to others and believes that others are similarly secretive. She relied upon cues in the behavior of others to evaluate her own situation. Her internist was aware of the high probability that Mrs. McCaine's symptoms were functional or neurotic in nature, but he did not wish to offend her by saying so, and he felt there was some room for doubt. When she returned from her surgical pilgrimage to another city, she continued to be his patient for further medical problems. Her estimated cost of the series of hospitalizations here and elsewhere, plus the medical fees, was $5,400. Insurance firms paid most of this.

In summary, committed sponsorship offered the best opportunity for the physician and patient to join in the diagnosis and treatment of health problems. Patients and physicians in general were pleased with their relationship, but in the majority of cases committed sponsorship simply made the technical aspects of patient care more tolerable, if not pleasant, for the patients and physicians, while about 25 per cent of the committed sponsorships constituted a threat to the patient. We wish to state clearly that the *physician by himself* was never found to be entirely responsible for this threat; it is equally clear at the same time that the *patient by himself* was not fully responsible. This type of sponsorship, in which the patient demanded and paid for the physician's time, was open to influences of the patient or physician, or both, which focused on the importance of pleasantry and good manners as opposed to solving the patient's problems. In only one of the 24 cases was this sponsorship an exemplary one, devoted to the task of professional management of both technical and personal aspects of patient care. The influences and fear of mental illness, plus the narrow training and correspondingly narrow framework of medical practice, may have contributed largely to these disturbing situations. Superficially, we found little to suggest that the patients or their physicians understood these dilemmas or wanted a change in their relationships. However, in the more problematic relationships, the deeper feelings of patients indicated dissatisfaction and annoyance. They knew something was not right but they kept their feelings to themselves. They did not communicate their dissatisfaction to their spouses or to their physicians.

Sponsorship was related significantly to hospital accommodation and service but not to the sex of the patient. The data summarized in Table 10 show that there were differences between any pair of the three accommodation groups. Private patients enjoyed almost exclusively, and suffered occasionally from, committed sponsorship, while the ward patients endured the most discontinuous and disorganized sponsorship (committee); semiprivate patients were in between.

The sponsorship of the surgeon has been mentioned in connection with his position in the hospital, particularly in regard to his role in the operating room. However, our data reveal that private patients were the only ones who were fully sponsored by surgeons. Semiprivate surgical patients had semi-committee or casual sponsorship as frequently as semiprivate medical patients. In the wards all the patients, medical and surgical, were under the sponsorship of the committee. The figures on the type of sponsorship found among the private medical and surgical patients are given in Table 10, section C; 51 per cent of the private surgical patients enjoyed a committed sponsorship, while only 14 per cent of the private medical patients did.

TABLE 10. PHYSICIAN SPONSORSHIP DURING HOSPITALIZATION, BY ACCOMMODATION AND SERVICE

Accommodation and Service	N	Patients by Type of Sponsorship			
		Committee	Semicommittee	Casual	Committed
A. ACCOMMODATION					
Private	65	—%	11%	54%	35%
Semiprivate	54	—	44	54	2
Ward	42	100	—	—	—
Total	161	26	19	40	15

Private compared with semiprivate, p < .05; private compared with ward, p < .05; semiprivate compared with ward, p < .05.

B. SERVICE					
Medicine	74	27%	26%	41%	7%
Surgery	87	25	14	39	22
Total	161	26	19	40	15

p < .05

C. PRIVATE PATIENTS BY SERVICE					
Medicine	28	—%	21%	64%	14%
Surgery	37	—	3	46	51
Total	65	—	11	54	35

p < .05

The sequence of doctor-patient relationships we have discussed under the concept of sponsorship was not an isolated phenomenon in the course of the patient's day-by-day experiences or in the career of the physicians. We determined by careful questioning of the patients and the physicians what their relationships were *before* and *after* this hospitalization as well as *during* the hospitalization we studied. The data on sponsorship before, during, and after hospitalization are summarized in Table 11. The very high coefficients of contingency both before and after hospitalization reveal that the doctor-patient relationship was a relatively stable one insofar as sponsorship is concerned; that is, patients who had a committee sponsorship during this hospitalization were accustomed to being cared for by medical students and house staff through previous use of the clinics and the Emergency Room of the hospital. After they were discharged they returned to the hospital's out-patient services for their care. This point is evident at a glance at the com-mittee-committee sponsorship cells of Table 11, sections A and B.

The private patients having a committed sponsorship with their physicians during hospitalization had, in very large part (twenty-one out of twenty-four patients), experienced the same type of sponsorship before they came to the hospital. Subsequent to hospitalization twenty-two out of the twenty-three surviving patients maintained a committed relationship with their physician. Committed sponsorship like committee sponsorship was limited almost en-tirely to a particular hospital accommodation; twenty-three out of the twenty-four patients who had committed sponsorship in the hospital were in private rooms; all forty-two of the committee-sponsored patients were on the wards.

TABLE 11. PHYSICIAN SPONSORSHIP BEFORE, DURING, AND AFTER HOSPITALIZATION

	Total	Patients by Sponsorship During Hospitalization			
		Committee	Semicommittee	Casual	Committed
A. BEFORE AND DURING HOSPITALIZATION					
Prehospitalization Sponsorship					
Committee	26%	73%	30%	8%	—%
Semicommittee	19	11	32	16	—
Casual	40	15	37	73	—
Committed	15	—	2	4	100
N =	(161)	(26)	(63)	(51)	(21)
p < .05; $\overline{C}$ = .87.					
B. DURING AND AFTER HOSPITALIZATION					
Posthospital Sponsorship					
Committee	25%	87%	23%	7%	—%
Semicommittee	20	7	42	24	—
Casual	41	7	35	68	—
Committed	14	—	—	1	100
N =	(155)*	(31)	(26)	(76)	(22)
p < .05; $\overline{C}$ = .71.					

* Six patients died in the hospital; thus, there is no posthospital sponsor for these patients.

Patients who experienced either a semicommittee or a casual sponsorship were housed either on the semiprivate or the private accommodations. Un-like the committed- and the committee-sponsorship patients, the semicom-mittee patients more or less shopped for physicians both before and after the hospitalization. The casually sponsored patients were predominantly sponsored by the same physicians before, during, and after this hospitalization. (See Table 11, sections A and B—casual-casual sponsorship.) There is no clear concentration of patients in any one cell either before or after hospitalization among those who experienced semicommittee sponsorship while in the hospital.

Sponsorship before, during, and after hospitalization was related significantly to the socioeconomic position of the patients. Patients who experienced semicommittee sponsorship were lower in the status system than those who were casually sponsored; both groups were in the middle range of scores on the Index of Social Position. These patients were members of families who were not medically indigent but did not have enough status and economic competence to command the committed attention of specialists.

The patient's view of the house officer cast some light on sponsorship. The further removed the patient was from the divisions in which teaching was most visible, the more the house officer was viewed as a student rather than a primary or supplementary physician responsible for diagnosis and treatment. To patients in the ward accommodations, any and all "doctors" were involved in the total performance of patient care, teaching, and research; they expected the house officers to care for them, or at least they hoped they would. Patients in the semiprivate and private accommodations had a sponsor who oftentimes found it convenient, especially in dealing with his higher-status patients, to justify the house officer's role and work as a necessary part of the teaching program of the Medical Center. This was viewed as an adjustment made by the physician in a committed sponsorship with higher-status patients. These physicians commonly implied (and their patients reported such impressions to us) that they were not only good practitioners but also teachers desired by a renowned university whose students were, therefore, in evidence and should be given a break for they had to learn. This view was not popular with house officers who felt that such physicians taught them little while requiring too much work of them. The house officer believed the patient's private doctor degraded him by reducing him to the role of student which he was trying so hard to abandon and thereby discounting his importance in the care of patients and the operation of the hospital.

The role of the physician in relation to private patients, especially in committed sponsorship, involved another interesting dimension of the physician's adaptation to his patient—the nature of what the physician told the patient about his disease. While private patients were more fully informed than semiprivate or ward patients, the information given to them about their diagnosis and treatment was sometimes erroneous. Private patients were given the wrong diagnosis knowingly or by a remarkably effective inference in 15 per cent of instances. There was a significant difference by service and sex which holds only for private patients. (See Table 12.) Private female patients on the medical service were most often misinformed. Five of these patients had cancer, five had mental illness, and three had heart disease.

TABLE 12. PHYSICIANS' REPORT OF DIAGNOSIS TO PRIVATE PATIENTS, BY SEX

Report of Diagnosis	Private Patients by Sex		
	Total	Female	Male
Complete and accurate	68%	53%	84%
Incomplete but accurate	12	15	10
Incomplete and inaccurate	5	9	—
Wrong diagnosis	15	24	7
N =	(65)	(34)	(31)
p < .05			

Seven of these thirteen patients were given an *ad hoc* diagnosis. (See Chapter 9, p. 151.) The feelings of patients and families about the diagnosis of these patients were strong and involved much anxiety. Implicit in the demands of patients for kindness and sympathy was the desire to be sheltered from unpleasantness, and some physicians willingly obliged.

We found that patients who enjoyed casual and committed sponsorship were more satisfied with their care and less suspicious than patients who were cared for by the committee and the semicommittee; they received more understanding and emotional support from their physicians, they had a more favorable outcome, and there was less economic hardship. Although comfort, convenience, and a feeling of security were important in adding to a patient's satisfaction, it is not easy to prove that they added to the patient's recovery. The favorable outcome of the patients who enjoyed committed sponsorship was ascribable more to the personal and social situation of the patient and to his less severe illness than it was to physician sponsorship.

Summary

From the perspective of sponsorship, the physician-patient relationship was directly and most clearly linked to the socioeconomic status of the patient. Committee, semicommittee, and casual sponsorships were impersonal and disinterested. Committed sponsorship was enjoyable but it demanded a price. Each type of sponsorship was associated with selected advantages and disadvantages. At the same time, it was abundantly clear that both patients and physicians believed committed sponsorship was the ideal relationship for the patient. We believe these patterns of sponsorship represented the manner in which the hospital, practitioners, and patients adjusted to community and hospital forces, most of which were beyond the control of the physician and the patient.

We draw two inferences from our analysis of sponsorship: (1) Physicians who exhibited a personal interest in patients were concerned about their practices or careers so that from self-interest they believed they could not offend or appear unkind even when necessary for rational patient management. (2) Rarely did a physician exhibit an effective skill in using himself and his sponsorship to the patient's therapeutic advantage when this was most urgently needed; in such instances, groping and even floundering were evident. While the attention commanded in committed sponsorship was pleasant and brought some betterment for patients and physicians, there seemed to be little advantage otherwise.

I_N THIS CHAPTER WE CENTER ATTENTION UPON THE NEED
for admission, the physician's diagnosis of the patient's medical or surgical
problems, the completeness and accuracy of the diagnosis, possible explanations of the etiology of the patient's illness, and the appropriateness of
the treatment prescribed. Our conclusions concerning each issue were based on
evidence from all the sources of information to which we had access: the
medical record, observations of behavior, and interviews with physicians,
nurses, the patient, and his spouse. The inferences we drew from the data
about the role of human relations may or may not agree with the decisions
made by the patients, their physicians, and family members on their efforts
to cope with the illness.

All patients sought help for problems which they or family members had
identified as requiring a physician's attention. Each was examined by a
physician who thought the patient's illness could be managed best in the
hospital. We divided the need for admission of patients to the hospital into
three categories: *urgent, elective,* and *optional.* If the illness was acute and
threatened to cause death, marked disability, or suffering, urgent admission
to the hospital was indicated. We define *urgent admission* as one involving
a distinct threat to the life of the patient or severe disability if the person
was not admitted immediately or within forty-eight hours. Mr. Monet was
admitted to the ward accommodation on the medical service because of delerium tremens, a generalized convulsion, gastrointestinal bleeding, and facial
erysipelas which threatened airway obstruction. Hospitalization was rated
as urgent.

When the illness or condition indicated that admission could be arranged at
a time convenient to the patient, the physician, and the hospital, we classified
the admission as elective. An *elective admission* was one that was required
sooner or later but the timing could be determined by the availability of a

bed, the work schedule of the physician, or the personal plans of the patient and his family. Mrs. Napp, a private surgical patient, had experienced two minor gall bladder attacks over a period of years. X-ray studies revealed stones in the gall bladder. She delayed surgery for several years until her children were old enough to take care of themselves during her absence from home. She was then admitted for surgery at her convenience and that of her doctor. Her admission was an elective one.

For both urgent and elective admissions hospitals offer a service which is unique; the patient needs this service and cannot obtain it elsewhere. In addition to the requirements of diagnosis and treatment of a specific illness, admission to the hospital may be arranged for other reasons. The admission of patients to the hospital for such reasons, when there was no obvious medical or surgical need, was viewed as optional. An *optional admission* was traceable to the desires of the patient, his spouse, the physician or a combination of the three. Mr. Trout is an example of optional admission. Mrs. Trout, who had lost both of her parents from malignancies within the previous two years, was worried about her husband's alcoholism and possible malignancies. Mr. Trout had been a heavy drinker for years. On the day prior to admission he had been drinking for several hours when he began to experience abdominal pain accompanied by nausea and vomiting. As Mr. Trout had no physician and his wife's regular physician was out of town, she called an alternate physician. This doctor was not familiar with the family and was less experienced than the regular physician. His uncertainty, combined with Mrs. Trout's anxiety, led him to recommend immediate hospitalization so he could get a consultation with the house officer in the hospital. Mrs. Trout felt her anxieties about cancer and alcoholism would be relieved by her husband's admission. Mr. Trout was a reluctant party to the action, but he was outvoted and finally agreed to come to the hospital.

The percentage of patients classified by their need for admission in each accommodation and service is given in the several sections of Table 13. We note in passing that there were no meaningful differences between the sexes for any accommodation or service group. Therefore, we shall not discuss the factor of sex on the need for admission. Examination of the figures in Table 13, section A, shows that the ward patients required admission most urgently. Conversely, the semiprivate and private patients had the highest proportion of optional admissions. Speaking generally, each accommodation group traced a distinct pattern in comparison with the other two accommodation groups. The ward patients were concentrated in the urgent category, the semiprivate patients in the elective group, and among the private patients the highest figure was for urgent admission.

When we compared the data on the need for admission by service (Table

TABLE 13. NEED FOR ADMISSION TO HOSPITAL, BY ACCOMMODATION AND SERVICE

Accommodation and Service	N	Patients by Need for Admission		
		Urgent	Elective	Optional
A. ACCOMMODATION				
Private	65	49%	23%	28%
Semiprivate	54	26	43	31
Ward	42	64	29	7

Private compared with semiprivate, p < .05; private compared with ward, p < .05; semiprivate compared with ward, p < .05.

B. SERVICE				
Medicine	74	51%	5%	43%
Surgery	87	40	53	7
p < .05				
C. PRIVATE ACCOMMODATION AND SERVICE				
Medicine	28	46%	4%	50%
Surgery	37	51	38	11
p < .05				
D. SEMIPRIVATE ACCOMMODATION AND SERVICE				
Medicine	26	35%	8%	58%
Surgery	28	18	75	7
p < .05				
E. WARD ACCOMMODATION AND SERVICE*				
Medicine	21	80%	5%	15%
Surgery	21	50	50	—
p < .05				

* Elective and optional admissions are combined in the chi-square analysis.

13, section B), we found a significant difference in the distribution between the two services. Patients admitted to the medical service were clustered into two groups—urgent admissions and optional admissions; only 5 per cent were in the elective group. On the other hand, the surgical patients were concentrated in the urgent and elective categories. Few surgical patients were admitted optionally.

The more detailed breakdown of the data on the need for admission by each accommodation and service, presented in Table 13, sections C, D, and E, reveals some interesting information on the use of the hospital by physicians and patients: At least 50 per cent of the medical patients in the semiprivate and private accommodations were optional admissions; very few were elective. While the proportions of optional admissions were close to one another in the private and semiprivate accommodations of the medical service, there were sharp differences between the two groups when we examined the data on each patient to determine why these admissions occurred. When semiprivate patients were ill, they commonly sought out general practitioners for help; they also usually followed the advice of their physicians. Admission to the semiprivate accommodations, particularly on the medical service, was arranged frequently by the patient's physician so that he might obtain a consultation with another physician. Although a consultation with a selected specialist might have solved the problem, the consultation was not sought outside the hospital by the patient or by his physician. The anxieties of patients, combined with the uncertainties of physicians, produced a crisis which to both the patient and the physician justified admission. In the private accommodation, especially among high-status patients, admission to the hospital was looked upon as a matter of convenience for the patient. These patients came and went when they pleased, as they pleased.

When we compared the need for admission among semiprivate and private patients with that among ward patients and admission to the medical service with that to the surgical service, a distinctly different pattern was traced. On the ward accommodations, three medical patients (15 per cent) were optional admissions. Two were hospitalized by a medical assistant resident because he judged them to be good teaching cases for the house staff, the medical students, and interested physicians. The third optional admission was refused initially by the house officer. This patient and his wife then recruited a community physician to request admission to the hospital ward accommodation. Reluctantly, the admitting resident agreed because of the policy of the medical service. (This policy is discussed in Chapter 7, p. 115.) No ward patients were admitted optionally on the surgical service.

At times, conflict about admission to the ward accommodation occurred between the house officer and the admitting officer. House officers had an expressed interest in admitting patients with diseases from which they, as students of medicine, could learn. There was a keen interest in patients for whom something could be done, preferably in a dramatic way. This was very satisfying to young physicians anxious to "save lives." They liked to review pathology; they were excited about it, but they wanted change. If the patient was responsive to their treatment, was appreciative, got well, and then went home—this was satisfying. If the patient's disease was rapidly progressive and the patient died, the young physicians could examine the results at the postmortem tables—this also was satisfying. But patients with slowly progressive or unchanging chronic diseases were of little interest to the house physicians after initial evaluation. The young physicians found it unpleasant to associate with patients facing progressive and irreversible disease. Thus, the house staff looked down upon the admission of uninteresting patients (turkeys), endured them when they could not avoid them, and "shipped" (discharged) them as soon as possible.

Although hospital economics and the choices of house officers influenced admissions to the wards, the patients themselves were a party to the transaction. They knew that "the ward" carried a stigma in the community. Moreover, it often led to economic impoverishment, as income ceased and savings were spent. Poor people who were ill delayed seeking medical attention, sometimes out of fear, sometimes to avoid hospital expenses and wage losses. They came to the clinic or the Emergency Room in great pain; often they were forced to seek help because there was no other alternative but more pain, disability, or possibly death.

Each of the three parties to the transaction—the patient, the house officer, and the admitting officer—was faced with a dilemma: The house officer was interested in learning to diagnose and treat disease. (Is the patient "a good learning case"? If not, can his admission be prevented?) The admissions officer did not want to deny the hospital's facilities to an urgent case, but he did not want the hospital to be forced to underwrite the cost of the hospitalization. The patient, whose life and well-being were most intimately and extensively involved, had the least powerful voice in deciding whether or not he would be admitted to the wards.

The semiprivate and private patients presented a different picture. Viewed objectively, the fact that they had established a professional relationship with a physician who sponsored them in the hospital changed their relationship with the hospital. The private physician had a primary interest in promoting his practice in his own behalf. This is the way he made his living, and he expected to make a good living from his practice. Physicians in private practice and their patients rarely differed in their opinions concerning the need or desirability for admission to the hospital. When differences did occur the physician, in order to promote his own ends by satisfying the patient, yielded to the patient's wishes. The physician did not want to lose the patient, and the patient did not want to change physicians. Admission to the hospital, therefore, resolved a crisis between the physician and his patient. (We recognize, of course, that physicians successfully opposing the choice of patients for hospitalization would not be included in this study. We emphasize, however, that when disagreement regarding hospitalization occurred physicians in private practice did not oppose the choice of their patients.) As noted, surgical patients required urgent or elective admission in most instances; few (7 per cent) were admitted optionally. This finding is attributed to the fact that most of these patients required major surgery which is done only in a hospital.

In brief, hospital admission for diagnosis and treatment was influenced in major ways by economic, educational, and social realities as well as by hospital service.

The diseases from which each patient suffered were diagnosed tentatively by a physician before admission to the hospital. A definite diagnosis was recorded in the medical record at the end of hospitalization. We studied the medical records of each patient and abstracted all the diagnoses physicians had made of his ills. When more than one diagnosis was given, we coded the one his physician used to justify the present hospitalization. This diagnosis is the one we discuss here and use in later sections of this chapter in reviewing the physician's performance in the care of his patients. For analytical purposes the specific coded diseases diagnosed for the 161 patients under study were consolidated into ten categories. The number and percentage of patients in each diagnostic category by accommodation are given in Table 14. There were some marked differences between the accommodations with respect to certain diagnostic groups; for example, 17 per cent of the semiprivate patients were diagnosed as suffering from gall bladder disease but only 2 per cent of the ward patients and 3 per cent of the private patients. Two other diagnostic categories in which the semiprivate patients differed markedly from the ward and private patients were miscellaneous diseases and cancer. (Included in the category of miscellaneous diseases were mumps, delerium tremens, neurological diseases, trauma, skin diseases, anemia, benign tumors, and so on.) Relatively few cancers were diagnosed among the semiprivate patients in contrast to those on the wards and the private accommodations. Diseases of the cardiovascular system and the gastrointestinal-biliary systems accounted for one half of all the patients' primary diagnosed diseases. Diagnosed mental illness was the least representative diagnosis in the series; one patient who was housed on a ward in the medical service was given this diagnosis.

When we view the diagnosis of the patients from the perspective of the service in which they were treated (see Table 14), we see that some diagnostic groups were confined to Medicine whereas others were limited to Surgery. Most disease groups, however, were found on both services but often in rather different proportions. Gall bladder disease and cancer clustered on the surgical service; cardiovascular diseases and diabetes were cared for mainly on the medical service.

The sex of the patient played a minor part in the kind of disease likely to be diagnosed. All of the myocardial infarctions, hernias, and chronic pulmonary diseases occurred among males. There were, however, secondary diagnosis of chronic pulmonary diseases or a history of myocardial infarction among the women. Females had 67 per cent of the cancer and all of the benign breast disease. Other differences were minor.

To identify and qualify the disease from which his patient suffers is the first task of the physician. He may then proceed to the next steps in caring for his patient—the prescription of treatment and an estimate of prognosis. The second and third steps in this process are dependent upon

TABLE 14. SPECIFIED DIAGNOSTIC GROUPS, BY ACCOMMODATION AND SERVICE

| Diagnostic Group | Total | Accommodation | | Service | | |
		Private	Semi-private	Ward	Medicine	Surgery
Myocardial infarction	6%	8%	4%	5%	12%	—%
Other cardiovascular disorders and diabetes	22	18	24	24	30	15
Gastrointestinal disorders	16	18	15	10	16	15
Gall bladder disease	7	3	17	2	4	10
Miscellaneous diseases	20	22	13	31	26	16
Cancer	15	18	9	17	8	21
Conditions requiring biopsy and minor surgery	7	8	11	2	—	14
Hernias	4	4	5	—	—	7
Chronic pulmonary disease	2	—	2	7	3	2
Mental illness	1	—	—	2	1	—
N =	(161)	(65)	(54)	(42)	(74)	(87)

the first; therefore, adequate diagnosis is of prime importance in the proper care of patients. This is the classical frame of reference that guides the physician as he goes about the practice of medicine. We began our research with this frame of reference as a point of departure. However, we formulated a general hypothesis which postulated that the three-step linkage between diagnosis of disease, prescription of treatment, and forecast of prognosis was contaminated or interfered with by a series of intervening variables—the socioeconomic status of the patient, the structure of the hospital's accommodations, the organization of medicine in the community, the physician's relationship to this patient, and the structure of the family. In order to review the adequacy and accuracy of the diagnosis, we studied the record of each patient and took into consideration his problems, his family, his relationship to the physician, the history of his symptoms, results of the physical examination and laboratory tests, and the course of the illness. Ideally, the diagnosis should have fitted the patient.

We developed four categories into which we placed our assessment of the adequacy and accuracy of the diagnoses the physicians had placed into the medical records: *properly diagnosed, underdiagnosed mentally, under or over-diagnosed physically,* and *misdiagnosed mentally and physically.*

When the evidence from all sources indicated a patient's symptoms were primarily organic in nature, the diagnosed organic disease was demonstrated, and mental disturbances were not productive of symptoms in a meaningful way, a patient was classified as *properly diagnosed.* In this category were included patients with hernias, heart attacks, infectious and neoplastic diseases, and so on. (Presentation of detailed personal or medical histories is believed to be unnecessary to illustrate this category.)

A patient was rated as *underdiagnosed mentally* when he was given a diagnosis of a physical disease although his behavior and symptoms of mental illness were demonstrated to his physician, were indicative of major disturbances sometimes psychotic in nature, and accounted, in whole or large part, for the symptoms. We found that the diagnosis of mental illness was never made by a nonpsychiatrist or applied to a high-status patient. Overdiagnosis of mental illness, therefore, could not occur. Underdiagnosis of mental illness was viewed as important in that it might have led the physician in a compensatory maneuver to overdiagnose physical disease—the doctor must have an explanation for the symptoms because the patient expects it.

Mr. Cuffstat, for example, was admitted to the ward medical service with an acute infectious disease, unrelated to a mental disorder. Attention was drawn to Mr. Cuffstat's mental status because of his manner of speaking and relating to others. He had a melancholy visage, described by several persons on the ward as appearing ready to cry; although he never did cry he smiled only rarely. He avoided looking directly at those who addressed him, examined him, or cared for him. He answered their questions tersely after a delay of sometimes up to 5 minutes. He produced very little information, but what he did say was usually found to be accurate. All the staff in the hospital from the attending physicians to the aides and the other patients found Mr. Cuffstat odd and "withdrawn." When the admitting intern requested a psychiatric consultation, the psychiatrist diagnosed a schizoid personality. This diagnosis was ignored by everyone and was not coded on the medical record. No psychiatric therapy was recommended by the psychiatrist, and the patient was discharged after nine days in the hospital.

Of Scandinavian descent, Mr. Cuffstat grew up on a farm in a midwestern state. He told us his boyhood on the farm was "crude and hard." He dreamed of being a musician, a philosopher, or an inventor, but his schooling was limited and finally he was drafted into the army. (We have no information about his record as a soldier.) After discharge from the army he became a vagrant for some time and consumed large amounts of alcohol; he often found himself penniless in various cities in the country. Eventually he came to this city and managed to get through two years of a local college before he had to quit to go to work. He was such a hard worker that his boss introduced him to his daughter and a marriage of convenience followed.

Mr. Cuffstat's wife, his three children, his in-laws, and the neighbors viewed him in much the same way as the staff of the hospital. Mr. Cuffstat lived with and worked for his father-in-law. Mrs. Cuffstat did not want to leave the family home, nor did the in-laws want them to leave. Although they complained about his lack of interest in them and in the everyday affairs of their life, they and the father-in-law particularly enjoyed his productivity at work. The father-in-law paid him a reasonable wage as a machinist and took back a more than generous food and rent allowance for him and his family. However, at the same time that the family exploited him they also protected him from the neighbors who thought he was "crazy." They realized something was wrong with him but they put up with his silent ways.

When Mr. Cuffstat's father-in-law and wife learned he was included in our study, they feared he would be committed to a mental hospital. They resisted the home visits, but finally granted one during an evening when they could be around to speak for him and shield him. His family did not know his diagnosis or what was planned in the way of treatment. They were not even certain that hospitalization was necessary. They chose generally not to visit in the hospital. When we wanted to interview Mrs. Cuffstat and asked Mr. Cuffstat if his family had visited recently he said, "I didn't need anything, so they didn't come."

As a part of his expression of frustration with his family and work, Mr. Cuffstat developed symptoms of peptic ulcer which came and went with the rising and falling of tension. He was fearful of cancer and suspicious of doctors, although apparently less suspicious of those in this city than the ones he and his family had known in the Midwest, whom he viewed as "degenerate drunkards from the Eastern civilization." Because mental illness was well-documented and accounted for some of Mr. Cuffstat's symptoms, we rated him as underdiagnosed mentally.

A patient was judged to be *under-* or *overdiagnosed physically* when the evidence from the medical record and the doctor's report, combined with the patient's history and his family situation, did not support the diagnosis the physician had selected. Mr. Cato is an example of a patient who was overdiagnosed physically. He experienced a heart attack about nine months prior to his admission to the hospital. On the night of his admission he had a most unpleasant evening playing poker. As tempers flared he developed chest pains which became worse after he went home; he was admitted to the hospital under suspicion of a second heart attack. However, there was much uncertainty about the evidence for this diagnosis. His private physician was a general practitioner who relied upon the house staff to care for his patients (semicommittee sponsorship). The house staff was uncertain about the diagnosis of heart attack, and the general practitioner in the face of this uncertainty chose to treat the patient initially for a heart attack. When Mr. Cato expressed his desire to leave the hospital, the general practitioner began to have second thoughts about his diagnosis and discharged Mr. Cato after twelve days of hospitalization.

Mrs. Cato, however, insisted upon taking her husband to a specialist. The specialist reviewed the evidence gathered from the two hospitalizations and a new examination. He concluded that it was impossible to tell whether or not a second heart attack had occurred, but in his opinion there was no further heart damage. Symptoms disappeared and the patient was advised to resume his usual work. Even after the patient's discharge the doctors in the hospital and the general practitioner applied the diagnosis of myocardial infarction, with no real evidence for such a diagnosis. They reported their diagnosis to the patient without hesitation or doubt. Although documentation for the diagnosis was lacking, it was coded in the medical record as myocardial infarction. Our diagnosis is chest pain of uncertain cause, and we rate Mr. Cato as overdiagnosed physically.

Mr. Thatus was a more obvious case. He had suffered from "bursitis" for two weeks prior to admission. He went to the physician at the plant where he worked, complaining of pain in his shoulder, and was treated with heat locally. The symptoms persisted and a private practitioner was called. Suspecting heart attack, the doctor referred Mr. Thatus for admission to the hospital. Within a short time he developed a fever, a high white corpuscle count, and pain in his chest. There were no chemical or electrocardiographic changes suggesting heart attack. Finally, the patient developed a skin rash diagnosed as erythema multiforme. The house staff and one of their consultant cardiologists believed there was much evidence for viral pericarditis, none for myocardial infarction. Within three weeks the condition cleared up and Mr. Thatus was discharged. His coded primary diagnosis was myocardial infarction, the secondary diagnosis erythema multiforme. The treatment ordered by the doctor was viewed by Mr. Thatus and his family as highly successful. They believe Mr. Thatus almost died. Indeed, they view his recovery as a spectacular therapeutic success for the physician who, in this instance, encouraged their belief by emphasizing the patient's close brush with death. One of the reasons why the family did not discover differences of opinion concerning the diagnosis is that the house staff rotations occurred one week after Mr. Thatus' admission. The new house staff "inherited" the patient and chose to let continue the therapeutic course struck upon partly by default. The diagnosis of myocardial infarction was not documented.

There were few instances of incomplete physical diagnosis which gave rise to misdiagnosis. Sometimes a careful history had not been taken concerning the symptoms of the patient. Mrs. Rush had experienced increased menstrual blood flow for a considerable period of time but had no other symptoms. From this she developed an iron-deficiency anemia. Since she was embarrassed to discuss this with her doctor, a friend and neighbor, and he apparently did not inquire about it, he remained unaware of her blood loss. Suspecting malignancy or renal disease, he admitted her to the hospital and ordered extensive X rays and laboratory studies, the results of all of which were normal except for anemia. He applied the diagnosis *anemia of unknown etiology*. Although the etiology was quite clear and the house officer was aware of this, he did not intervene. The physician's uncertainty was communicated to Mrs. Rush who remained worried about the cause of her anemia for several months. We rated Mrs. Rush as a patient underdiagnosed physically.

Physical underdiagnosis was commonly associated with alcoholism. Four patients suffering from alcoholism were underdiagnosed. There was much unpleasantness in dealing with alcoholic patients. Families faced major problems and so did the professionals. The withdrawal of the doctors from these patients was impressive. They underdiagnosed physically more in these instances than they did in any other group. Mr. Monet (mentioned earlier) was admitted to the hospital with erysipelas and gastrointestinal bleeding. The house staff made the diagnosis of rheumatic heart disease with mitral insufficiency. The patient did suffer from these diseases but also he had suffered a seizure during recovery from a drinking bout and showed evidence of liver damage. His family, ashamed of his drinking, tried to hide it from neighbors and even from the doctors. All parties to the illness chose to ignore the alcoholism and its implications for this patient.

In this case underdiagnosis permitted the doctors to avoid the personal and social issues involved and not offend the patient and his family. Indeed, the doctors were pleased with the passive, pleasant, joking ways of Mr. Monet who, intentionally or otherwise, misled them. He was a man of many troubles from a family with equally as many. As his shame was great and there was some residual pride, attempts were made to avoid the stigma of alcoholism. The house staff did not pursue the question of liver or brain damage. They were pleased with their diagnosis of rheumatic heart disease with mitral stenosis; they also had an opportunity to learn something from the patient about erysipelas and gastrointestinal bleeding. Mr. Monet was discharged from the hospital without comment concerning his alcoholic abuse and neglect of himself. After a convalescence during which Mrs. Monet tried to reform him, he resumed his work and drinking simultaneously. His life then became one of constant drinking by night and attempts to recover from intoxication by day. He was probably never free from the influence of alcohol. Sometime after he was discharged from the hospital he ran over and killed a child with his car. It was not determined if he was intoxicated at that time. Although Mr. Monet was treated and released from the hospital, one very important diagnosis from the standpoint of both his physical and mental well-being was ignored.

When the evidence in the medical record did not support the diagnosis given by the physician, we evaluated all the data we had accumulated and reached a probable diagnosis. When the data showed a clear linkage of the patient's problems to his mental status, we judged this person to be *misdiagnosed both physically and mentally.* The majority of patients placed in this category were underdiagnosed mentally and overdiagnosed physically. Each of three typical patients in this category—Mrs. Helms, Mr. Lubeck, and Mrs. Sobel—was overwhelmed by family problems, and the physician in each case looked for physiological answers to explain the symptoms described to him by the patient.

Mrs. Helms, age 52, began to have viselike headaches one year prior to admission to the hospital as a private medical patient. Two months before her admission her headaches became more severe. She complained about her symptoms to the nurse at the plant where she was employed as a supervisor. The nurse discovered high blood pressure and sent her home with the recommendation to consult her physician. This frightened Mrs. Helms so that she immediately called her physician who saw her briefly in his office. He did not take a history or examine her. He prescribed some pills and a two-week bed rest for her. On hearing this, her husband was dissatisfied and telephoned the physician who then repeated his advice. Mr. Helms believed his wife's symptoms were the result of tension on her job. He called a second physician, a friend of the first one, who would not see Mrs. Helm on ethical grounds. For two weeks dissatisfaction mounted while Mrs. Helms remained in bed. The first doctor was finally persuaded to call a consultant, an internist, who took her history, examined her, and recommended that she get up from bed and stop medication. By this time Mrs. Helms, feeling weak and incapable of ambulating comfortably, concluded something must be radically wrong; she chose to stay in bed although she did not inform the doctors of her decision. After the family physician discussed the case with the consultant he reinstructed Mrs. Helms concerning medication, but she continued on bed rest against the doctors' advice and took medications about which the doctors did not agree. On those few occasions when she got up from bed, she had dizzy moments resembling fainting spells, although she never actually fainted. These "fainting" spells were reported to the consultant as well as to the family physician. They accepted her report as adequate documentation of recurring syncopal episodes and recommended admission to the hospital for further studies. Mr. Helms had confidence that the doctors would find the cause of the symptoms, treat Mrs. Helms, and make her better.

While the doctors were considering the possibility of a brain tumor and vascular insufficiency of the brain, Mrs. Helm had other things in mind. She had enjoyed a reasonably privileged early childhood until her father, a graduate of an Ivy League college, died leaving her at age 16 and her mother to support three younger siblings and themselves. Mrs. Helms managed to get a high school diploma and go to business college for two years before she was forced to leave school and go to work. The loss of her father, her inability to attend a noted woman's college, and the need to work for a living were the first major disappointments in her life. Others followed when she married a man of different ethnic background and less education. She had only one pregnancy and one child, a daughter. This was such a trying experience that she never had another pregnancy. In order to save money for her daughter's college education Mrs. Helms had gone to work when the girl entered high school. However, on graduating from high school the daughter rebelled against the wishes of her mother; she left home and joined the WAVES. The daughter had "let her mother down," and Mrs. Helms' symptoms developed a few days later. When the daughter became homesick yet could not get out of the WAVES, the mother's headaches became worse. To solve her problem, the daughter swiftly married a Navy man and became pregnant. The son-in-law went to sea, and when Mrs. Helms became bedridden the daughter was called home. Mrs. Helms didn't think her hospitalization was necessary; she felt she was not "that sick," she had got her daughter home, and she was enjoying the attention. Admission to the hospital startled her. She told us, "Things have swelled all out of proportion."

Mrs. Helms' diagnosis was entered in the medical record as *cerebrovascular insufficiency, probable,* and reported to her without the qualification of the "probable." Our diagnosis is tension headaches, and admission is rated as optional. (Mrs. Helms' case is discussed further in Chapter 14, pp. 293–94.)

Mr. Lubeck, who was 60 years old, had aches and pains from his head to his feet and episodes of crying, alternating with episodes of unexplained laughter. His family was ashamed of him and he thought he was losing his mind. He was afraid he would die of cancer, as his mother had, or of heart disease, as his father had. Mrs. Lubeck took him to the doctor. If nothing could be done for him medically, she wanted, at the very least, advice on how to live with him. She agreed to the admission to the hospital in order to get this question settled.

Mr. Lubeck's symptoms were evaluated one by one; numerous X-ray and chemical studies were done. The X rays of the joints and abdomen showed he had moderate osteoarthritis of the spine and diverticulosis of the large intestine. The results of all other tests and the physical examination were normal. The surgical consultant wrote the following note in the medical record:

Only significant findings are arthritis and diverticulosis. I think it must be assumed that the abdominal pain is secondary to *diverticulitis,* for which a low residue diet will be instituted. Although cervical pain is undoubtedly real, the patient's depressive affect and his history of psychotic depression in the past warrant a good trial on Trilafon.

Neither the surgical consultant nor any other physician explained the pain in the neck or any other part of the body. They attributed Mr. Lubeck's symptoms to diseases that conceivably might be present such as osteoarthritis and diverticulitis. The osteoarthritic changes were documented; the diverticulitis was not, but a diagnosis of diverticulitis was made and his symptoms were attributed to it. No psychiatrist was called to evaluate the disturbed affect. No diagnosis of mental disease was applied. The doctor attempted to convince Mr. Lubeck that he did not suffer from either heart disease or cancer as he feared. He considered his task completed and discharged the patient. Mrs. Lubeck was faced with utter frustration since her questions revolving around the problem of living with her husband were not answered.

A third patient in this category, Mrs. Sobel, had suffered from numerous complaints for many years. In the background of her life there were many frustrations and disillusionments. She had to leave school and go to work at the age of 16 to help support the family when her father became ill of a hypochondriacal disorder. Eventually he recovered to support the family again but it was too late for Mrs. Sobel to get an education. She wanted to marry a man who could give her a large income and a high social position. She married one who had aspirations but did not achieve them. According to Mrs. Sobel, she "married the wrong brother"; she was referring to her brother-in-law who became a lawyer with the financial assistance of her husband and father-in-law.

Over the years Mrs. Sobel endured a variety of misfortunes including the loss of three children from Rh incompatibilities. She was disillusioned in her marriage, not only with her husband's occupation and status but also with her failure to have healthy infants. Her obstetrician counseled her to have further children by artificial insemination from a suitable donor. Although she favored the recommendation, Mr. Sobel rejected it. When we interviewed her Mrs. Sobel rationalized that the outcome was perhaps fortunate because the "younger generation is impossible today."

Mrs. Sobel resented her low social position. She aspired to improve herself by cultivating a friendship with her physician who gave her prescriptions but comparatively little time. However, he did tolerate her and she referred numerous patients to him. During most of her adult life Mrs. Sobel had suffered from severe hypochondriasis. She had many complaints of bowel and metabolic disorders. She accumulated various diagnoses and was treated with various diets and drugs for her supposed bowel disorder, hypothyroidism, and nerves. She had a hysterectomy and extraction of all her teeth. She was very much a child to her husband, as he was to her. In the months before her hospitalization she felt her husband had been working hard and paying too little attention to her. He had been ill and hospitalized; she felt that it was her turn. She bothered the doctor, and her husband urged him also, to the point where he admitted her to the private medical service of the hospital for further diagnostic studies.

The diagnostic process involved an awareness on the part of the doctors of the lack of documented physical disease of any kind. They had offered a diagnosis previously and they continued to believe that she had a functional bowel disorder. In an effort to reverse the trend to hypochondriasis, her doctor refused to give her the diagnosis of hypothyroidism but he treated her with thyroid medication anyway.

In brief, although the doctor recognized the nature of the symptoms, he did not make a diagnosis primarily of psychoneurosis. Rather, he offered an organic diagnosis (hypothyroidism), which he, himself, only partially believed. Curiously, he coded *hyper*thyroidism in her medical record and gave her ambiguous cues regarding his opinions. Her clinical symptoms and laboratory findings did not support either diagnosis. It is clear from the data that Mrs. Sobel had become frustrated, disillusioned, disappointed, and symptomatic. She was misdiagnosed physically and mentally.

TABLE 15. ACCURACY AND COMPLETENESS OF DIAGNOSIS OF PATIENTS, BY SERVICE

| | | Patients by Service | |
Accuracy and Completeness	Total	Medicine	Surgery
Diagnosed correctly	62%	46%	75%
Underdiagnosed mentally	26	30	23
Misdiagnosed physically	4	9	—
Misdiagnosed physically and mentally	8	15	2
N =	(161)	(74)	(87)
p < .05			

Viewed statistically, 62 per cent of the patients were diagnosed correctly while 38 per cent were diagnosed incorrectly. There were no significant differences by accommodation or sex. However, there was a significant difference by service, as seen in Table 15. An examination of the figures in Table 15 shows that there were significantly more correct diagnoses on the surgical service than on the medical service. There were relatively small differences between the medical and the surgical services for the underdiagnosis of mental disturbance; however, this was where the largest proportion of the errors were concentrated on both services. Seven patients were misdiagnosed physically; all were on the medical service, and six of the seven were males.

Likewise, misdiagnosis, physical and mental, was concentrated on the medical service; in this category there were more women than men, but not enough to make the difference a significant one.

Our review of the diagnoses the responsible physicians made demonstrated that the physicians exerted no tangible effort to diagnose mental illness even though it was evident and frequently contributed to the patient's symptoms. The diagnosis of appendicitis may have been made by a practitioner of one specialty (an internist or general practitioner) and treated by another specialist (a surgeon), but diseases treated in the special field of psychiatry were not diagnosed by nonpsychiatrists. Physicians had a prime concern with sick organs; when sick organs were found symptoms of the patient were attributed to them; if sick organs could not be found the symptoms remained unexplained or were attributed in some instances to functional disorders. Even then, a psychiatric diagnosis was not applied.

Based upon the assumption that the physicians' and patients' self-expectations influenced the way each performed in searching for a diagnosis, we asked the physicians routinely if they wished to know more about the patients as individuals; 98 per cent of the replies were negative. The house officers revealed no interest in the patient as a person beyond what they had learned in their histories. Their reactions were negative in spite of the cue contained in our question. Though we did not ask this question of private physicians as specifically as we did of the house officers, the former gave no indication of more interest. The reaction demonstrates that house officers, and probably private physicians, were satisfied with their limited knowledge about the patient as a social personality. We asked also in each instance if the physicians desired more information about the patient's disease, and 67 per cent of these replies were negative while the remaining replies indicated an interest in knowing more about the disease in a physical sense. This, in the light of our findings, is startling!

We asked each patient which of three things he considered more important to the doctor in establishing a diagnosis: his personal history, the doctor's physical examinations, or laboratory tests. The patients placed a remarkable emphasis upon physical examination and laboratory tests. They underrated the importance of their own histories, with no differences by service, sex, or accommodation; 65 per cent of the patients told us that examination and tests were of most importance. Mr. Monet said, "The tests, of course." Mr. Pagus emphasized the physical examination: "It's got to be done before they decide anything. It's the main thing in deciding what's the trouble." Thirty per cent of the patients did not discriminate among the choices or simply said they did not know. Mr. Taldo realized the importance of the history but told us that all three were important in making a diagnosis: "They need all of them and if you keep your mouth shut and don't talk you don't help yourself at all." Mr. Grundy said, "All three coincide, but I guess the tests are most important. Some patients can't talk, and tests determine their illness." Only 5 per cent indicated they thought their own history was the most important aid to the doctor in establishing a diagnosis. In these cases the patient realized he was telling the doctor the diagnosis. They said: "I told him I had a rupture." "My veins are poor." "I knew it was my heart." Mr. Gordon indicated that the interview was the most important. He qualified this, however, by telling us, "You've gotta tell them the truth. The doctor knows what he is doing."

Some patients viewed the examination as a test. Mr. Jetson said, "The examination is a test. The doctor's tests are most important [in establishing a diagnosis]." Some patients tended to view the body as operating like a machine and saw the examinations and tests as the only means through which the mechanism's defects could be understood. Mr. Croff, reporting the tests as most important to the doctor, said, "They show the level of the blood." Mr. Church, who was in the hospital more to get away from his work and his home than anything else, indicated that the tests were most important; about the examination he said, "I thought it was necessary or they wouldn't have done it. I guess I looked forward to it. That's why I'm here." Mrs. Selvo said the tests were most important but also that the examination was important as well: "The doctors examined me for a reason—to find out what's wrong with me." Mrs. Pasto indicated a feeling found among many of the patients that even the examinations and tests did not give the answers: "Sometimes they have to operate before they know."

Some patients were belligerent toward the doctor concerning the history. One said if she told the doctors anything it wouldn't be the truth: "Since they're so smart, at least according to their own estimates, they can find out by themselves without any assistance from me. I came here to be cared for, and I expect them to do it." Another said that her history was most important in establishing a diagnosis but exhibited doubts about her answers: "It ain't up to me to tell them." A patient with a skin disease said, "The doctor can make the diagnosis but he won't know the history unless I tell him." Still another patient emphasized the importance of his history: "I told him the diagnosis. I have a hernia."

Even among those patients who chose the history as being the most important for the doctor in making the diagnosis, there was no strong feeling that it was vital or in any sense irreplaceable. On the other hand, the nature of the laboratory tests mystified most patients; the results were viewed as almost uncanny, magical, or superhuman. Some patients thought the tests revealed something very special about them. One man said the blood tests were to determine whether a person was "a commie, social, or antisocial." (He was not psychotic and was quite serious about this.) In their ignorance of the real meaning of the tests they obviously had distorted images of their value and underrated the significance of their own histories.

There may have been other reasons for the patients' emphasis upon the importance of the tests and examinations. If the diagnosis could have been established by history, presumably admission to the hospital might have been unnecessary except for treatment purposes. The fact that all of these patients were in the hospital may mean that other attempts at diagnosis and treatment had failed. The mere fact, therefore, of being in the hospital focused attention away from the story of the patient himself and upon diagnostic and treatment procedures which often were feared. Such procedures, therefore, emerged as perhaps more important than they really were. Probably the physicians in their haste and primary concern with these matters prompted the patients to focus upon them just as the physicians themselves did.

Did the patient tell the physician about his physical ills and symptoms? We found that 78 per cent of the patients reported their physical illnesses to the physicians; in 20 per cent of the patients there was a moderate withholding of information and in 2 per cent a marked withholding or distortion of information. There were no differences by accommodation, service, or sex, but ward patients tended to communicate less adequately than others.

Did the patient discuss his feelings about himself and his family? Sixty-three per cent gave little or no indication how they felt, 35 per cent gave some indication, and only 2 per cent revealed their feelings in some detail. The answers were not significantly related to accommodation, service, or sex.

Physicians inquired selectively and patients communicated selectively. Presumably, this pattern of relating is based upon the expectations patients and physicians had of each other and of themselves. Considering these breaches in communication, *can we expect physicians to understand the personal and social factors which lie behind the patients' symptoms?* Should we expect the physician to diagnose the patient's problem accurately, or *should society be content with a score for accuracy in diagnosis of 46 per cent on the medical service and 75 per cent on the surgical service?*

Each patient had a unique personal background, social history, and current situation. This uniqueness consisted of a set of past experiences, attitudes, habits, and feelings we call a "way of life." Symptoms of illness often arose from diseased tissues, malfunctioning bodies, disturbed personal and social situations, or from several different conditioning factors simultaneously. Patients with heart disease or cancer might have had symptoms readily attributable to the diseased organ but their symptoms, in part or in whole, might have originated from their fears as well. Symptoms might have been necessary to establish or legitimize "illness" from which the patient could gain in some way. When we examined holistically the patient's symptoms from the vantage point of understanding his way of life and the personal and social problems enmeshed in it, a new perspective of his disease emerged. We repeat that in our assessments of etiological factors which probably gave rise to the patient's symptoms we drew upon data provided by the medical record—history, progress notes, nurses' notes, and laboratory reports—supplemented by interviews with hospital and family physicians and nurses, interviews with patients and family members during and after hospitalization, and observations of patients, family members, and those around them in the hospital and the homes of the patients. From the viewpoint of possible etiology of the patient's symptoms we grouped our results into four categories.

In the first category, the symptoms arose from the attitudes, fears, behavior, tensions, and so forth of a person who was emotionally distraught, sometimes mentally ill. There is lack of evidence that physical disease, if any was present, was the primary cause of the symptoms of the patient. In this category *the illness was a response to a way of life.*

In the second category, the patient was *organically ill because of his way of life;* his symptoms may have arisen from his illness as well as from his way of life. Neglect or abuse of the self may have occurred. Alcoholism is an example; vomiting in the face of personal and social crisis is another. The way of life caused specific organ disease or body malfunction.

In the third category *the symptoms were related partially to a way of life.* There were influential personal and social characteristics which combined with the vulnerability of an organ or organ system to produce the disease. For example, patients with peptic ulcers were placed in this category when their way of life was related clearly to the worsening of the malady.

In the fourth category *no apparent links were visible between the symptoms of patients and their way of life.* Malignancies are illustrative of diseases in this grouping.

When we classified the patients in terms of these four categories, no significant differences were found between the three accommodations or the two sexes, but there were sharp differences between the two services— medical patients have far more links between their diseases and their ways of life than surgical patients. The distribution by service is shown in Table 16.

Disease was a way of life for 20 per cent of the medical and 2 per cent of the surgical patients. All of these patients were emotionally disturbed and some of them were seriously ill mentally. Mr. Notter suffered from the time he was a young man from chronic symptoms that were diagnosed psy-

TABLE 16. LINKS BETWEEN DISEASE AND THE PATIENT'S WAY OF
LIFE, BY SERVICE

Etiological Category	Total	Patients by Service	
		Medical	Surgical
Disease was a way of life	11%	20%	2%
Disease was a result of a way of life	7	14	1
Disease was partially related to a way of life	8	8	9
Disease was unrelated to a way of life	74	58	88
N =	(161)	(74)	(87)
p < .05			

chiatrically as paranoid schizophrenia. He was disabled from it and was in a
state mental hospital on several occasions. On advice from the mental hospital the welfare department which was giving his family financial support
made an effort to have him maintained at home although this was most
trying for the family. Physicians at this center twenty-two years ago had
given Mr. Notter a diagnosis of epilepsy. Although the evidence for the
diagnosis was never very convincing and notes by consulting neurologists
denied that such a diagnosis was applicable, several doctors did believe he had
epilepsy. Mr. Notter believed it himself and was treated accordingly. It was
his custom for years to appear at the emergency service and demand attention
from the doctors; sometimes this would include examinations and prescriptions, and occasionally it resulted in clinic appointments or admission to the
hospital. Four years before this admission Mr. Notter had a heart attack
but he recovered satisfactorily without disability or cardiac enlargement.
At the time of the heart attack symptoms of epilepsy disappeared. Mr. Notter
and his family soon discovered that when they reported chest pain to the
doctors in the Medical Center it brought faster action than when they reported
symptoms of an epileptic seizure.

In the months prior to the hospitalization we studied, Mr. Notter had
become increasingly difficult to live with. He abused the family and his
obscenity was a source of embarrassment. When the crisis reached a critical
point, Mrs. Notter brought her husband into the emergency service with a
complaint of severe pain in his chest. The family hoped to be free of him
for a while. He was admitted as having a possible heart attack. The diagnosis
of angina pectoris was applied. This was a "safe" choice, just as the earlier
diagnosis of epilepsy had been, but it probably was inaccurate and, in a sense,
irresponsible. Mr. Notter was discharged in two days. Both the patient and his
family knew they were manipulating the doctors and the hospital. There is
much evidence to support a social and behavioral explanation of the symp-

toms. However, when the doctors reported the diagnosis, the patient and his family became less certain about the situational causes of the symptoms, thus adding to the confusion.

Mr. Miles, another patient in this category, was primarily afraid of disease. For twenty-seven years he believed that he would die of a heart attack in his late fifties as his father had done. He became fearful of any shortness of breath. Now in his late fifties, he began to develop pains in his chest. He and his wife became more frightened as the symptoms developed. He was faced with a critical phase of his life—that of coming to terms with aging and possibly an early death. His latent fears became manifest, and action was taken resulting in this hospitalization. Although he had some hypertension, there was no evidence of heart disease or that the pain he reported was attributable to defective circulation within the heart. After spending nineteen days and much money on hospital and medical care, Mr. Miles grew tired of double talk and the uncertainty of the physicians. He left the hospital, abandoned the doctors and their advice, and went back to work with no further symptoms. The crisis was over, at least for the moment.

The other patients in this category were primarily disturbed emotionally and fearful of disease. Their symptoms arose from emotions rather than from physical disease, which, though sometimes found, was of minor consequence. There was no hint in the doctors' discharge diagnosis of the nature of the problems.

After examining the diagnoses from the viewpoint of etiology, we can say that most diagnoses offered by physicians for patients whose diseases were viewed by us as a way of life are "supposed," or *ad hoc,* diagnoses. They named a condition that might have given rise to the symptoms the patients reported, but a thorough review of the patient and the effective social environment in which he functioned indicates a probably different etiology. The *ad hoc* diagnoses and the probable causes of symptoms are given for these 16 patients in the tabulation on p. 172.

Fifteen of these sixteen patients were cared for on the medical service. Only two were admitted as ward patients; the others were cared for on the private or semiprivate accommodations under the direction of private practitioners. There was often disagreement in the diagnosis of these patients. In Mr. Jetson's case, the assistant resident did not believe the private physician's diagnosis was accurate or had anything to do with the symptoms. He dismissed the matter with a smile saying, "Perhaps his doctor has lost his sense of perspective, but I haven't lost my sense of humor."

The coded diagnosis of hyperthyroidism for Mrs. Sobel was also reported to us in the interview with her doctor. Strangely, the house officer reported hypothyroidism, and quite clearly the medical record and the therapy offered

Patient	Ad Hoc Diagnosis	Probable Etiology of Symptoms
Ash	Undiagnosed disease—fainting spell (patient was told he had "mild heart attack").	Fear of aging and loss of virility.
Balter	Radiculopathy.	Mental breakdown, probably schizophrenia.
Chandler	Hypothyroidism.	Hypochondriasis.
Crane	Undiagnosed disease—abdominal pain.	Fear of aging, depression.
Figaro	Uterine fibroids.	Functional gastrointestinal symptoms resulting from reaction to social stress including impoverishment resulting from condition of disabled schizophrenic husband.
Grundy	Psychophysiologic reaction—headaches.	Mental breakdown, schizophrenia.
Helms	Cerebrovascular insufficiency, probable.	Tension, with headaches, from past and current situational social stress.
Hutch	Angina pectoris.	Grief and fear-reaction following recent death of brother from heart attack.
Irving	Deformity of nose.	Fear of menopause and loss of husband to another woman.
Jetson	Steracoraceous ulceration of rectum.	Fear of cancer as recently diagnosed in two siblings—one dead, one dying.
Letche	Probable essential vascular hypertension.	Fear of aging and dying as father did.
Lubeck	Diverticulitis.	Manic-depressive psychosis.
McCaine	Scoliosis—dorsal spine.	Cancer phobia.
Miles	Pre-infarction angina.	Fear of death from heart disease.
Notter	Angina pectoris.	Fear of heart disease—social manipulation, an adjustment to schizophrenia.
Sobel	Hyperthyroidism.	Hypochondriasis.

indicated that hypothyroidism was the intended diagnosis. However, there was no evidence to support either of these diagnoses.

The *ad hoc* diagnoses were sometimes not believed by the physicians who made them. They were transmitted variously to patients who sometimes believed them and sometimes did not. Although ignorant of medical matters and sometimes grossly disturbed with mental illness, these patients were perceptive and capable of reasoning independently. Sometimes they reached the same conclusion as the doctor in spite of what the doctor told them, but often they reached conclusions quite contradictory to those offered by the doctors. In dissatisfaction and confusion, some patients went to other physicians and other hospitals to get answers to their questions; sometimes they found the answers and sometimes they did not.

We found eleven patients whose diseases were largely a result of their way of life but who did have diseased organs. As in the first group, they were concentrated on the medical service. They were ill because they were neglected or abused themselves or because their personal or social stresses were manifested through a malfunction of an organ or body part. Six of these eleven patients were alcoholics. Others suffered from periodic vomiting or occasional episodes of diarrhea associated with their stresses. One patient suffered from tachycardia when she was particularly anxious, as she usually was.

Mrs. Peacock typifies this group. Following the birth of a daughter fifteen years ago she complained of pain and itching about the anus which caused a great deal of scratching and painful bowel movements. Over the years she developed an intense preoccupation with the functions of the gastrointestinal tract. She was childlike, extremely anxious, and, in her words, "chicken." She was anxious about her eating patterns as well as those of her daughter; although both were obese she thought neither ate enough. She had a chronic cathartic habit. She had had other symptoms which led to extractions of teeth, a hysterectomy, and a few visits to a psychiatrist.

Mrs. Peacock had been taking her symptoms to various physicians for years, severely taxing the family budget, but nothing was recommended that helped her until recently when she pushed her surgeon into admitting her to the hospital for removal of the minor but troubling hemorrhoids. At the time of admission to the hospital she was complaining also of chest, abdominal, and perineal pains. She had developed a new cycle of itching and scratching about the anus. This, associated with her cathartic habit and compulsions concerning elimination, led to the aggravation, if not the production, of the hemorrhoids and a fissure.

There were no immediately visible links between the symptoms and the diseases of patients and the patients' ways of life in 119 cases, 74 per cent of all the patients. In many instances links were suspected, but information about the disease and the personal and social histories did not allow us to state with some certainty that the disease was linked to the way of life. In this group were patients with heart attacks, malignancies, hernias, breast conditions, most gastrointestinal and vascular disorders, and conditions suspected to be caused by occupational hazards and smoking. In brief, though it may be contended that there were links between the symptoms and some of the diseases of patients in this category, these links were less obvious.

From this view of symptoms and the attendant disease, we conclude that the social and personal forces, which we have called a way of life, accounted directly for 34 per cent of admissions to the medical service and 3 per cent to the surgical service. Such forces were also strongly influential in an additional 8 per cent of medical patients and 9 per cent of surgical patients. In sum, 42 per cent of the medical patients and 12 per cent of the surgical patients revealed readily demonstrable ways of life which were etiologic to the symptoms and diseases resulting in this hospitalization. (See Table 16, p. 170.)

There were marked or extreme fears of cancer, heart disease, and mental illness or a combination of these conditions in 55 per cent of the patients. Among these patients exposure to illness in their families was high. Most patients did not mention their fears to their physicians, and the doctors, in turn, indicated little interest in the fears of the patients. Many patients were not relieved of their fears until after the tissues were examined following surgery and a negative report given. Five patients shopped for physicians until an operation was agreed upon even though it was not advised. Some of these operations were done in this hospital and some elsewhere. We found that an anxious, fearful, childlike patient could develop symptoms of acute or chronic diseases. On several occasions patients convinced their physicians that they were suffering variously from acute gall bladder attacks, heart attacks, convulsive disorders, and so forth although the evidence indicated that the symptoms were a response to a basic crisis in their lives. When patients reported pains without the context and background of the symptoms, the doctor was presented with a problem.

A physician made a diagnosis of radiculopathy on Mrs. Balter's symptoms. However, he really did not believe this diagnosis and was uncertain about what to do. He reported to us, in part:

> Right now she's being catered to by her family and there's no therapy, no physical therapy, no exercises. I think the way this probably will turn out is we won't find anything. We'll have her on a graded program of increasing physical activity and exercises, telling her that this is the way to relieve discomfort and saying it's something like a disc and letting her work it out for herself. However, she's a practical nurse; she's a little sophisticated, and I wonder if she's going to think that what we're saying is that she's not really sick but cracked. I think she may. She may be the kind who, as in the past, will still go on looking for someone to tell her that she's got something definite wrong.
>
> When you have the feeling that the patient's trouble is functional, you always feel a little more hard pressed than usual because you feel it's unfair to the patient. You tend to work harder and look further for something organic and you're always troubled that you might be missing something—that perhaps the patient isn't really a crock.

Mrs. Crane offered another example of much uncertainty and groping. She had had a hysterectomy during an earlier hospitalization for reasons not clearly stated. In the present hospitalization she thought she had a virus or "something like that." The tests done in the hospital were expensive, uncomfortable, and of no avail. To us she expressed doubts about her physician, accusing him of "double talking" and of not knowing what he was doing. She thought he spent very little time with her. The physician, in turn, believed Mrs. Crane was neurotic. He told us, "Something is wrong with her, but I can't quite put my finger on it." In his uncertainty, he encouraged the intern to explore numerous possibilities and even invited suggestions from the researchers. We, of course, offered no suggestions, but the intern went ahead with numerous ones, which he and the private practitioner then proceeded to scrutinize carefully. One night during the hospitalization, Mrs. Crane developed severe abdominal pain and reported it to the intern, who became convinced that the pain was caused by an acute gall bladder attack. This was disproved. He then searched for other possibilities including endometriosis, although such a diagnosis did not appear to be a likely one either. The private practitioner did not name a specific condition in the medical record, but he did infer that the symptoms were caused by some specific organ disease which he was unable to identify. While annoyed with the ambiguities of the doctors, Mrs. Crane forgave them because she was in the hospital long enough to get a rest. She told us, "At least I didn't have to get up in the morning and look after the family."

We have shown that the physician's failure to understand the patient's way of life was associated with inaccurate diagnosis. To analyze the next step—the management of the patient following the diagnosis—we reviewed the total body of data we had accumulated on each patient and his family; then we assigned the patient to one of the following categories: *appropriate management for the main problem; partially appropriate management; symptomatic management;* and *inappropriate management.* All patients whose chief problems were perceived accurately and treated accordingly by the doctor were assigned to the first category. Mr. Pagus had chronic pulmonary disease and was managed specifically for this problem; the fact that he was depressed and dying was incidental. Similarly, Mr. Cuffstat, although mentally ill, was admitted specifically with high fever; he was treated for pneumonia, his chief immediate problem.

The second category involved appropriate but incomplete management of the present problems of the patient. Mrs. Tidd was admitted with pneumonia; it was well known to the physicians that she also was very depressed, but they diagnosed and treated the pneumonia and ignored the depression. Soon after discharge she was readmitted to the hospital for treatment of a psychotic depression. This time her admission was on the psychiatric division. We do not know that attention to the depressed state at the earlier admission would have improved it; we wish only to indicate the actions of the physicians.

The symptomatic management of patients comprises the third category. The disease may have been understood and it may have been diagnosed in whole or in part, but its treatment was strictly symptomatic; no attempt was made to get to the bottom of the chief problem. Mr. Monet was treated for symptoms resulting primarily from his severe problem of alcoholism but not for the alcoholism itself. We do not wish to imply that symptomatic treatment is poor or inappropriate treatment, as it may have been optimal under the circumstances; we do wish to point out, however, that in these cases no attempt was made to discover or remove the causes of the disease.

Patients placed in the fourth category were treated for diagnoses of illnesses they did not have or under conditions in which the indications were very unclear. Mrs. Leadon was a surgical patient in this category. When family pressures got too high she asked her surgeon to do breast biopsies on her; she looked forward to these interludes with pleasure. Although she feared surgery, she hoped to find a new mass in her breast to take to the doctor so he would admit her to the hospital. A similar pattern was illustrated by Mrs. Wallick who wanted surgery. Although surgery was denied her here, she got it at another hospital.

The number and percentage of patients in each category of management are given in Table 17. Appropriateness of management was related to service but not to accommodation or sex. The medical patients clearly had less appropriate management. Their physicians were not looking to the source of the patients' problems. Physicians and patients were looking for answers where they could not be found.

The data in Table 17 show that 43 per cent of the medical patients and 76 per cent of the surgical patients were managed appropriately by their

TABLE 17. APPROPRIATENESS OF PATIENT MANAGEMENT, BY SERVICE

Patient Management		Patients by Service	
	Total	Medicine	Surgery
Appropriate	61%	43%	76%
Partially appropriate	22	26	19
Symptomatic	7	11	3
Inappropriate	10	20	2
N =	(161)	(74)	(87)
$p < .05$			

TABLE 18. RELATIONSHIP BETWEEN DIAGNOSTIC RATINGS AND APPROPRIATENESS OF
PATIENT MANAGEMENT, BY SERVICE

Diagnostic Rating	Management by Physician	
	Appropriate	Inappropriate
A. MEDICINE		
Diagnosed correctly	85%	17%
Underdiagnosed mentally	9	45
Errors in physical diagnosis	6	38
N =	(32)	(42)
$p < 05; \overline{C} = .86.$		
B. SURGERY		
Diagnosed correctly	91	24
Underdiagnosed mentally	9*	67*
Errors in physical diagnosis	—	9*
N =	(66)	(21)
$p < .05; \overline{C} = .74.$		

* These cells were combined in the chi-square analysis.

physicians. On the other hand, 57 per cent of the medical patients and 24 per cent of the surgical patients were mismanaged in some way. With these data in mind, we turn to another question: *Was the management of the patient linked to the diagnosis the physician made of his illness?* The answer to this question is a crucial test of the hypothesis under examination in this study. The data pertinent to it are contained in Table 18. On the medical service, 85 per cent of the patients who were appropriately managed were diagnosed correctly; on the surgical service 91 per cent of the patients who were appropiately managed were properly diagnosed. The largest percentage of mismanaged patients on both medical and surgical services was composed of patients who were underdiagnosed mentally. However, in 38 per cent of the inappropriately managed patients on the medical service there were errors in physical diagnosis. On both services errors in diagnosis were linked to inappropriate management.

Summary

We have shown that the illnesses of ward patients were severe and advanced, and their needs for admission tended to be urgent. Semiprivate patients were admitted least urgently. Admission for consultation was far more common among them than among the ward or the private patients. Consultations outside the hospital were more readily available to private patients who used specialists almost exclusively than to semiprivate patients. Private patients were more knowledgeable about hospitals and medical practice; in using this knowledge they secured consultations with specialists and presumably sometimes avoided hospitalization. In addition, patients who had their own private physicians used the hospital more often than ward patients for functional illnesses even though such ills were not recognized openly or treated for what they were.

From the perspectives of etiology, accuracy and completeness of diagnosis, and appropriateness of patient management, we found that medical patients, particularly those in the semiprivate and private accommodations, stood out in several ways in comparison with surgical patients: They had more diseases and symptoms attributable to personal and social adversities; there were more errors in diagnosis, and their management was less appropriate. Patients reported their life histories to physicians only partially and infrequently, and even when they did physicians tended to ignore these reports. Errors in diagnosis were linked clearly to the patient's and the physician's failure to take into consideration major factors in the patient's history. Inappropriate management of the patient followed.

Ideally, the diagnosis and treatment of a person's ills should take into consideration the two dimensions of his being, the physical and the emotional. The physical aspects of an individual—sex, age, height, weight, complexion, hair color, and bodily contour—are easily observable. The attributes expressive of his psyche—the manner of speech and thought, attitudes toward self and others, emotional sets, moods, reactions to the social and physical environment, handling of personal feelings, in short *the selfness*—are less discernible; nevertheless, they are a vital part of the person.

Numerous medical specialties have developed to treat the different organs and organ systems associated with the physical dimensions of the human body, *the soma*, but only one has focused on *the psyche*, namely psychiatry. A person afflicted with an illness defined by a physician as treatable by medication, surgery, or a combination of the two is likely to be sent to a general hospital. Such a patient may also be disturbed mentally and be in as great need of professional help for his emotional difficulties as he is for his physical difficulties. Yet, this aspect of his illness may be overlooked.

In order to determine the possible influence of the patient's personality structure on his present illness it was necessary to make an examination of his mental status. However, fear of psychiatrists was a constant threat to patients as well as to a considerable number of internists and surgeons, and our pilot study led us to the conclusion that the incorporation of an open psychiatric examination in the protocol would jeopardize the study. We decided finally to base our assessment of mental status on a number of interrelated factors: the life history of the patient before this illness; his behavior during hospitalization—reactions to physicians, hospital staff, spouse, other family members, and roommates in the hospital; and, finally, behavior in the family during the home visits. The data upon which we made our judgment of each patient's mental status were collected over a period of weeks, sometimes months, by the primary data collectors, by observers in the patient's room, and from interviews with the patient's physicians, members of the hospital staff, the patient, and the spouse. After all the data were assembled, they were systematically studied and a final judgment of a particular patient's mental status was made independently by Duff and Hollingshead. When we differed in our assessment of a person's mental status, the whole record was restudied by each of us; then we discussed our evaluation of the person's mental status until we reached agreement.

We divided the patients into four categories: *mentally healthy, moderately disturbed, severely disturbed,* and *psychotic.* These categories were not psychiatric diagnoses but clinical judgments derived from the kinds of data described in the preceding paragraph. The behavior giving rise to a specific judgment of mental status is illustrated by a narrative statement about one representative of each category. Each of the four persons whose story is presented was selected from all patients in a particular category. If another patient had been drawn, details would have differed from the one presented but the salient features that led us to place him in the specific category would have been similar for any patient in that category.

A Mentally Healthy Person: Harry Carter

Mr. Carter, who was 55 years of age, had lived all of his life in this city. His father was born in Canada of English stock; his mother was born in this city to Irish immigrants. He attended the city's public schools and completed the tenth grade. After holding a number of unskilled and semi-skilled jobs in the years following his withdrawal from high school, he obtained an unskilled laborer's position with the city through the political influence exerted by an employer of his father, and he remained with the city for more than thirty years. When we conducted our interviews he was the foreman of an outdoor work crew, with civil service status, regularly earning $120 per week. He got along well with associates on the job, the city administration, both major political parties, and the public. He belonged to several fraternal organizations and recreational associations.

Mr. Carter's marriage of 37 years was the first and only marriage for both the husband and wife. Mrs. Carter was born and reared in this city. She came from an Irish and German background. The Carters had one adult son who attended the public schools, completed two years of work in a junior college, and was a salesman for a concern with national connections and activities. He was married in his early twenties to a girl who completed nurse's training in this hospital's school of nursing. The son and his wife had three children.

The three generations of the Carter family were well adjusted to one another. There were close relationships between Mr. and Mrs. Carter and their son and his wife; the children adored their grandparents. Mr. Carter visited often with his brothers and sisters living in the community. He was on friendly terms also with Mrs. Carter's brothers and sisters who were, in large part, local residents. So far as we were able to determine there were no basic conflicts in this family.

The story of Mr. Carter's hospitalization is as follows: On a Sunday morning he awoke with severe chest pain and breathing difficulty. He arose from his bed against his wife's advice, dressed, and insisted on driving 10 miles to his son's home for help. He climbed a flight of stairs and aroused his son's family. (Mr. Carter told us later that, from his reading and conversations with friends who had had heart attacks, he judged his severe pain to be a heart seizure, but he didn't want to believe it.) The daughter-in-law immediately called a specialist she knew and was told to get an ambulance to take him to the hospital. This physician called the hospital, telling the house officer that Mr. Carter should be admitted, probably on the ward service, but he did not offer to sponsor Mr. Carter as his patient.

Mrs. Carter and the daughter-in-law came to the hospital in the ambulance with Mr. Carter. The daughter-in-law was familiar with procedures and with the admissions officer, and she had a favorable view of the ability of the house officers on the medical service. She knew that if Mr. Carter were cared for on the semiprivate or private accommodations there would be doctors' bills to pay in addition to the hospital bill. She insisted that her father-in-law be admitted to the ward accommodation, and she successfully manipulated the social system of the hospital so that Mr. Carter was admitted to the ward accommodation. The diagnosis was myocardial infarction.

During the first hours, Mrs. Carter was distraught. Until the crisis passed she hardly spoke. Each day she came to the hospital and stayed with Mr. Carter for several hours, simply sitting beside his bed and holding his hand or watching him. When the daughter-in-law, who was employed in a doctor's office, completed her work each afternoon, she came to Mr. Carter's room, talked for a few minutes, and left with her mother-in-law. The two women then drove to the younger Mrs. Carter's home where the family ate dinner together. Usually after dinner, the mother returned to the hospital accompanied by her son.

This was the first admission to a hospital Mr. Carter had experienced in his life. In required periodic physical examinations he was found to be in good health; during the many years he worked for the city he was absent from his job only fifteen days beyond the authorized vacations. During the last five years he lost just one day from work, attributable to a cold.

When Mr. Carter was able to discuss his illness with us he was apprehensive about it and its implications. He had been in severe pain and was fearful of the possibility of death. We could observe his tenseness as he squirmed in his bed and occasionally set his mouth in a fixed grin before answering our questions. He indicated that he went over his experience many times in his mind, and he told us, "When I put two and two together I usually come up with an answer satisfactory to myself." Several times he told us, "One has a great deal of time to think lying here in bed."

In recalling his experience in the hospital he said he realized that the nurses, doctors, and patients all functioned in a crisis atmosphere. He accepted the fact that students were going to take care of him. He said, "In their line students have to learn on people. They can't practice on dummies forever." He thought many of their questions—such as "Do you have any leg pain?"—were silly. He volunteered the information that ". . . the doctors here know the score. They don't pull their punches. You learn they'll sit on you if you step out of line."

The head nurse thought Mr. Carter, unlike most patients, realized that the hospital was a complicated institution, that organization was necessary, and that patience and understanding were virtues all too frequently ignored. She summarized her reactions to him by saying:

> He is a popular patient. He is close with his wife and he is good to his brothers when they visit him. He has a nice son with three children. They are all friendly, pleasant people. He is grateful to us when we do something for him. He says we make him feel very comfortable.

An aide viewed the family as closely knit and devoted to one another. A student nurse said:

> The average patient in his condition on the ward is indifferent and mean. Mr. Carter is a nice patient. He is satisfied with what's done for him. He is not demanding, and he knows how to wait patiently.

The night nurse told us:

> He's always kind and courteous. He understands his condition and follows orders. If he is told to stay out of bed or dangle for ten minutes or so, that's what he does. He realizes if he overdoes it, he could knock himself back another couple of weeks.

Another nurse remarked that when patients had to be moved from his room for reasons beyond the control of the nurses, these patients usually asked to be returned to "Mr. Carter's room." The medical student assigned to him thought Mr. Carter's family more interested in the patient than families of most ward patients were. The house officer told us Mr. Carter got along well with everyone.

These several reports made independently by the respondents are congruent. Mr. Carter was viewed by the hospital staff as an "unusual ward patient," and he *was* unusual in several ways: First, of the patients we studied on the ward accommodations Mr. Carter was the only one who was mentally healthy before admission. Second, Mr. Carter made a sincere effort to adjust to the practice of medicine on the ward as he experienced it. Third, because of his employment status and the fact that the city had full hospital insurance on its employees, Mr. Carter hardly belonged on the ward.

Mr. Carter was sure he would overcome his illness and would be able to return home and to work in a short period of time. He told us, "I will be all right. I have the loving support of the other half of my life, my wife." Unquestionably, he was supported by Mrs. Carter and he received the support also of his son, daughter-in-law, brothers, two sisters, and three grandchildren.

The data on Mr. Carter led us to the conclusion that *in the years before his present illness* he was mentally healthy. We stress this point here because we assessed the mental status of each person *before* the onset of the present illness and again *during* the current hospitalization. This was done to enable us to separate the effects of the hospitalization from the probable pre-illness emotional state of the patient.

Throughout the hospitalization Mr. Carter was moderately disturbed by his illness, his loss of control of his activities, the sights and sounds of sick and dying patients, and the doctors' orders that he lie quietly or they "would sit on" him. During the third week of hospitalization he became discouraged. There were times when he did not care to talk about his illness experience which he was trying to forget. His wife remarked that he was catching on to the idea that he had been a very sick man. As we observed members of the staff go about their duties in caring for the patients in the room, we noticed the sharp differences in the ways Mr. Carter responded to the various staff members: He was courteous with the aides, the licensed practical nurses, and the student nurses, but his reactions to the medical students and the staff physicians, whom he feared, were guarded and noncommittal—these were the persons who would "sit on" him, "not pull their punches," and "tell me off if I'm not careful."

The house officer in charge of Mr. Carter's care told us he did not think Mr. Carter was troubled by emotional problems. Speaking generally, he was correct but this young physician did not perceive the patient's anxiety about his illness while he was in the hospital and was not aware of his fears.

Six weeks after his attack Mr. Carter returned to work and began to carry on his usual activities with little or no impairment. Mrs. Carter was concerned about her husband but was not protective of him. In referring to his illness she said: "He walked easy and talked easy. His job was not a demanding one, and it gave him sufficient free time so that he could come home during the day to rest. I don't know what could have caused his attack." A year after the hospitalization she reported that he was taking it a little easier. She told us, "Now he rests more frequently and doesn't try to cover as much territory."

In our judgment, the data we gathered on this family indicate that Mr. Carter was healthy in his interpersonal relationships and in his intrapsychic life. During the hospitalization when the shock of a sudden illness had overwhelmed him, a moderate emotional disturbance was expressed. There is no evidence of social or emotional impairment before he became ill. After the illness experience he was able to do all the work he had done previously, enjoy his family, and lead an active social life. We infer that Mr. Carter's mental status before and after the illness warranted an assessment of healthy.

A Moderately Disturbed Person: Louis Romeo

Mr. Romeo was born in Italy forty-nine years ago, youngest in a family of eight children. At 2 years of age he was brought by his parents to this city, where he has lived since then. When Mr. Romeo was 5 years old, his father and mother were killed in automobile accidents about three months apart. An older sister who was married and had children his age became his foster mother. After completing the eighth grade in the city schools, he sought work to help out the family in its strained economic circumstances.

Mr. Romeo married for the first time when he was 21 years of age; there were no children from this marriage, and his wife died of a ruptured aorta when she was 25 years old. He married his present wife when he was 28 years old; they had three children. Mr. Romeo was a route salesman for a local company, which had employed him for eighteen years. Two years before his hospitalization he was made a supervisor of eight route salesmen. He described his job as being very demanding and nerve-wracking: "They're pushin' me all the time. I knew I'd have a heart attack. I wouldn't be surprised if a lot of the fellows that work there end up the same way." He said, "The wife and kids are always demandin' things." As a result he worked overtime to earn from $115 to $120 per week.

In the last eighteen years he missed only one day of work. He got to work every morning by 6:00. After completing his own route he often had to substitute for a deliveryman who didn't come to work. After completing the route deliveries he returned to the office to do the clerical work necessary in his job as supervisor, often working until 6 or 7 in the evening. When he came home he usually ate, watched television for a short while, and fell asleep to be ready for the next day's work.

Mr. Romeo had been afraid of doctors and hospitals for a long while. On his job he delivered supplies to doctors' offices and often he joked with them, but he told us he was "scared stiff" of a medical examination and had not been to a doctor for "more than twenty years." He had long had a phobia about pills and was afraid of picking up viruses and other diseases on his job. He had not been to a dentist in his life. He told us: "My teeth are rotting out of my head." In the year before his hospitalization he went to an optometrist to be fitted for glasses. When we inquired about Mr. Romeo's fear of physicians, he told us he didn't know why he felt this way but he knew they were "a bunch of enemies." The only person with whom he discussed health matters was the sister who reared him. He refused to talk about illness with any other member of the family.

This was the first hospital admission for Mr. Romeo. On the Friday evening before admission, Mr. Romeo came home after a work week of sixty hours, ate his supper, shaved, dressed, and with Mrs. Romeo set out for their social club on foot. As he was walking up a hill he felt a sharp, oppressive pain in his chest. They stopped and rested for a few minutes, then walked on to the club and played cards for several hours. On Saturday evening they went to a dance given by his fraternal order. They ate heavily, danced, and enjoyed themselves thoroughly. About 1:00 Sunday morning, as Mr. Romeo was watching a young woman do the twist, the pain returned but he ignored it. (Mrs. Romeo claimed later that his attack was brought on by his enjoyment of the girl's dancing. He told us, "She was magnificent!") About an hour later Mr. Romeo drove the family car home although he was in considerable pain. After several more hours of relentless pain he allowed his wife to call a physician. The physician came to the house and ordered an ambulance to take Mr. Romeo to the hospital. The admitting officer told us later that Mrs. Romeo, who had ridden to the hospital in the ambulance with her husband, was so nervous during the admissions process that they hurried him through. They requested a semiprivate room but since none was available he was assigned to a private room. The diagnosis was coronary occlusion.

During the first few days of his hospitalization Mr. Romeo did not follow the house officer's instructions. He rolled around in the bed, sat up, moved his feet, sat on the side of the bed. He was so restless that the house officer decided he had to be sedated heavily. Mr. Romeo accepted the medication without asking about it and slipped into a stuporous state.

When Mr. Romeo was selected for this study, his physician said: "This is a man who has a disturbed emotional background." After visiting the patient's room for the first time the fieldworker wrote:

> There is some problem within this family. The wife and the daughter have very little to say to Mr. Romeo. He listens to the radio and reads the newspaper. At the end of my observation Mr. Romeo commented that perhaps his wife should go home and stay put. She replied that she planned to do so because she did not intend to come back again today. His response was, "Don't you like your husband?" There was a pause and silence which was filled in by him saying, "Well, there are plenty of nurses here."

The second day a different fieldworker wrote:

> Today Mr. Romeo told me almost too enthusiastically in front of his wife that he was glad to have me come. I started to explain the project to her and she was cool. He broke in with "She's watching me like a hawk." Before I could ask the meaning of that statement, he added, "with all these pretty girls."

This fieldworker was convinced that Mrs. Romeo categorized her as one of the "pretty girls" whom her husband saw in the hospital.

Quite frequently Mr. Romeo sent his wife home saying that she looked tired. When she got home, he often called her to come right back. He told us she was afraid to drive, to which she retorted: "Afraid?—You won't let me drive!" She found it a great hardship to rely on public transportation and had a great deal to say about her trips to the hospital upsetting her work schedule. The teen-age daughter came to the hospital after school with her younger brother; while visiting in the patient's room the two children and their mother ate sandwiches that Mrs. Romeo brought from home as they waited for a ride with a neighbor whose husband was also a patient in the hospital. Mrs. Romeo felt neglected while her husband was in the hospital. She complained bitterly about the work load she was going to face when he came home, that she would have additional meals to prepare, that he would be "in the way." She did not relish the opportunity his recuperation period would offer to have conversations with him because she was not accustomed to holding conversations with him.

Mrs. Romeo was concerned about finances. They had many obligations to meet and only a few hundred dollars saved. She talked at length about how the bills were to be met, about her husband's disablement, and about the small allowance the union forced the company to pay while he was ill, which she found inadequate for their needs. She worried over the drop in income she faced when her husband returned to work and was unable to work overtime. She said:

Right now with my husband in the hospital we are not going places or doing anything, but this can't go on forever. The family must continue to operate. We must have food on the table, clothes on our backs, some money to run the car and to make payments on the house and furniture and to keep the boy in college [the state university].

Throughout the years Mr. Romeo had visited patients in hospitals but he never enjoyed doing so. The smell nauseated him. When he had to visit he stayed only a few minutes. He told us when he came here he was very nervous and repeated: "I never liked hospitals." We learned later that a week before Mr. Romeo became ill a next-door neighbor was rushed to the hospital with a coronary attack. Mr. Romeo learned of his neighbor's illness while he was backing his car out of the driveway to go to work and saw the ambulance pulling up to the neighbor's house. Two weeks before that a cousin of his, who was also 49 years old, had a coronary thrombosis and died within an hour.

Mr. Romeo was afraid of all persons on the staff. He did not ask the physicians what caused his illness, how long he was going to be in the hospital, or why he was told to do certain things. He simply took the medicine given him and tried to follow orders, even though he found this very difficult. When we asked him why he didn't question the doctors about his illness he said, "It's a military secret." He thought the length of time he would be in the hospital also was a "military secret." He couldn't tell us why; he said only, "The doctors know, but they won't tell me."

Mr. Romeo complained about the hospital to us and to his wife, but not to the doctors or nurses. One day during a noontime observation when a student nurse brought him his lunch, he smiled and thanked her, but as she left the room and he started to eat he looked at the observer and said, "Oh, brother, I'll have to go home to my wife's cooking to get a solid meal. They give these things fancy names but there's nothing to eat."

Mr. Romeo considered the hospital a dangerous place. He was afraid if he visited other patients he would pick up a disease that "might knock me off." Although he kept the door of his room open at all times because he was afraid of being alone, he stayed in his room the entire three weeks he was there. He told us later that he got to the point where he could locate all the holes in the ceiling. When we asked him what he thought of the experience he said, "I couldn't live through it again." He told his wife one day, "I didn't sleep last night. I was awake all night. I think this week didn't happen. It's all a bad dream."

Mr. Romeo's speech was jerky and his thoughts somewhat erratic. His conversation did not flow evenly into sentences or paragraphs. In conversation he was "ahead of the game"; before a question was finished he answered "Yup, yup." He told us he felt constantly driven to be "one up" on people. He wanted to give the right answer and was uncomfortable if he did not understand the reason for the questions. He realized he was "a wise guy"; he said he had learned "it doesn't pay," but he continued to behave like a "wise guy." He told us he was a "drivin', rushin' man; this is part of my blood." Mrs. Romeo dominated the interviews, answered questions for her husband, frequently drowned him out when he was trying to express his opinions, and at other times either contradicted what he was saying or attempted to make his responses seem foolish. He then became less self-assured, and his speech ran together and was halting. He tried to compete with his wife by talking along with her but he did not talk back to her. (We believe he was too passive an individual to put up a fight.) Basically, Mrs. Romeo was a self-centered woman who was insensitive to her husband's feelings although she tried to cover up his nervousness. She ridiculed his fear of his heart condition and his desire to follow the doctor's orders when the orders conflicted with orders she wanted to give. Mr. Romeo felt that he should follow the physician's orders even at home. He told us his wife would probably try to enforce her own ideas, but he said, "She can be overthrown."

The private physician who sponsored Mr. Romeo's hospitalization viewed the Romeos as a "model family." He made brief daily visits during the three weeks Mr. Romeo was in the hospital, and Mrs. Romeo telephoned him twice about her husband's progress. Mr. Romeo complained to us about the doctor's charges: "Two minutes and $10." However, he said nothing to the physician about this. The physician thought Mrs. Romeo was "much better" than the wives of most patients. He said, "Generally, we're harassed day and night by relatives about the patient's condition." He thought Mr. Romeo was a "good patient" and Mrs. Romeo was a good patient's wife because they didn't "put the pressure on."

The house officer said that Mr. Romeo was undemanding: "He doesn't treat the staff as servants the way other private patients do. Most private patients are inclined to be demanding and unfair in their treatment of nurses and staff on the floor." The staff liked Mr. Romeo because he "never tried to push us around."

The head nurse on the day shift found him cooperative but "too exuberant in his relationships with the nurses on the floor." She, personally, tried to calm him down, help him to realize his condition, and restrain him. The evening head nurse viewed Mr. Romeo as an active patient. An aide told us there were a number of little things that bothered him; when she started to do something for him he wanted it finished before she left him; if the nurses called her to do something else, he became impatient. She learned to avoid friction with him by getting everything done before she left his room.

At the time of the home visit Mr. Romeo told us he felt obliged to follow the advice given to him in the hospital by the physician. He was convinced that "returning to the old job" was not "a smart thing to do," but he had no preparation for any other kind of work. He attributed the coronary thrombosis to the work conditions there which he felt would never change. He had always been a man "on the go," working hard and pushing to get ahead. Now, he realized that the job was pushing him; its demands were merciless. He said that when he went back to work he would be willing to take a salary cut even if it involved becoming "nothing but a route sales-man again." He later told us he would not go back to the same line of work at all because it might bring on another heart attack, but he would probably have to stay with the company because it would be hard to get other work at his age.

When Mr. Romeo first became ill and left his home and work he told us he felt like a "bird who has been let out of a cage." Before he left the hospital he said his confinement to his room (self-imposed) was like being "in a cage again." Later, during the home visit, he wryly told us he "was back in the cage."

For the Romeos, this illness precipitated elements of anxiety and de-pression. They were worried when they discussed their concerns that the future would not be better and might even be worse. The illness accentuated the passivity and anxiety of Mr. Romeo who felt frustrated at the thought of having to go back to the work conditions of his job which he asso-ciated with bringing on his heart attack. These were bitter weeks also for Mrs. Romeo. Their only income was from the small union allowance, and the bills continued to mount for ten weeks as Mr. Romeo slept, watched television, and waited for "the tear in my heart to mend." Mrs. Romeo's anxiety was exacerbated by the fact that the neighbor next door, who had the alleged heart attack a week before Mr. Romeo, was mowing his lawn and trimming the hedge five weeks after he came home from the hospital.

Finally, consistent with his pattern of complaining yet accepting, Mr. Romeo returned to work. The company did not want him back, but the pro-tection afforded by long-standing union membership forced them to rehire him. However, he became a route deliveryman, not a supervisor, earning only about $85 per week.

Throughout his life Mr. Romeo functioned relatively well in his family and on the job. He had worked hard to raise his family and give his children a better start in life than he had had. However, he lacked the capacity to state his feelings openly. He accepted almost everything with an uneasy anxiety: his work, his home life, even participation in this project. On the job the customers were always right; if they complained he had to make adjustments according to their dictates in order to meet competition. When his fellow employees were absent from work he was the one who had to fill in for them. He tried to appear to his family as "brave as a lion," but when he referred to his wife and children as "a bunch of rabbits," he was projecting his feelings about himself; he knew that he was the real "rabbit."

Mr. Romeo was the least successful member of his paternal family. He told us he had not done as well as his brothers and brothers-in-law, but he did not regret not going into business with them because he was able to take care of his family and still live his own life. He rationalized the difference between himself and the others by claiming that he didn't want to accumulate anything so "why make it?" Mr. Romeo thought of himself as a nervous individual who went along with the existing order, whatever it happened to be. He complained bitterly but not to those persons who might do something about his complaints.

All this information led us to classify Mr. Romeo as moderately disturbed before his heart attack. During the hospitalization he was severely disturbed in his relations with his family, the staff, and the private physician. Acute anxiety was masked by his hyperactive attempts to flirt with the nurses and his morbid fear of other patients, the hospital's corridors, and other rooms. After his return home he became depressed, withdrawn, and fearful until his wife's nagging and the family's physical needs drove him back to the hated job. Rifts in the family, Mr. Romeo's reluctance to allow his wife to drive the car, his inability before his illness to earn what Mrs. Romeo thought the family needed, and quarrels over recreation, household items, and the ambitions of the children indicate that this was a family in which the raw edges of the anxieties of the spouses rubbed one another to the point of impairment of their efficiency as members of the family and the community.

A Severely Disturbed Person: Sarah Glass

Mrs. Glass was born in Russia sixty-two years ago. When she was three years of age her mother died. Within a year her father remarried, and a few months later the father and the new wife emigrated to New York City with Sarah and her two-year-old brother from the first marriage. The father and stepmother found jobs and left the children at home each day with relatives. In those years eight members of the family lived in a single room. Mrs. Glass described her father's second wife as a "real old-fashioned stepmother," mean and very strict; she seldom gave the children enough to eat. Sarah was so unhappy that at the age of 8 she went to live with an aunt and an uncle and their five children. She claimed that she cared for the children, scrubbed floors, washed dishes, did the laundry, and ironed the pleats in the little girls' dresses until two o'clock in the morning. She told us she did not mind the hard work because she was given some pretty clothes by her aunt and was allowed to go to school until she had finished the ninth grade. On many occasions the cousins teased her unpleasantly. The oldest child used to say, "Why don't you go to live with your own father?" When she became miserable she cried herself to sleep or tried to forget her troubles by imagining she was Cinderella. The other children never helped her with her tasks; if she asked for their help they said, "No, you're supposed to do it." The aunt was aware of the bad feeling between Sarah and the children, but she did nothing to make things easier for her niece. However, even when conditions were at their worst, Sarah thought it was better than living with her stepmother.

At the age of 19, forty-three years ago, Sarah married. It was the first and only marriage for both partners. Mrs. Glass believed their ability to stay together was attributable to their common background—Mr. Glass was an "orphan too"; he also had a "stern and mean stepmother." He was the oldest of five boys whose mother died when he was 8 years old. His father married twice more, producing two children from the second marriage and one from the third. Somewhere in the saga of the elder Mr. Glass's marital history, he, his eight children, and the third wife came to America from Russia.

Mrs. Glass described her husband as an extremely ambitious man. At an early age he was selling newspapers on the streets of New York in addition to bootblacking on weekends. He worked at many jobs to pay his way through elementary and high school and two years of business college. When the Glasses were first married, he worked on three different jobs at the same time in an effort to get ahead: in a shipyard during the day, in his father's barbershop in the evenings, and in a motion picture theater on weekends. He was always watching for an odd job to bring in more money. Mrs. Glass told us: "What he is today, he has made by himself." The Glasses have been "down and out" three times in their married life, but somehow they have always "come back." Mrs. Glass reported to us that financial strains have caused nervous problems for her.

Her husband looked at their financial ups-and-downs a bit differently; he said, "She shouldn't worry about them as it will all come out in the wash." She said: "He is wonderful in his ability to take things so calmly." Mr. and Mrs. Glass now own a profitable retail business. He is happy being his own boss; he likes this better than working for other people. She has helped in the business for many years but plans to retire soon to collect social security. However, she said that she would come into the store one or two afternoons a week to sell from behind the counter.

Mr. and Mrs. Glass had lived in apartments all the years they had been in this community. For the seven years before the hospitalization they lived in an apartment in a suburban town which Mrs. Glass favored. Her husband, against her wishes, insisted on moving to a recently built luxury apartment close to his place of business. Since she did not want to move Mrs. Glass decided the time had come for her to seek medical attention for a long-standing chronic condition. She telephoned for advice to a surgeon who had operated on her leg eight years before and was told that he was in surgery but he would try to see her as soon as possible. Once having made up her mind, Mrs. Glass was unwilling to wait; she told the secretary she was in so much pain she would go to the Emergency Room of the hospital. The surgeon then called the Emergency Room and reported that he would see her as soon as possible. He asked the resident to examine her in the meantime to see what care was necessary. The house officer found her right ankle was inflamed and swollen; he thought she should be admitted to the surgical service, and the surgeon confirmed this decision. Mrs. Glass then requested a semiprivate accommodation because of the expense of a private room and, more particularly, because she did not want to be alone.

This was the fourteenth admission of Sarah Glass to a hospital; it was her second admission to this hospital. Eight years prior to her current admission, her present surgeon operated on her left leg and removed varicose veins. He told her at that time that she should have a similar operation on her right leg also, but she rejected this advice. The argument between Mrs. Glass and her husband about moving led to her decision to go into the hospital. She told us later she had the choice of helping with the move or going to the hospital; she decided to go to the hospital in order to punish her husband by letting him handle the move all alone. When doctors examined her leg and learned that for several days Mrs. Glass had been nauseated, vomiting every day, and finding a great deal of phlegm in her throat each morning, they decided she should stay in the hospital for treatment of her leg and the nausea. She thought this would be two or three days at most but her stay in the hospital dragged on for five weeks.

Mrs. Glass's previous hospitalizations were, in large part, associated with her reproductive history. When she was 20 years old she gave birth to a daughter. During the early months of pregnancy she felt nauseated, vomited often, and was particularly distraught during intercourse. When the baby was about one year old Mrs. Glass became pregnant a second time. After a few weeks she decided not to go through with this pregnancy. Without telling her husband that she was pregnant she went to an abortionist, a woman whom a neighbor had said "would fix her for a small fee." There were two more abortions before a son was born. When she became pregnant again shortly after this, she told her husband she intended to have an abortion and he insisted that she have it performed by a physician. This was followed by two more abortions and a hospitalization for a tubal pregnancy. After this, she became pregnant again and then gave birth to her youngest child, a daughter. She developed rheumatic fever, was hospitalized for several weeks, returned home, and became pregnant again. Two more abortions followed. The last abortion she described in detail, telling of the plop in the pail that she heard as she lay on the operating table. Afterwards, she regretted the last abortion and both she and her husband cried. She explained this series of abortions by saying she had become pregnant at inopportune times, she was terribly nauseated each time, and she was young and foolish. (Despite her explanations, the fact is that at the time of the last abortion she was 40 years old.)

The day after Mrs. Glass was admitted to the hospital she rallied her family around her. The elder daughter came with her husband from New York City. The younger daughter who lived in a nearby suburban town stayed for several hours. In the afternoon Mr. Glass came. During the evening the son and his wife, who lived in a city some 50 miles away, came. By the end of the day the three children, two in-laws, and the husband were crowded into the room along with three other patients. No thought was given to the emotional and physical needs of the other patients. This was the only occasion on which we saw the family all together.

The day the family came to the hospital the surgeon told Mr. and Mrs. Glass he planned to operate upon her as soon as the necessary tests were completed. Two days later he stripped the veins from her right leg, cut a growth from her thigh, and make a skin graft on an ulcer on her right ankle. Mrs. Glass did not respond well to the surgery and the accompanying medication. She remained nauseated and vomited more or less regularly every day. A gastrointestinal series of X rays was done but no abnormality was found. Then a gall bladder series was done because of her constant complaints of burping, stomach pains, and vomiting. During the twelve hours before the tests she was not allowed food or liquids. She told us this made her so extremely uncomfortable that the pain in her leg felt "almost good." On the eleventh day after surgery when she was still vomiting clear fluid, the physicians concluded it was attributable to an emotional state rather than an organic condition. She told us later that before they found this out "the physicians tortured me, just tortured me."

As her hospitalization went on she claimed she had a terrible urge to urinate or defecate but when she went to the bathroom she couldn't. She went into lengthy detail about her elimination problems, and at the same time she belched loudly several times, clearly adding to the normal noise of burping. She told us proudly she was taking Alka Seltzer without her doctor's knowledge because she thought this was a good medicine for her condition and she liked "putting something over on the nurses."

Whatever the nurses or aides did for her was wrong. She described what appeared to us to be a delicious steak dinner as tasting "like a sour dishcloth." She launched into a long series of protests about the food, the staff, her family, and the data collectors. One day she dramatically sent her untouched lunch back to the kitchen claiming it had been delivered in the middle of all her agony. She demanded that the head nurse or the house officer check with the surgeon before any procedure was done on her. She complained about the lack of attention she was receiving from her two daughters and her son. She claimed her husband was neglecting her. When he did come she whined continuously in a demanding voice and he responded in irritated tones. She berated the data collector for not coming more often; when she did come Mrs. Glass complained about everything and urged her to come again so they "could talk." The data collector wrote: "It probably depends on which feeling wins out—her desire to tell me all of her problems or her annoyance with me for not being more attentive."

The floor nurses viewed Mrs. Glass as "an inconsiderate vulgar person." She overemphasized all her personal needs, and her personal habits were disgusting to the nurses: She showed her ugly sore to whoever would look at it; she spit directly into a waste can without using tissues; she made as much noise as possible when vomiting which nauseated the other patients in the room. She was uncooperative about medication and care. She decided that the pills the staff were giving her were going to make her sick but the pills she had brought from home were good for her. The charge nurse told us:

> She didn't cooperate on anything and complained about everything. She tells you exactly how to do things and you can never do it right for her. She makes things sound as bad as possible. The other patients resent her demands along with her refusal to get up and walk. She has been babied by her family and has developed a tendency to act helpless.

Later in her hospitalization the surgeon ordered the dressing on her leg changed once a week. Mrs. Glass thought it should be changed once a day and she created difficulties for the nurses and house staff until it was changed daily.

The head nurse apologized for her description of Mrs. Glass as the "pisser on the floor," going on to explain that Mrs. Glass had everybody "pissed off." She was moved to two different rooms, and shortly after each move the other patients individually demanded that they be moved out of her room; at the same time she expressed annoyance with these patients because they talked too much. Finally, the supervisor told Mrs. Glass the hospital was moving her to a private room, but Mrs. Glass created such a storm of protest that the supervisor moved all the patients out of her room and left her alone in a four-bed room. A house officer, in referring to her peculiar personality, said, "It's manifest to each of her roommates in turn; they soon demand to get away from her." Mrs. Glass, however, told the data collectors she got along "very well" with the other women in her room and with the doctors, nurses, aides, and visitors to other patients. She told us many times, "I tell them everything is wonderful and they are very nice to me."

Both house officers believed Mrs. Glass could have been taken care of very well at home several weeks before she was discharged from the hospital, but her husband and her private specialist preferred to have her "exhausted in the hospital rather than to have to cope with her emotional problems at home." She told her private internist and the surgeon that the nursing care was grossly inadequate. She pleaded with them to let her go home because she would be better off there. Finally, her physician discharged her on Christmas Eve. There was glee on the floor. The nurses told us: "This is the best Christmas present we ever had."

While Mrs. Glass was in the hospital her surgeon viewed her as a "very unhappy person in general." He realized she looked to her family for sympathy. He thought she received it most of the time from her husband; he didn't know about her relationship to her children. He attributed the turmoil of her hospital stay to poor nursing care. He took the data collector out of Mrs. Glass's room to have a long talk with her about the way poor nursing care was affecting the progress of her recovery. After Mrs. Glass left the hospital she continued to call the surgeon to demand that he come to her apartment and examine her. Between visits to the apartment she called him on the telephone to ask for information, solace, and confirmation of her personal difficulties. In the words of the surgeon, "She became a pest."

During the home visit Mrs. Glass gave us further insight into her post-hospital relationships with the surgeon. She said he had become very "neglectful" of her, and he was getting worse. She complained that he didn't even call when he didn't come as promised. She told us:

I tell him, "Look when you tell me you're coming and you can't come, would you please call and tell me." He must think I'm awfully fresh. I said, "If you can't come, just call up and tell me what to do." He just looks at me.

Mrs. Glass continued to call the surgeon but she complained that each home visit cost her $15. She was outraged that he charged her $450 for the surgery and an additional $60 for visits made in the hospital.

During the home visit Mrs. Glass told us she had called several of the women with whom she had become acquainted while she was in the hospital. She invited each one to call and have tea with her, but each one was "too busy." Wistfully, she said, "They all seem to be recovering from their illnesses. I am the only one who's not getting any better."

Mrs. Glass told us also about her brother. Until the home visit she had denied having a brother. She told us she claimed to be the only child in the family because in this way she did not have to explain her brother's whereabouts to people who did not understand her personal problems. When she went as a young child to live with her aunt and uncle to escape from the mean stepmother, her brother was left at home. The parents continued to work, leaving him alone at home a great deal throughout his childhood. When he was in his teens he joined the navy, served four years, and was honorably discharged. He drifted from place to place, had many different jobs, eventually enlisted in the army, and was sent to Cuba where he deserted and hid in the jungle. Mrs. Glass claims that for three nights in a row before her brother returned from Cuba, she dreamed he had deserted and come home on a boat looking like a tramp. When she told her husband about it he told her to forget it and not to worry about it. Three days later her brother turned up at her home as she had dreamed. They gave him food, a bath, and clean clothing. For many days he sat in the house with the shades drawn, asking if anybody was looking for him; then he gave himself up and served a sentence for desertion. After he was released from the army stockade he came to live with the Glasses. He often arose in the middle of the night and took long walks, sometimes walking from Brooklyn to Coney Island. During this period he went from job to job. When Mr. and Mrs. Glass moved to this state some twenty-five years ago, the brother went to live with his father and stepmother.

One day Mrs. Glass's father telephoned to tell her he had had the brother committed to a mental institution. About ten years ago, at Mrs. Glass's request, the brother was transferred to a state hospital in this state where he has remained. She described her brother as a harmless fellow who never talked: "He is all closed in. You can't reach him. He just doesn't talk." Mrs. Glass visited him every two or three weeks. She reported that she was the only person in the world who ever visited him.

At the end of the home visit Mrs. Glass told us she did not like the hospital or any of the staff. She said:

At night I would beg the nurse to give me a bedpan. The nurse used to say, "Mrs. Glass, I will do what I can but I'm all alone here and I have thirty-two patients. I just can't be all over the place at one time." Now am I supposed to wait when I am in pain? I don't care how many patients she has. It is *me* that I want taken care of. Do you understand me?

At the conclusion of the interview, Mrs. Glass insisted that the interviewer stay and observe her painful trip from the couch, where she had been sitting, to a bed where she was going to have her lunch. Then she dismissed the interviewer abruptly, letting the maid show her to the door while she started to wolf down the lunch the maid had brought to her.

So far as we were able to tell, Mr. Glass was primarily interested in building his business and giving his wife the things she demanded, such as a maid, fine clothes, and expensive furniture. He told us they had been married for forty-three years and in all that time he had had nothing in mind but the family's welfare. To him this meant making money, "getting ahead in life." His wife's emotional needs were outside the purview of his vision and apparently outside his interests. He thought he was close to her emotionally and that she did the best she could. We believe the behavioral manifestations of Mrs. Glass's activities substantiate the judgment that she was severely neurotic. Clearly, this woman was incapacitated to such an extent that she created turmoil around her.

A Psychotic Person: Lois Czesaba

Mrs. Czesaba was born forty years ago in the United States. She was descended on both her father's and mother's side from a mixture of early German settlers and American stock of English origin, combined with assorted ancestors who came from Ireland, Wales, Belgium, and other northern European countries. Her husband was born in Poland but reared in a nearby town; he managed a gasoline station in this city. At the time the hospitalization took place they had been married approximately three years and lived in a one-family house in a suburban town.

When we first saw Mrs. Czesaba she lay on top of the bed in a filmy transparent nightgown. She looked at us, turned on her back, pulled the top of her nightgown down on her breasts, flexed the left leg so she showed the inner side of her thigh, and smiled in a vague, far-away manner. She had no objections to being included in the study; in fact, she welcomed attention. Throughout this first conversation she was exhibitionistic, talkative, seductive, and teasing as she assured us she would cause us no trouble. When we were ready to leave, she said without any connection to the previous discussion,

"It's better to know the Devil you know than the Devil you don't know."

When we came the second time Mrs. Czesaba said for no apparent reason, "I'm still here. I'm not going any place." She then said that she was having trouble talking since her false teeth were not in her mouth. She reached to the stand beside her bed and fixed a complete set of upper and lower dentures in her mouth. We learned later that all of her teeth had been extracted when she was 37 years old.

Mrs. Czesaba was the only child of a third marriage for both her father and mother. The father had two daughters by one of these marriages and the mother had one daughter by her second marriage before she married Mrs. Czesaba's father. She told us she was the "favorite son my father never had." She described this treasured relationship with satisfaction. Her parents lived in this community for a number of years before their deaths. Mrs. Czesaba's father died at the age of 84, two years before this hospitalization. We asked her how she felt about this and she asked us how we thought one should take things like this. We soon learned that this was her characteristic way of responding to questions. About three months before the hospitalization she found her mother dead in bed. Her response to this death was a weight loss of over 20 pounds in two months which she told us was "just baby fat."

Lois Czesaba started taking dancing lessons when she was three years old. During adolescence she began to entertain commercial audiences with her acrobatic and strip-tease dancing throughout the eastern part of the United States, Cuba, and Panama. She followed this career until she was married at the age of 17. Before she was divorced from this husband she had several miscarriages and one son whom she kept and reared. She did not return to the entertainment field after her divorce because of a fall which injured her knee. She learned the trade of hairdressing and was a hairdresser until she married a second time. Between the time Mrs. Czesaba divorced her first husband and married her present husband she was admitted to hospitals for dilation and curettage three times. There were several miscarriages and at least two pregnancies that ended in abortion during this interlude.

Mrs. Czesaba realized she had been rebellious in her relationship with her first husband. She deliberately didn't treat him the way her mother had told her she should treat a husband. Apparently she learned a lesson from this because she told us that she treated her second husband entirely the opposite of the way she treated her first husband. She reported that she was attempting to raise her 2-year-old son from her present husband differently from the way she raised her older son. Mrs. Czesaba ridiculed her husband when he wasn't present: she referred to him as "a greaseball" and a "fat butterball" although he is rather slender. She said that she learned very early in her marriage that sharing thoughts with him upset the family so she decided to keep things to herself and not allow her husband to know what was going on or how she was really feeling. This worked the other way as well, since Mr. Czesaba did not share his thoughts with his wife. She felt by acting this way she satisfied herself and worked through her troubles of the moment, but she confused her husband and angered him. He ignored her and she realized it. Her way of dealing with people was to tease and joke, clown, and use verbal and gestural attention-getting devices. She attempted to be seductive to men, crossing her legs so that a large part of her thigh showed, pulling at her blouse to expose the upper part of her breasts, and smiling broadly to display her "store-boughten" teeth.

Mrs. Czesaba told us her husband was a person who had deep feelings and great concerns. When he was quiet she believed things were bothering him and she got after him to get his worries off his chest. Mr. Czesaba said his wife tried to solve her problems by talking a great deal. When she was particularly concerned about anything, she disappeared for hours at a time. She often took a bus downtown, walked the streets, shopped, bought a piece of dress goods, and came home to make a dress for herself or a suit for the little boy, or sometimes she drove with her half-sister to New York City, had a meal, went to a show, and returned. Mrs. Czesaba told us several times that she had, on occasion, seriously thought of "taking a powder," just "disappearing for good."

When troubles mounted and became too great for Mrs. Czesaba to bear she badgered her husband into taking "a long trip." She talked him into leaving his job, packed up their belongings, and closed the house; the family then "went on the bum" for months at a time. She said, "We are a bunch of gypsy bohemians." The year before the hospitalization, the Czesabas went to Florida for three months. They spent their time "on the beach." They took a trip to the Bahamas and traveled to other parts of the South.

Approximately one month before this admission, Mrs. Czesaba found a lump in her left breast. She feared she had cancer and immediately went to her family physician. In all of the later conversations we had with Mrs. Czesaba she never again mentioned the possibility of cancer. She was afraid of death but she did not use the word; she always said "leave" or "go away."

Many times in the hospital Mrs. Czesaba made incoherent statements completely out of context. When she was on her way to the operating room she said in a low deep voice, "Don't let them burn me at the stake." As she was wheeled into the operating room we heard her mutter, "I don't like this at all. I'm too fat. I'll burn well." The day after the operation she turned to the observer and said, "I hope the fire is out by tonight." The second day after the operation she said to the observer, "I'm still on fire," and later in the observation, "You know it must be an awful feeling to be shot. It must feel something like this."

Mrs. Czesaba described in detail how the interns, medical students, and an assistant resident examined her breasts. She told us all the doctors liked the feel of her right breast. (The interesting point here is that the tumor was in her left breast.) She attempted to ignore the tumor by saying, "If something has to be done, it has to be done." She clearly enjoyed having "the doctors feel me."

Mrs. Czesaba told us that she kept "a happy face" when she was with people but that she cried in private. The first night she was in the hospital she cried inconsolably until she was given a sedative so that she could sleep and forget her anxieties. Nurses and physicians who came in contact with her realized she was distraught while she was in the hospital and that she attempted to cover up her anxieties by overjoviality and claims that "everything is fine." She became agitated at questions about health problems before this illness. When we asked her if she ever woke up at night she said, "Honey, I don't think there is a human being that doesn't wake up at nights." We asked routinely, "Do you ever feel you are going to lose your mind?" She said, "Uffh," and with obvious agitation climbed out of bed, walked around the room, and then just stared at us. When we asked if she thought there was time to do the things she wanted to do, she said, "There haven't been enough hours in the day at any time to do what I want to do. I'm just one of those sons of the garden who can go with four hours of sleep and feel fine." (We never found out what she meant by "sons of the garden.")

Mrs. Czesaba's 21-year-old son realized his mother was subject to extreme emotional stress. When his grandmother died he took thirty days of leave from the army for fear that his mother "would crack up." This exhausted his leave for the year, but Mrs. Czesaba could not understand why he didn't come home for Christmas to be with her. Sometimes she referred to him as "my adopted son." In the course of her ramblings she told us about her "crazy home life"; then she grinned broadly and with a vacant stare said, "I have no problems and no troubles. Don't you wish you were me?"

Whenever she discussed members of her family she talked about her half-sister first; her husband entered the discussion after various other relatives. In spite of this she worked hard to get her husband's attention. When he visited her she gave him the impression she was in great pain. Clutching her breast she once told him how painful "the football" was. A moment after he left, she was out of bed doing an exhibitionistic dance with sexual overtones; there was no indication that her breast was hurting her. At other times she ignored the fact that she was under medication and her breast was bandaged.

When she decided to put on one of her "shows" it made no difference who was in the room or where she was in the hospital. She mimicked with verbal accents and gestures Jews, Poles, Italians, Negroes, or anyone else whom she wanted to take off on at the moment. Once, noticing our interest, she stopped inexplicably to inquire if there were "any screwballs around." She said she was going to charge us an entertainment tax and resumed her "show." We asked if she considered us "screwballs" and she replied, "I have my serious moments, but not often enough."

In our associations with Mrs. Czesaba she often referred to her activities as "putting on a circus"; she thought of herself as the star in the center ring of the "make-believe stage of life." During the latter part of her hospitalization, she wandered up and down the hall putting on shows in the rooms of all the patients. She told us:

> I'm friendly. I poke my head in the door to say hello. I kid with them. I ask them how they like the floor show and if their seats are okay. Then they chime right in the fun. I don't know if I'm helpful, but at least I make them smile.

Mrs. Czesaba seriously proposed to the head nurse that fashion shows be put on in the hospital so that everyone would know "what kind of johnnie is in style." She had an infuriating habit of insulting people. One afternoon while we were carrying on an observation she said to a nurse who came into the room, "How is Pipsqueak today?" One woman in Mrs. Czesaba's room was so upset by her clowning and inappropriate remarks that she cried and kept the curtains closed around her bed. Mrs. Czesaba, completely misinterpreting this behavior, told us: "I gave her doctor hell for not treating her better."

The nurses realized that Mrs. Czesaba was disturbed emotionally. The night nurse said Mrs. Czesaba made every effort to convince her that she was in great pain from the biopsy, demanding medications so she could sleep. This nurse said she didn't know the woman well because "she slept most of the time under heavy sedation, thank God." The head nurse said with a knowing smile, "This woman is pleasant enough on the surface, but I don't know what she had in the back. . . ." The nurse did not finish this sentence. She could not understand why Mrs. Czesaba was kept in the hospital so long for a simple breast biopsy.

The house officer told us that when he came into the room for the first time and introduced himself to Mrs. Czesaba, he said to her that he had not met her before. She responded with a wave of her hand and said, "I'm Mrs. Czesaba and I feel fine. You started at the wrong end. I've already told you everything." This was the way she did things, in her own words, "upside down and wrong end to." The house officer told us also that he realized she was acting out in her saucy, flip behavior. She told him while he was examining her, "It's a comfort to know that men are a sicker race than women." The surgeon said this woman was putting on a false front regarding her illness. He thought if we intended to understand her we should look into the family situation.

We observed Mrs. Czesaba the day she left the hospital with her husband. She clutched her left breast, looking very pained. We believe that she was "putting on a show" for the benefit of her husband, probably to gain his sympathy.

During the home visit we learned that for several weeks after she left the hospital Mrs. Czesaba rallied members of her and her husband's family around her to do the housework. Her half-sister was the leader in this volunteer work crew. The half-sister's daughter and the wife of her husband's brother came to the house daily to take care of the 2-year-old boy. Mrs. Czesaba told us, "This has been a fair up here." Later in the visit she said, "I've been on easy street since I was sick."

While Mrs. Czesaba was in the hospital she told us that everyone there was good to her, treated her well, and kept her happy, but during the home visit she referred to the nurses in the hospital as "stinkpots" and said, "I tried to act as nutty as I could while I was there to keep everybody happy." It is true that she amused the patients, but the fact is she interfered with all of the activities on the floor: She "told off" her roommate's physician and also "told off" some of the other patients' doctors; once she went into a telephone booth and tried to get a private-duty nurse for a patient. After this, she told us, "Poppa patted me on the head for that. I get lots of pats on my head for the things I do." Again, during the home visit, she described herself as "the nuttiest nut in a nutty family."

Nine months after her discharge from the hospital we visited the family again. Mrs. Czesaba at this time characterized herself as "going crazier than ever." She told us that the time between her hospitalization and the follow-up had been "a screwy one, but life's like that—just one screwy thing after another." She said later in the conversation, "I may be screwy but I plan things systematically."

The biopsy of Mrs. Czesaba's breast showed no malignancy. She was greatly relieved while she was in the hospital and at the home visit after the hospitalization. However, when we made the follow-up visit she was very concerned that she would not live long enough to see her child grow up and "be prepared for life." She told us, "It may be different from the way other people think but that's the way I think about things."

At the time this visit was made Mr. Czesaba had lost his job at the service station and Mrs. Czesaba was agitated by her need to "get going." They had sold their home and all the furniture and were preparing to "go on the bum." (While the interview was underway two purchasers of furniture came to the house for things they had bought—the television set and the sofa and chairs from the living room; we finished the interview sitting on the floor.) Mrs. Czesaba was looking forward unconcernedly to the trip to Florida or "wherever the road takes us." Mr. Czesaba was sorely worried, but he thought his wife would be happier "on the road" than in this community. To preserve the marriage a little longer he had consented to her inordinate demands to move on.

As long as we knew her this woman behaved in inapppropriate ways, hallucinating verbally and gesturally. She looked upon people as stagehands who made her theatrical performances possible; they were entertained by her as she continued to dance through life. She was perceptive of the fact that our expressions did not reveal our thoughts. She sometimes told us what she thought we were thinking. To the end, Mrs. Czesaba was concerned that we were gathering information in an effort to evaluate her mental status. Her half-sister was firmly convinced that this was what we were doing. Mrs. Czesaba said, "I can tell by the expression on your face what you are hearing." She reassured herself by repeating, "You're not really psychoanalyzing me." Finally, she observed that our association with her would result in our laughing either with her or at her. We explained that we were trying to understand her as a human being.

We are not convinced that we were able to penetrate to the real self of this woman. She was close to no one, except possibly her half-sister. We have insufficient data on associations with other family members to make a judgment about the meaning she had to them. She laughed her way through life in inappropriate ways, utilizing her illness to make secondary gains within her family, particularly with her husband.

In summary, we had the impression we were trying to communicate with an adolescent girl who was acting out, felt dependent and unsure of herself, and was living in a world of fantasy. She had regressed to the point where she was unable to handle most everyday problems in a meaningful way. It is clear that she was ineffective in her relationships with her husband and superficial in her friendships with other persons.

We turn now from the detailed behavioral data presented on particular individuals—for the purpose of illustrating what we mean by mental status assessments of *mentally healthy, moderately disturbed, severely disturbed,* and *psychotic*—to a tabular presentation of the distribution of the 4 categories of mental status among the 161 persons in the study. Before discussing the statistical materials, we repeat that we made *two* assessments of mental status for each person because we desired to estimate the impact of the illness and its accompanying hospitalization on the person's usual mental status. First, we relied upon the life history and the behavioral characteristics of the person

TABLE 19. ASSESSMENT OF MENTAL STATUS PRIOR TO THIS ILLNESS, BY
ACCOMMODATION

Pre-illness Mental Status	Total	Patients by Accommodation		
		Private	Semiprivate	Ward
Healthy*	9%	8%	17%	2%
Moderately disturbed*	29	26	28	36
Severely disturbed	49	60	42	38
Psychotic	13	6	13	24
N =	(161)	(65)	(54)	(42)

Private compared with semiprivate, $p > .05$; private compared with ward, $p < .05$; semiprivate compared with ward, $p > .05$.

* These categories were combined in the chi-square analysis.

for our judgment of his mental status prior to the present illness. We refer to this assessment as the pre-illness mental status. Second, we examined the patient's behavior while he was in the hospital and made an in-hospital assessment of mental status.

The distribution of mental status prior to the present illness is given in Table 19. An examination of the figures in the Total column shows that the largest proportion of persons, 49 per cent, were severely disturbed, and the smallest proportion, 9 per cent, were mentally healthy. The distribution of the pre-illness mental status by accommodation differs from one category to another and from one accommodation to another. The difference, however, is significant only between the private and the ward patients. The largest disparities between the ward and the private patients are concentrated in the two polar categories—mentally healthy and psychotic.

The percentage figures for each accommodation and mental status category during hospitalization are presented in Table 20. During hospitalization mental status was considerably different from what it was judged to be prior to the present illness. During hospitalization there was an increase in per-

TABLE 20. DEMONSTRATION OF MENTAL DISTURBANCE DURING
HOSPITALIZATION, BY ACCOMMODATION

In-hospital Mental Disturbance	Total	Patients by Accommodation		
		Private	Semiprivate	Ward
None	—	—	—	—
Moderate	25%	15%	39%	21%
Severe	53	65	39	55
Overtly psychotic	22	20	22	24
N =	(161)	(65)	(54)	(42)

Private compared with semiprivate, $p < .05$; private compared with ward, $p > .05$; semiprivate compared with ward, $p > .05$.

sonality disturbance; not one person was given an assessment of mentally healthy. Within each accommodation there is a distinct increase in emotional disturbance among the patients. A study of the figures in Tables 19 and 20 demonstrates this difference. A shift from less severe to more severe personality disturbance during hospitalization occurred also in all accommodations. The only significant difference in mental status during the present hospitalization was between the private patients and the semiprivate patients. This difference is attributable to the heavy concentration of severely disturbed persons within the private accommodations.

TABLE 21. PRE-ILLNESS MENTAL STATUS COMPARED WITH IN-HOSPITAL
MENTAL STATUS DURING THIS ILLNESS

Pre-illness Mental Status	Mentally healthy	In-hospital Mental Status Moderately disturbed	Severely disturbed	Overtly psychotic
Healthy	—%	12%	11%	3%
Moderately disturbed	—	41	33	6
Severely disturbed	—	44	54	40
Psychotic	—	3	2	51
N =	—	(41)	(85)	(35)

p < .05; $\overline{C}$ = .64.

The comparisons we have made between the mental status of persons prior to the present illness and that during hospitalization for this illness indicate that, in a considerable number of persons, mental status changed during hospitalization. However, there was continuity from one time period to another. This is shown by comparing the mental status of each person before the illness with his mental status during hospitalization. The distribution by mental status category and time period is given in Table 21. While none of the mentally healthy persons in the pre-illness phase of his life was judged to be mentally healthy in the hospital, only five of the fifteen persons —or one out of three—in this category were judged to be moderately disturbed in hospital whereas nine of the fifteen exhibited severely disturbed behavior and one was overtly psychotic while in the hospital. At the other end of the mental status gradient, one person who was overtly psychotic before the present illness revealed only mildly disturbed behavior while in hospital and two of the psychotics appeared to be only severely disturbed while in hospital. However, 18 of the 21 persons given a mental status rating of psychotic before the present illness continued to display psychotic behavior during hospitalization. The shifts in mental status from the pre-illness phase to the phase we observed in hospital may be calculated by comparing the numbers in each column with the numbers in the rows in Table 21. The

TABLE 22. INTERRELATIONS BETWEEN PRE-ILLNESS MENTAL STATUS AND MANIFESTATION OF SYMPTOMS IN THE PRESENT ILLNESS

	Pre-illness Mental Status			
Manifestation of Symptoms	Mentally healthy	Moderately disturbed	Severely disturbed	Psychotic
Little or no relation to mental status	53%	39%	13%	5%
Moderately related to mental status	27	39	35	33
Largely determined by mental status	20	22	34	43
Identical to mental status	—	—	18	19
N =	(15)	(46)	(79)	(21)

$p < .05$; $\overline{C} = .44$.

overall association is demonstrated by the corrected coefficient of contingency of .64.

We examined interrelationships between the patient's mental status prior to the onset of the illness and the manifestation of his symptoms in this illness by constructing a contingency table with the manifestation of symptoms as the rows and the pre-illness mental status of the patient as the categories for the columns. The categorizations and the percentage figures for each row and column are shown in Table 22. The probability statement indicates that the patient's present symptoms in hospital were related significantly to his pre-illness mental status. A person may have had a disease that was definitely related to his mental status—peptic ulcer, for instance—or he may have had a disease that had no connection with his mental status—cancer, so far as we know, would be such a disease; the important point is that the figures in Table 22 trace a distinct gradient across the top row. A definite association appears between mental status and the possible etiology of symptoms.

Persons who came into contact with patients were questioned systematically on the way they viewed the emotional state of each patient while they were interacting with him during his hospitalization. Usually, the first person to interview a patient when he came to the hospital was the admissions officer. The day after each patient was admitted to the hospital we questioned the officer who admitted him. It should be remembered that this officer saw the patient only once and for a brief time; her interest was directed toward determining what kind of accommodation the patient desired and evaluating his ability to pay for the hospitalization. Observation of the incoming patient's emotional state was an incidental part of her work, yet it is surprising how accurately some admissions officers assessed the mental status of persons they saw for only a few minutes. However, we found that in only one patient out of twenty did admissions officers have some perception of the patient's emotional state. (There were no differences by accommodation.)

A physician had many more opportunities to evaluate the mental status of a patient than did an admissions officer. The physician was trained, presumably, to understand the emotional dimensions of illness as well as physical and organic pathology. Certainly, he was responsible for the diagnosis, treatment, and overall care of his patients. We accepted the physician's claims regarding responsibility for the care of patients; moreover, we assumed that the perception of the emotional state of the patient while under the physician's care was an integral part of good patient care. With this assumption as a reference point, we expected a physician to have a reasonably accurate perception of his patient's mental status while he was in the hospital. However, the physician's perception of the patient's mental status was related to accommodation, as seen in Table 23; this, in turn, was associated with sponsorship.

TABLE 23. PHYSICIAN'S PERCEPTION OF PATIENTS' MENTAL STATUS, BY ACCOMMODATION

Physician's Perception of Mental Status	Total	Patients by Accommodation		
		Private	Semiprivate	Ward
Correct	11%	22%	6%	2%
Partial	42	40	37	52
None	47	38	57	46
N =	(161)	(65)	(64)	(42)

Private compared with semiprivate, p < .05; private compared with ward, p < .05; semiprivate compared with ward, p > .05.

The emotional status of private patients was more likely to be perceived accurately by their physicians than the emotional state of either the semiprivate or ward patients. On the other hand, the largest percentage of patients whose physicians partially perceived their mental status was on the wards. The highest proportion of patients with physicians who had no perception of their emotional states was on the semiprivate accommodations. The perception of the patients' mental status by their physicians was significantly different when private patients were compared with either semiprivate or ward patients. No significant differences were found between the physician's perception of mental status by service or sex.

We now raise the question: *Is the perception of the patient's emotional condition by the physician associated with the severity of his mental disturbance?* Briefly, the answer is yes. This relationship, as measured by the corrected coefficient of contingency, is .58. Without going into detail, our data show that unless the patient was disturbed to a marked degree the physician either ignored his mental status or did not notice it. Even in the case of 34 per cent of the patients who were overtly psychotic while in the hospital, their physicians were not aware of their mental status.

The limited perceptions physicians had of a patient's mental status may be traceable to the lack of communication between patients and physicians. We questioned the patients specifically regarding discussions with their physicians. We found that only 2 per cent of the patients talked with their physicians about their disturbed feelings while they were in the hospital. An additional 35 per cent communicated, in selective ways, how they felt about themselves, their spouses, family members, jobs, home life, perceptions of their illness, and so on, while 63 per cent did not talk with their physicians about their feelings about themselves, other persons, and their life situation. (There were no significant differences by accommodation, service, or sex.) We are not in a position to determine if this reluctance on the part of the patients to communicate their feelings, emotions, and attitudes to the physician was traceable to the hesitancy of the physician to probe into areas other than those required in gathering the precise information called for by his efforts to make a physical diagnosis, or if it was due to the inability of the patient to communicate his feelings to a high-status professional who often indicated to the patient how busy he was.

Personnel in the nursing department were even less perceptive of the patients' emotional status than were the physicians. Registered nurses perceived partially or correctly the mental status of only one third of the patients; they were not aware of the in-hospital emotional disturbance of two thirds of the patients. Licensed practical nurses were the most perceptive of emotional status; they were aware, partially or fully, of the patients' emotional difficulties in four cases out of five. Nurse's aides had no perception of the mental status of three patients out of four. The specific percentages for each type of nursing personnel are given in Table 24.

Twenty-four per cent of the patients were treated for their in-hospital mental disturbances by physicians, physicians and nurses, or nurses without

TABLE 24. NURSING PERSONNEL'S PERCEPTION OF PATIENTS'
MENTAL STATUS

Perception of Mental Status by Nursing Personnel*	Nursing Personnel		
	Registered nurse	Practical nurse	Nurse's aide
Correct	8%	4%	2%
Partial	26	76	23
None	66	20	75
Number of patients	(161)	(161)	(161)

* There are no significant differences in the perception of the nursing personnel between the accommodations, the sexes, or the two services.

the aid of physicians; 70 per cent of this select group were private patients, and the remainder were divided equally between the ward and semiprivate accommodations. This concentration among the private patients is significant in comparison with both semiprivate and ward patients although there were no meaningful differences between the semiprivate and the ward patients. Most of the treatment was administered by physicians or a combination of physicians and nurses. Few patients were treated by nurses alone; the proportion who were is similar for the three groups.

The treatment of patients for mental disturbance while in hospital was judged to be successful or partially successful in different proportions for the three accommodation groups. There was a significantly higher rate of successful therapy among the private patients than among ward patients. There were no meaningful differences between patients who were given treatment for their emotional difficulties on the semiprivate and those on private accommodations; likewise, there were no differences when we compare the successes or failures in treatment for emotional disturbance on the two services or in the two sexes. In sum, success or failure in treatment for emotional troubles was associated with socioeconomic status, as reflected in the accommodations, rather than with the medical service or the sex of the patient.

Although all of the patients exhibited emotional disturbances while they were in hospital and 22 per cent were overtly psychotic, psychiatrists were called for consultation to see only six patients. Moreover, only two persons were drawn in the sample, both ward patients, who had been cared for in the psychiatric outpatient clinic before they were admitted to the hospital. One of these, Mrs. Tidd, was in active therapy at the time of admission to the medical service with a suspected case of pneumonia. The resident who had been handling the psychiatric therapy visited her once, on his own initiative, to suggest to the intern on the medical service who was in charge of the case the kind of drug he had found useful and to offer his "emotional support to this poor, miserable woman." From then until after her discharge from the hospital, Mrs. Tidd was not seen by anyone from the psychiatric service. The second psychiatric outpatient, Mrs. Stantzen, was admitted to the ward accommodation upon the insistence of the psychiatric clinic after she had made an attempt at suicide. Her stay was brief and marked by open conflict between the house staff on the medical service and the psychiatrist from the clinic. The medical intern thought this patient should be sent to the state hospital; the psychiatric resident disagreed. After a few days the patient was discharged, primarily upon the insistence of the psychiatric resident who preferred that she be sent home rather than to the state hospital.

The circumstances associated with each of the six patients who had a psychiatric consultation while in the hospital were briefly as follows: The medical service requested a psychiatric consultation for one ward patient. An assistant resident visited him and attempted to talk with him for about one half hour. The patient was elusive, silent, and withdrawn. The psychiatric resident gave him a label *schizoid* and returned to the Department of Psychiatry. The patient continued his strange behavior until his discharge.

Psychiatric consultations were requested for three semiprivate patients. The first, Mr. Simions, was an agitated medical patient with vague gastrointestinal symptoms. He was seen by a private psychiatrist once, but he became more disturbed after he "locked horns with the psychiatrist" than before. The internist said he recognized the "deadlock" between the patient and the psychiatrist so he dealt with the illness "mechanistically." The psychological factors in the illness were not evaluated.

Mr. Mapoli, a medical patient, was seen once by a consulting psychiatrist after he attempted suicide in the hospital. Following a consultation with the psychiatrist, the internist decided to handle the patient's emotional problems himself and extracted a promise from Mr. Mapoli "that there would be no more of this foolishness." The internist, in this instance, explained his reluctance to have the psychiatrist see Mr. Mapoli again:

> There are some physicians who know how to deal with personality problems and emotional difficulties and who feel responsible in this regard. There are other physicians who are cold and indifferent. I don't think you can make any real distinction between specialties in this regard. I think it's a matter of individual people and personalities rather than specialties.

We came across the same type of reasoning several times in our interviews with physicians. The argument was that for the best care of patients the personality and attitudes of the physician are the important factors that influence the emotional status of the patient; acquired professional knowledge, techniques, and performances are secondary considerations.

Mr. Hoyt, a semiprivate patient on the surgical service, was so agitated that the assistant resident in Surgery asked a psychiatrist to see him. The patient was in the terminal phases of malignancy and a firm suicidal threat had been made. The psychiatrist talked with him but was unable to solve the patient's real problem—fear of imminent death. The young surgeon who requested the consultation apologized to us for having called a psychiatrist:

> When things are really getting out of hand, one has to call in a psychiatrist. I've not been impressed, though, that psychiatrists are very much help—unless a patient is really acutely in emotional trouble, I think that support for a surgical patient must come from the temporary father figure who is almost always the surgeon because he's in charge of everything. Obviously, if a patient is frankly

schizophrenic he needs a psychiatrist, but the usual type of emotional problems we see just need a strong personality to hold the patient up, and this can easily be done by us.

Two private patients were seen by psychiatrists: Mr. Church was a severely disturbed, high-status person who presented a wide range of vague symptoms. His internist requested a consultation with a psychiatrist who talked with the patient. Mr. Church was very angry. He told his internist that he was getting along very well by himself and if he needed a psychiatrist he would seek out a competent one himself. The internist accepted Mr. Church's judgment which ended the matter. Mrs. Ingraham, a very agitated patient on Medicine who was so disturbed she was not able to handle her interpersonal relations with her husband or with any of the nurses or house staff in the hospital, was seen by a psychiatrist for evaluation at the request of her surgeon. She vented her wrath upon the psychiatrist; he saw her only once. (The story of Mrs. Ingraham is discussed in some detail in Chapter 16, pp. 340–42.)

Although eight patients were seen by a psychiatrist during their hospitalization (six on requested consultations and two known psychiatric patients), we have no evidence that any one of them received even a small amount of psychiatric therapy while in the hospital, with the exception of Mrs. Tidd, mentioned earlier, who entered a ward accommodation with pneumonia from the psychiatric outpatient clinic and was given some tranquilizing pills at the suggestion of a psychiatric resident.

The low level of communication between psychiatrists, on the one hand, and internists, surgeons, and patients, on the other, may be attributable to several factors: the stigma of mental illness; the low status of psychiatric treatment as compared to medical or surgical treatment; and the vagueness and high cost of psychiatric therapy. Patients being treated in a general hospital for an organic condition did not want to be labeled as "psychiatric cases." Few spouses were willing to accept psychiatric consultation if it could possibly be avoided, and they appeared to believe their spouses' emotional problems could be attributed to something other than mental illness. Our data reveal clearly that internists and surgeons believed they were fully capable of handling the emotional problems of their patients unless "things get out of hand." They did not desire to have their patients labeled mentally ill. Moreover, a major figure in the Department of Psychiatry threw some light on another point; in an orientation address to the new house staff while we were collecting data, he said: "When the private psychiatrist is called to see a patient in the Community Division he can charge $50 or $75 or anything he wants." We infer that this was a warning to the new house officers not to ask for a psychiatric consultation if they had the financial welfare of their patients in mind.

The patients, themselves, and their spouses were more perceptive of their emotional status than were any of the hospital personnel. The patients realized they might be facing imminent death, and they were worried, fearful, tense, anxious, and felt threatened by their illness. Although almost the same percentage of patients and spouses (97 per cent and 96 per cent respectively) were aware of the patients' emotional disturbances, there were differences between the patient and spouse in their comprehension of the emotional problems besetting the patient: 52 per cent of the patients but only 43 per cent of the spouses had a correct perception of the factors threatening the patient; 45 per cent of the patients and 53 per cent of the spouses understood that the patients were upset, scared, resigned, or fighting their emotions but had only a partial perception of the real meaning of these anxieties.

Although the patients and spouses were aware of the emotional difficulties with which they were coping, they were adamant in their desire to avoid a label of mental illness. Both believed the emotional disturbances they perceived in themselves and in the other member of the spouse pair were attributable to the physical illness and the anxieties associated with the hospitalization. In sum, they, like the other members of the human group involved in the care of sick people, *subordinated the psyche to the soma,* or in the words of Mrs. Czesaba, "It is better to know the Devil you know than the Devil you don't know." The Devil these persons knew was illness attributed to an organic disease; the Devil they did not know, and did not want to know under any circumstances, was mental illness, especially if it was recognized as such and so labeled by a phychiatrist.

Summary

The attributes of *the psyche,* which are less disernible than those of *the soma,* are a vital part of the human personality and account for many of the symptoms of patients. Yet, often in the diagnosis and treatment of a person's ills, this aspect of his problem is overlooked. To judge the actuality of this assertion, both pre-illness and in-hospital mental status evaluations were given to each patient. Based on a number of interrelated factors, the patients were divided for this purpose into four categories: mentally healthy, moderately disturbed, severely disturbed, and psychotic.

Before the illness, the largest proportion of patients were severely neurotic while only 9 per cent were judged to be mentally healthy. During hospitalization mental status changed in a considerable number of persons although a relationship was maintained between the pre-illness and the in-hospital mental status. There was also a significant relationship between the patient's symptomatology and his pre-hospital mental status.

The perception of a patient's mental status by his physician was related to accommodation and to the severity of the mental disturbance; it was not related significantly to sex or the service of treatment. The emotional status of a private patient was more likely to be perceived accurately than that of a semiprivate or ward patient; the emotional status of a moderately disturbed patient was hardly ever perceived by his physician. The mental status of only 11 per cent of the patients was perceived accurately by their physicians. Nursing personnel were even less perceptive in understanding the emotional status of the patients. Although all of the patients exhibited emotional disturbances while in hospital, only 2 per cent discussed their emotions with their physicians. This may have been due partly to the busy physicians' lack of encouragement to communicate and partly to the fear of the patients and their families of the stigma of mental illness. Only eight patients were seen by psychiatrists during hospitalization. Nonpsychiatric physicians discounted the professional knowledge and techniques learned in the specialized field of psychiatry. They assumed that the physician in charge was more important in treating emotional problems of a hospitalized patient than a psychiatrist.

In brief, a patient may have been in as great need of professional treatment for his emotional difficulties as for his physical difficulties; yet during hospitalization he was treated by medical specialists who were concerned primarily with the organs and organ systems of *the soma*. These specialists infrequently perceived problems of *the psyche* and even then rarely called for help from the psychiatrist.

PART IV TREATMENT AND
INTERPERSONAL RELATIONS

CHAPTER 11 PHYSICIANS, NURSES, AND PATIENTS

Fᴿᴼᴹ ᴛʜᴇ ʙᴇɢɪɴɴɪɴɢ ᴏꜰ ᴏᴜʀ ꜱᴛᴜᴅʏ ᴡᴇ ᴇɴᴠɪꜱᴀɢᴇᴅ ᴛʜᴇ
registered nurse and the physician as key persons mobilized by the hospital
to deal with the medical, physical, and emotional needs of patients. However, from the points of view of the physicians, nurses, and patients, the
role of the nurse was subordinate to that of the physician as diagnostician
and therapist planning the course of treatment for the patient. In Chapter 5
we pointed out that the physician viewed the nurse's role in the hospital and
in the care of patients as primarily one of carrying out his orders and reporting the patient's progress to him. Nurses reiterated this viewpoint, and the
patients also saw the nurse as an agent of the physician and as a provider of
hospital services to him. In this chapter we examine the relationship of
physicians and patients to the roles of the nursing personnel as they carried
out their assigned duties on the patient-care divisions.

The data we present on nurse-patient relationships were drawn from five
different sources: (1) day-to-day observations; (2) focused interviews with
Department of Nursing personnel who cared for each patient; (3) focused
observations in the patients' rooms; (4) the medical record of the patient;
and (5) interviews with the patient. In addition to the data gathered by each
of these procedures we have drawn upon our detailed knowledge of the
hospital, professional relationships within it, and the community's social
system.

In the ward accommodations the head nurse functioned as a coprofessional
with the physician. She helped the intern, especially the "green" intern,
as well as the medical students and residents. She was aware of the assistance
she gave them and that they, in turn, helped her with the care of patients.
The bond between head nurse and young physicians was, therefore, such that
authority in patient care was sometimes not well defined. One head nurse
told us:

217

We have to tell the house officers sometimes that we can't take the initiative to write or change orders. We often remind them to write an order or to change it. Sometimes the registered nurse forgets where she leaves off as a nurse and finds she is acting like a doctor. Nurses sometimes take it upon themselves to switch an intramuscular injection, as ordered, to an oral medication. The more the nurses act on their own, the more the house officer expects of them. Gradually, he just takes it for granted that it is the nurses's duty to change some of these things.

Nurses on the wards viewed the doctors with mixed feelings. While recognizing the importance of young physicians in patient care, the nurses sometimes worried about the implications of their student status and research interests. In general, though, the registered nurses joined the physicians and the medical students in their excitement about the diagnosis and treatment of disease. The situation was summed up in three words by a head nurse on a medical ward while she was discussing the working relationship between house officers, medical students, and nurses: "We get results."

Within the semiprivate and private accommodations, the head nurses' views of doctors offered a different model of their role: the private patient and the private doctor had to be served and satisfied. (The administrators, both hospital and nursing, agreed with this conception of the physician-nurse relationship in these accommodations.) The head nurses recognized their dependence upon many doctors. They knew that the house staff was under the direction of the private doctors who represented organized medicine in the community. "There are," as one nurse said," a multitude of them." Each private practitioner had his own way of dealing with patients and the numerous kinds of problems they had, and the nurses, house officers, and others in the hospital had to make allowances and adjustments according to the interests of each private practitioner. The nurses complained about this "multitude" of directors because of the confusion it caused. Nevertheless, they appreciated the stability experienced practitioners contributed to patient care.

A head nurse on a private division, while discussing the role of the private practitioner in the hospital, stated:

It's his case. He gives the orders and we carry them out. Some doctors are here practically all the time doing all they can. They never neglect their patients. If they can't handle the case they get consultations. They never leave a stone unturned. They show a great deal of interest in patients.

This nurse was talking about committed sponsorships. She was implying that some doctors with less committed types of sponsorship neglected their patients.

On the ward divisions, where the medical supervision the house officer received was in accord with the interests of the faculty of the School of Medicine rather than with the pursuit of the private practice of medicine, research and teaching predominated, but on the semiprivate and private accommodations the private physician was "the boss"; his interests in his patient and in his practice overrode the interests of the house officer. This divergence of interests sometimes resulted in conflict between the house officer and the private physician, and when such disagreements emerged the nurse was often caught in the middle. On these accommodations, however, the registered nurses knew that the house officer was subordinate to the private practitioner.

A head nurse on a private medical division made some pointed remarks concerning the relationship of house officers to private doctors:

> The house officers give the orders from which we [the nurses] meet the needs of the patient; they work with a private doctor, or should work with a private doctor, on a case—some of them work with private doctors and some of them don't. It's a matter of personality. Some are very aggressive and think they should be the one to write the orders and care for the patient. On the wards they write their own orders and are their own boss, but here they resent the fact that patients have private physicians who also write orders. At times this causes much difficulty and hard feelings between private physicians and the house officers. The nurses get involved when the private physician writes an order and the intern gets upset and tells us we have no right to honor it. I feel if the private physician is on a case he has the privilege of writing orders. Sometimes, you just get thrown between the two and you try to pacify them. It's a very difficult situation.

Another head nurse said:

> The house officers get a history and so forth. The private doctor tells them what he wants. They take care of the patient when the private doctor is not there and report to the private doctor anything special. They learn by experience how to take care of the different cases. They learn where their mistakes are. Sometimes they are left quite a lot on their own to care for the patient.

The head nurse's view of the relationship between the hospital authorities and the physicians was shaped largely by the fact that she was subordinate to the doctors and the hospital. She viewed the house officers as institutional physicians and the local private practitioners as entrepreneurs. She subscribed to the belief that the attending physician was "the boss." Patients sometimes believed this and sometimes they did not. Certainly, the more prestigious patients believed their doctors were self-directing; these were the laymen and physicians who formulated policy for the hospital.

One head nurse on a private medical division described her relationship to the private physician and the patient in these terms:

The private physician represents to the patient a person he should have complete trust in because he's someone in whose hands the patients have placed their lives. So what the private physician says usually goes. The physician may not be the center of patient care but the patient with a private physician sees his physician as the one who can answer all the questions and solve the problems.

Such a relationship made the nurse-patient interaction easier; it was certainly the ideal relationship between physician and patient, but the ideal and the factual were not always congruent. The same nurse quoted above described the greatest shortcomings of private physicians:

> . . . the lack of communication with the house staff. They tell the patients something has to be done and leave no order for it. Then the patient wonders why it hasn't been done. The nurse turns to the house staff for help and the house staff knows nothing about it. The fact is that the private physicians are very busy. They usually are in a hurry and rush in and rush out. They don't stay and give the patient a chance to ask questions. This is pretty much true of all of them. It's a rare physician who takes the time to really get to know a patient. Often, the private physician overlooks the orders for a patient on a discharge or instructions to the patient as to what he can or cannot do at home. He may also forget to sign a patient out. All of these things have repercussions for the nurses and the house staff.

This head nurse went on to describe the position of a member of the house-staff as a "learning doctor" who was sometimes rebellious toward the private physician. When he was more advanced in his training he often objected to limitations put upon him and wanted to do more than the private physician or the patient would allow. In brief, the performances of attending physicians and house staff with patients influenced the relationships of nurses with their patients.

On the wards personnel changes were practically continuous. The head nurses faced a changing human scene from day to day and from week to week: Patients came and went almost daily. Students were assigned by the School of Medicine or one of the schools of nursing in the hospital. Trainees in one of the several programs operated by the hospital arrived in "batches." House officers came and went as they were assigned and reassigned to different divisions and services. Even head nurses sometimes came and went. Some head nurses were excited by the constantly changing scene; others were overwhelmed by the chaos.

The following report by a data collector is descriptive of the activities of a head nurse on a ward accommodation at the beginning of the day shift:

> When I arrived on the unit, Miss ———— [the head nurse] was making rounds to check the treatment of patients. She checked oxygen tents, intravenous tubing,

the lunch schedule of her staff, and some medications she was soon to give. Although she went to the bedside of several patients, she did not speak directly to anyone. She then returned to her nursing station where she began to tell me about the staff assigned to her division. She said, "I'm supposed to haxe six registered nurses on this floor, but for months I've had only myself and one other. I didn't have any holidays off last year because I had no one to relieve me. I'm very fussy about the aides and the LPN's and what they do. They tend to stay off on weekends or nights just when I need them most. They don't take responsibility like the nurses do. I am allotted six aides but I have only two. Aides are off on the other floors all the time and I have to send mine on weekends to replace them. I don't think that's fair and I don't understand why the other head nurses don't crack down."

Miss —— then went on to discuss the students: "I get them in batches of nine with one instructor, but they aren't too much help because they ask so many questions and their instructor doesn't know the patients on the floor so I really need another graduate nurse to do my work when they are here. And then the students are here only Tuesday through Friday. Monday is class day for them and, of course, they have weekends off. Then, we get the practical nurse students. I complain when we get *them* in batches because they don't know what to do here; they don't know our routine for patients. Also, if too many students are here my regular help is sent away and then nothing gets done, and the doctors don't realize this and want things done right. Whenever I have what I consider to be an adequate staff the administration just takes them away from me and sends them someplace else."

Our observers attended "nursing reports" which took place when one shift finished and the next shift came on for duty. The reports dealt with patients and personnel assignments. Discussion centered primarily on treatment, food and fluid intake, elimination, collection of urine and stool specimens, and so on. The communications between the several members of the Department of Nursing who attended nursing report were task oriented. The patients were generally divided into two categories: *problem* and *no problem*. The definition of a *problem* is related to the degree to which the patient needed physical care or was unable or unwilling to comply with orders. Some typical remarks from our observations of the nursing reports were as follows:

"He's a problem—we can't get a urine specimen."
"She's not a problem. She got up and bathed herself."
"He's almost always wet or wants to turn. Then his relatives want to help him. They want to do it immediately and they want to tell us how to do it and when."
"She's a problem. She's hard to keep dry and she's getting very red buttocks. If we put her on her side we can't put anything under her to catch the urine. Then she gets wet."

"She's a problem. She's very dirty, untidy, and fat. She came in that way, and we can't get her cleaned up."

One head nurse told her shift relief, "We transferred Mrs. ———. She was a problem. The odor was terrible. She went to Surgery and they'll keep her on the surgical floor." The other answered briefly, "Good." In other words, *problem* patients obstructed work and *no problem* patients facilitated work.

Following the report at the nursing station, there was commonly brief "walking rounds," attended primarily by the head nurse who was going off duty and the head nurse who was coming on duty. One observer reported, "They go quickly from room to room and rarely speak to a patient." The following report of "walking rounds" on a surgical floor is typical of the problems registered nurses faced in their relations with patients and personnel assigned by the Department of Nursing. The data collector wrote:

> After the report was finished the night nurse left the division immediately. The aides went to their assigned duties. The day nurse in charge started walking rounds with two LPNs. After seeing four patients the head nurse was called to give a preoperative medication. She told the LPNs to proceed down the hall making rounds. They didn't know what this meant but they continued to go from room to room, just drifting and observing. They talked only with one patient who was reasonably comfortable, recovering from thrombophlebitis. Presently, the head nurse returned and said to me, "It's always this way on Monday morning. We have the bustle of staffing change and the breakfast trays along with getting patients to the operating room."

On the ward accommodations, one was impressed by the number of staff people hurrying between the patients in their beds and the treatment rooms and offices. The interaction between the patients and the nurses was limited in large part to the giving of preoperative medication and miscellaneous chores connected with housekeeping.

The experiences of Mr. Natrio, a low-status patient, illustrate the nature of the nurse-patient and physician-patient relationship in the wards. Mr. Natrio was admitted for the removal of basal cell tumors located over many parts of his body. Mr. Natrio had been afraid to come to the hospital for many years. He had heard tales about doctors who "experiment on people in Eastern's hospital." During the year before this admission his tumors became large, and complications of infection and painful ulceration developed. After twenty years of fearful suffering he came to the hospital for help. Under the duress of his pain, he rationalized that the doctors he had been told would operate on him were "expert" surgeons.

Mr. Natrio was very frightened as he entered the hospital. Because he was quiet and "good," he was ignored. He was hallucinating from time to time during the hospitalization and had a history of mental illness which was documented in his medical record, but the nurses and doctors overlooked this note in his history. The tumors were large and their removal was to be followed by skin grafting. The intern was excited about the prospect of doing the rather extensive "cutting, tying, and patching." Mr. Natrio was a "good prospect," a "fine learning case."

On the day of surgery Mr. Natrio became progressively more fearful that he would die, but the doctors and registered nurses did not notice his anxieties. Even the nurse who routinely gave him preoperative medication did not realize he was disturbed. Only an aide who had recently lost a family member from skin cancer noticed how upset he was. She thought he was "pathetic," and she tried to be very kind to him. Mr. Natrio interpreted her sympathy as evidence of his imminent death.

For several days after the surgery Mr. Natrio was extremely sensitive to everything that was said to him. The doctors joked with him concerning the surgery and the removal of the sutures, but he could not understand the jokes as his comprehension of English was poor and they could not speak Italian. One afternoon they told him they would come to remove the sutures at 5 o'clock the following morning. Mr. Natrio could not understand why this procedure was scheduled for such an hour. He did not raise the question with either the doctors or the nurses, but he spent a sleepless night only to discover that the intern and his medical student assistants did not appear for the removal of the sutures until midmorning. Many similar stories could be told, but this one should suffice to indicate observed relationships between patients on the wards and those entrusted with their care.

The behavior of the nurses on the semiprivate divisions revealed few differences from that observed on the wards. The patients, however, were quite different both medically and socially, and there were proportionately fewer student nurses present. Other than this, the report procedures and the tasks of the respective staff members were much the same.

In the private accommodations, head nurses were found at their desks or in the treatment room most of the time, but they routinely visited the rooms of the patients at the time of report. Although visiting was brief, the patient was greeted and a question or two were asked. There were few "batches" of new students to be directed; for the most part there were no medical students and there were private-duty nurses for special patients. The head nurses were guarded in their comments to the staff coming on duty. Patients, as a rule, were not openly categorized as problems, but a fussy, vocal, critical, or disturbed patient was usually the subject of comments. While attention may have been called to "Mrs. Jaw," who was overtalkative, excuses were made for her because she was ill and in pain.

Private patients of high social status attracted more attention from nurses and physicians than private patients of lower social status even though their hospital accommodations were the same. The head nurse spent a much longer time with VIPs, who usually attracted supervisors or a nursing administrator as well. We illustrate this type of specified treatment by reference to a case history: Mr. Benton was admitted to a private medical accommodation with a mass in his neck. He was identified upon his admission by the head nurse as an "executive type." The intern told us, "He's a businessman—a very busy man—and it was a sacrifice for him to come to the hospital." The nurse said, "He didn't think it was protocol for the intern to talk with him until he had talked with his private doctor. At first he was reluctant to co-operate and even shooed the doctor out while he was on the telephone." During the diagnostic study his identity as a VIP was communicated to the technicians in the X-ray department by one of the physicians who called out "West, West" when Mr. Benton was wheeled onto the floor. This indicated that a patient was arriving who required special handling. A senior technician on X-ray introduced herself immediately and spent considerable time listening to Mr. Benton's expressions of anxiety. Appreciating his agitation, she tried to reassure him but, at the same time, she was careful to avoid conveying unfounded assurance. Upon the completion of diagnostic studies a decision was reached to perform exploratory surgery.

Although the staff was aware that a medical patient would normally be transferred to a surgical division after surgery, when Mr. Benton indicated his satisfaction with his room and the nursing staff, agreement was reached readily that no transfer would be made. On the day of the surgery, however, the head nurse on the medical division had a day off, and the substitute head nurse, unaware of the agreement, arranged for a transfer from the private medical division to a private surgical division. After surgery Mr. Benton was very upset to discover himself in a different room on a different floor; he began to wonder if the transfer meant he had a serious malignancy. When the head nurse returned the next day and discovered that Mr. Benton had been transferred, she went immediately to visit him and apologize for the transfer. She kept in contact with the pathology laboratory until the report became available. She then personally and immediately transmitted the report to Mr. Benton—"inflammatory, not malignant." The head nurse did not consult the internist, the surgeon, or the house officer before she made her report to Mr. Benton. (It is unlikely that this nurse would have transmitted the report to the patient if malignancy had been found.) When the doctors learned what she had done, they were pleased that she had taken this action and relieved the patient's anxieties. They confirmed the favorable report to him, and he was given medication for his inflamed lymph node and discharged from the hospital promptly. He was most grateful for the care and attention he had received, particularly from the head nurse, although he had expected no less. The head nurse told us she had a personal attachment to most of her patients in the private accommodation: "These patients expect more attention."

This nurse was correct. Such patients did expect attention and they received it. We observed, in the less prestigious accommodations, temporary involvement of head nurses with patients concerning specific problems, physical or emotional, but visiting of this type never was seen in the ward or semiprivate accommodations.

Focused interviews with personnel in the Department of Nursing provided us with detailed quantifiable information on what the respondents thought their relations with the patients were. We systematically interviewed either four or five persons in the Department of Nursing who were responsible for each patient's care. The persons selected for the focused interviews were known to have interacted with the patient most frequently while he was on the division; presumably these individuals knew the patient best. We interviewed one registered nurse on the day and one on the evening shift; we then selected licensed practical nurses, aides, or student nurses for the other interviews. The interviews usually were held on the last day of hospitalization or the day following the discharge so that the nursing staff would have the maximum time to become knowledgeable about the patient but not enough time to forget the patient through working with other patients.

The number of persons in the Department of Nursing who were interviewed about their relationships with patients is presented in Table 25.

TABLE 25. INTERVIEWS WITH NURSING DEPARTMENT PERSONNEL ABOUT PATIENTS, BY ACCOMMODATION*

Nursing Department Personnel	Interviews About Patients by Accommodation			
	Total	Private	Semiprivate	Ward
Registered nurse (staff)	357	137	125	95
Registered nurse (private-duty)	39	32	4	3
Student nurse	47	—	25	22
Ancillary (LPN or aide)	259	109	78	72
Total	702	278	232	192
Mean number of persons interviewed per patient	4.4	4.3	4.3	4.5

*This table summarizes the *number* of interviews we had with each type of nursing personnel in each accommodation.

Even though we timed the interviews carefully to ensure that the respondent would know, hopefully, the most about the patient, it was clear from the beginning to the end of the fieldwork that there was confusion among a considerable number of registered nurses, student nurses, licensed practical nurses, and aides as to which patient we were discussing. This occurred in spite of the fact that we always gave the respondent the patient's name before beginning the interview and that our questions were simple ones about their relationship while this patient was under her care. The confused respondents often told us things appropriate to another patient. Sometimes we had to remind them of the patient's name a second time and give them further personal clues before they could recall the particular person. These vague and confused responses occurred in the face of our efforts to interview only those persons who had the most extensive contact over a period of several days with the patient. Their inability to recall a particular patient or to identify him by name while the patient was still on the division or had been discharged only the day before is some indication of the quality of the interpersonal relationships that existed between different members of the nursing staff and the patients.

We assumed that a patient's diagnosis and the physician's plans for treatment were essential prerequisites for the intelligent care of a sick person. Therefore, we were surprised to learn that less than one half of the registered nurses, about one licensed practical nurse in three, and one nurse's aide in four knew the patient's diagnosis and the treatment his physician had planned for him. Nursing personnel on the wards were most likely to know the medical problems of the patients and what was being done in the way of treatment. The percentages of those who had knowledge of diagnostic and treatment details of ward patients were: registered nurses, 62 per cent; licensed practical nurses, 35 per cent; nurse's aides, 32 per cent. Significantly fewer Department of Nursing staff members on the private and semiprivate accommodations knew what the diagnosis and treatment plans were for the patients under their charge. The percentages for private and semiprivate accommodations, respectively, were: registered nurses, 38 and 41 per cent; licensed practical nurses, 26 and 24 per cent; nurse's aides, 19 and 24 per cent. This greater awareness by nursing personnel of the ward patients' medical problems and plans for their alleviation may be attributable to the fact that the nursing staff carried a greater responsibility for the patients on the ward accommodations in comparison with the semiprivate and private accommodations. A second possible explanation is the severity of the ward patients' illnesses. (See Chapter 9.)

A third possible explanation was volunteered by an internist who knew the hospital very well. He believed the key to understanding the high level of ignorance about diagnosis and treatment plans for specific patients, discovered among registered nurses on the semiprivate and private accommodations, was attributable to the number of private-duty nurses on these services. He thought the private-duty nurses "know" their patients, whereas "the hospital nurses are concerned with administration and housekeeping chores." He asserted that the registered nurses employed by the hospital left the nursing care of the semiprivate and private patients to the private-duty nurses. Our data do not support his *ad hoc* generalization. The private-duty nurses *were* concentrated on the private accommodations, but, if the presence of private-duty nurses explained the low percentage of registered nurses who had a grasp of their patients' medical problems, we should have found a much greater difference between the private and semiprivate accommodations in the percentages of hospital-employed registered nurses who knew about the medical problems of their patients. However, no significant differences were found. Furthermore, later in this chapter we demonstrate that private-duty nurses were also lacking in knowledge about the illnesses of their personal patients.

Registered nurses, in the majority of instances, followed orders given by physicians and did things for patients without knowing why and how these things related to what was wrong with the person under treatment. We do not assert that the nurse and her staff should always have been aware of the diagnostic and treatment details, but we do think it is of interest to note that the diagnosis of a patient's illness and the treatment plan worked out by his physician were not understood by considerably more than one half of the persons who were responsible for carrying it out.

We systematically asked each respondent on the nursing staff if she knew how the patient viewed his illness. We found that only a small proportion of the nursing staff knew anything about the attitudes of the patients toward their medical ills. On the private accommodations 15 per cent of the registered nurses, 5 per cent of the licensed practical nurses, but no nurse's aides had any knowledge of the patients' conception of their illness; on the semiprivate accommodations the corresponding figures were: registered nurses, 6 per cent; licensed practical nurses, 2 per cent; nurse's aides, none; on the wards only 2 per cent of the licensed practical nurses and none of the registered nurses and nurse's aides had any information on the patients' views of their illness. Although the highest percentage of awareness was in the private accommodations and more registered nurses knew about the private patients than those in other accommodations, only one registered nurse in seven had some knowledge of how patients understood their illness.

The emotional component in illness was understood to a limited extent by some three out of four members of the nursing staff. There were a few differ-

TABLE 26. NURSING STAFF'S KNOWLEDGE OF PATIENTS' EMOTIONAL PROBLEMS IN THIS ILLNESS, BY ACCOMMODATION

Nursing Personnel	Patients by Accommodation		
	Private	Semiprivate	Ward
A. REGISTERED NURSES			
Understood emotional problems	3%	2%	5%
Partially understood emotional problems	62	70	71
Did not understand emotional problems	35	28	24
B. LICENSED PRACTICAL NURSES			
Understood emotional problems	3	2	7
Partially understood emotional problems	77	72	79
Did not understand emotional problems	20	26	14
C. NURSE'S AIDES			
Understood emotional problems	2	—	7
Partially understood emotional problems	75	74	76
Did not understand emotional problems	23	26	17
N =	(65)	(54)	(42)

No significant differences.

ences from accommodation to accommodation and from one group of nursing employees to another. (See Table 26.) Those on the nursing staff who had a detailed and extensive knowledge of the patients' emotional problems as they were related to this illness ranged from none among the aides on the semi-private divisions to 7 per cent among aides and licensed practical nurses on the wards. We think it is worthy of note that the aides and licensed practical nurses had as much understanding of the emotional content of the illness as the registered nurses.

The preceding discussion focused on the nursing staff's knowledge of the patients, their illnesses, and their views of their illnesses. Now, we raise questions about relationships between nursing personnel and their patients. *Did the nursing staff identify with the patients? Did they sympathi with the patients?* We express this dimension of possible relationships betw een nurses and patients in terms of empathy. Several points are of interest regarding the data on empathy. (See Table 27.) First, a high proportion of registered nurses, licensed practical nurses, and aides exhibited no empathy toward the patients. Second, the lack of empathy between nursing personnel and patients was characteristic for all accommodations. Third, evidence of empathy was more frequent between nursing staff and the private patients for each of the three nursing groups than for the semiprivate or ward patients. However, the differences in each part of Table 27 were not significant for any group.

We asked each respondent if caring for a particular patient was satisfying to her. We found there were no significant differences among the answers

TABLE 27. EVIDENCE OF EMPATHY BETWEEN NURSING STAFF AND PATIENTS,
BY ACCOMMODATION

Nursing Personnel	Patients by Accommodation		
	Private	Semiprivate	Ward
A. REGISTERED NURSES			
Evidence of empathy	17%	8%	7%
Evidence of some empathy	12	22	19
No evidence of empathy	71	70	74
B. LICENSED PRACTICAL NURSES			
Evidence of empathy	15	9	9
Evidence of some empathy	5	17	10
No evidence of empathy	80	74	81
C. NURSE'S AIDES			
Evidence of empathy	18	6	14
Evidence of some empathy	8	13	5
No evidence of empathy	74	81	81
N =	(65)	(54)	(42)

No significant differences.

we received from the registered nurses, licensed practical nurses, and nurse's aides. Therefore, we present only findings for all nursing staff: Slightly more than one half of the nursing staff believed that caring for patients was satisfying; about one in three thought that caring for patients was satisfying in limited ways; an unqualified no was given by a small proportion in each accommodation, but the highest percentage of dissatisfaction was on the wards. The answers to our questions for private, semiprivate, and ward accommodations, respectively, were as follows: found satisfaction—55 per cent, 61 per cent, 50 per cent; found some satisfaction—40 per cent, 28 per cent, 33 per cent; found no satisfaction—5 per cent, 11 per cent, 17 per cent. Those who did not find caring for a particular patient satisfying gave the following reasons for their dissatisfaction: aversion to the patient's illness and/or the patient's personal habits; the patient's complaints; and arguments between the respondent and the patient.

During our visit to each patient's home after his discharge, we inquired about his reaction to the nursing care he had received while he was in the hospital. (We were not able to differentiate here between the different nursing groups because most patients did not differentiate consistently between registered nurses, licensed practical nurses, nurse's aides, and students.) We found that patients in each accommodation did not get as much satisfaction from the nursing care they received as the nursing personnel did from the care they gave. Fewer private patients were dissatisfied than those in semiprivate and ward accommodations, but proportionately more semiprivate and ward patients were fully satisfied than patients on the private divisions. Overall, two patients out of three were satisfied with their nursing care. The remainder were dissatisfied for one reason or another.

We compared the responses of the nursing staff to questions about satisfaction with those of the patients to find the answers to the following questions: *Did the nurses find satisfaction in caring for the same patients who were satisfied with their nursing care? When a nurse was dissatisfied with a patient, was the patient also dissatisfied with the nurse? Was there a mutually reinforcing relationship operating between these participants in the process of nursing care during hospitalization?* The comparisons revealed that there were significant correlations between the satisfaction of patients with nurses and nurses with patients. On the private accommodations 40 per cent of the patients and nurses were satisfied with one another; the largest segment of the dissatisfied group, 26 per cent, showed mutual disapproval of the relationship in one or more ways. Patients and nurses on the semiprivate accommodations exhibited a similar distribution of likes and dislikes, and the nurse-patient relationship on the wards was similar to that on the other accommodations. The percentage figures for each group are summarized in Table 28.

We have separated student nurses' responses from those of other nursing personnel wherever possible since, of all the nursing staff working with ward patients, student nurses had the most intensive involvement and 60 per cent

TABLE 28. RELATIONSHIP BETWEEN SATISFACTION OF NURSES AND SATISFACTION OF PATIENTS, BY ACCOMMODATION

Accommodation	N	Nurses' Reactions	
		Satisfied	Mixed and dissatisfied
A. PRIVATE PATIENTS			
Satisfied	(38)	40%	19%
Mixed and dissatisfied	(27)	15	26
N =	(65)	(36)	(29)
p < .05; $\bar{C}$ = .47.			
B. SEMIPRIVATE PATIENTS			
Satisfied	(36)	56%	11%
Mixed and dissatisfied	(18)	6	27
N =	(54)	(33)	(21)
p < .05; $\bar{C}$ = .84.			
C. WARD PATIENTS			
Satisfied	(27)	43%	21%
Mixed and dissatisfied	(15)	7	29
N =	(42)	(21)	(21)
p < .05; $\bar{C}$ = .64.			

of student nurses caring for ward patients were dissatisfied with either the patients or their own inability to provide suitable care for them; in contrast, only 28 per cent were dissatisfied with their care of semiprivate patients. The student nurses were dismayed to find registered nurses spending so little time with ward patients. Left largely on their own, the student nurses had great difficulty applying what they had been taught in their classes. They had ideals for themselves and the roles they hoped to play as nurses. Their work assignments forced them to cope with physical and social problems that overwhelmed the patients. Many came to the conclusion that their dreams of playing ministering angel were not going to be realized on the wards. Some senior nurses and physicians were concerned over the lack of supervision and the trauma the students faced on the wards. One physician said, "It's pretty ghastly for these young girls when they are dumped into the hurly-burly wards." The students were startled by the appearance and the behavior of critically ill, lower-status patients. The shock of coming face to face with dire poverty and serious disease in an advanced state was compounded by the failure of the instructors in the hospital's School of Nursing to tell the idealistic teenagers what they should expect on the wards.

We assumed that perceptions nursing personnel had of the patient's social status in the community might be a meaningful aspect of the nurse-patient relationship. To test this assumption, two items of information were necessary: *the nurse's judgment* of the social status of a patient, and *the actual* social status of the patient. When these two items of information were compared we found that three out of four persons in the Department of Nursing were relatively accurate in their placement of patients in the status system. There were few variations in judgment from one category of nursing personnel to another and from one type of accommodation to another. Therefore, we combined into a single table the data on the degree of accuracy exhibited by registered nurses, licensed practical nurses, and aides in judging social status. (See Table 29.)

TABLE 29.   ACCURACY OF NURSING STAFF'S PERCEPTION OF
PATIENTS' SOCIAL STATUS, BY ACCOMMODATION

Nursing Staff	Accuracy by Accommodation		
	Private	Semiprivate	Ward
Registered nurses	91%	65%	86%
Licensed practical nurses	82	54	81
Nurse's aides	82	52	77
N =	(65)	(54)	(42)

Private compared with semiprivate, $p < .05$; private compared with ward, $p > .05$; semiprivate compared with ward, $p < .05$.

Members of the nursing staff had less perception of the social position of semiprivate patients than of either ward or private patients. The private patients were most easily identified because of their choice of accommodation, their clothes, their speech, and their personal physicians. The ward patients were conspicuous in their poverty and lack of private physicians, and the nursing staff was aware that only the poor and the very sick were in the wards. The semiprivate patients were least ill and, on this count, could be more readily ignored; they also were generally viewed as good working people who paid their bills but were not rich. An important finding encompassed in Table 29 is this: The nursing personnel were more aware of the patients' social status than of the patients' views of their illnesses. One registered nurse told us, "They wear their social selves; you have to ask them about their illnesses." Clearly, nursing personnel had a good working knowledge of the social structure of the community.

On the wards the social position of nurses was higher than that of the patients. The nurses on the wards, accordingly, were in a more rewarding status position vis-à-vis patients than in the semiprivate and private accommodations. This status difference was commented upon consistently by the head nurses:

> The ward patients are very glad for anything. They don't expect much. They're very nice usually, but I know if a patient is displaced so that you have a ward patient on the private side nurses frown on it a great deal. The patient doesn't get the care he should be getting because he's a ward type and he's poor. The nurses are kind of Grundy, you know. The ward patient is probably unshaven and unclean and they're not used to this. I think it makes a great deal of difference.

Families of patients also made a difference to the nurses. One nurse reported, "The families of private patients can tattle to the doctors. They can make trouble. The families of ward patients just don't know whom to turn to." The nurses indicated that ward patients seldom made inordinate demands upon them. Except for giving medications and assisting doctors with the acutely ill and dying, registered nurses were rarely present at the side of these patients. Yet, they had a large measure of autonomy in decisions regarding the care of patients under their supervision and they studied the medical records of these patients because they realized the responsibility that the organization of the wards placed upon them.

Formal observations of interrelationships between patients and all other persons who interacted with them were made on the first, third, and fifth day of each patient's stay in the hospital. (Patients who remained less than five days provided fewer than the planned total of twelve observations per patient. We did not observe after the fifth day in the hospital.) The observations were timed between 9 and 10 A.M., 12 NOON and 1 P.M., 3 and 4 P.M., and 7 and 8 P.M. Each observation period was 20 minutes in length. All observations were recorded as they occurred by a trained member of our staff. A special schedule was used so that we had uniform observation data on each patient. The number of 20-minute observations by accommodation and the mean number per patient were:

20-Minute Observations

Accommodation	Total	Mean Number per Patient
Private	656	10.1
Semiprivate	560	10.4
Ward	424	10.4
Total	1,640	10.2

The number of observations differed for each accommodation because the number of patients did, but the mean number of observations per patient showed no significant variation from one accommodation to another.

In drawing upon these data the questions we asked were interrelated: *How much time during an observation period of 20 minutes did registered nurses employed by the hospital spend with patients? Did nurses spend more time than physicians with patients?* These questions are of interest because they involved the three key persons in the patient-care process—patients, physicians, and nurses. They involved also physician-patient relationships and nurse-patient relationships. We gained the impression from our background interviews that, although the nurses were in the hospital for 8 hours a day while the doctors came and went, physicians and hospital administrators believed that the registered nurses spent no more time at the bedside of patients than physicians did. We are now in a position to examine this assertion.

During each 20-minute observation the interaction times between a patient and others were recorded. *Interaction time* is defined as that time devoted by any person to conversation or activity which directly involved the patient. The results are summarized in Table 30. The figures in Table 30 show significantly different amounts of time attending physicians interacted with patients in each of the three accommodations. They reveal also that the amount of time the house staff and medical students interacted with patients and the amount of time staff registered nurses spent with patients were not significantly different from one accommodation to another.

The time staff registered nurses spent with patients was divided into two general kinds of behavior: conversation, and a combination of conversation and activities associated with the care of the patient. The distribution of the interaction time spent by staff registered nurses with their patients is re-

TABLE 30. INTERACTION OF PHYSICIANS AND NURSES WITH PATIENTS DURING 20-MINUTE OBSERVATION PERIOD, BY ACCOMMODATION*

Interaction	Time with Patients by Accommodation, in minutes		
	Private	Semiprivate	Ward
Attending physician–patient	.41	.19	.01
House staff†–patient	.41	.41	.58
Registered nurse–patient	.87	.63	.75
Total	1.69	1.23	1.34

* The figures in this table represent mean minutes spent in interaction.

† House staff includes all interns, residents, and medical students.

corded in Table 31. The ratio of talk only in comparison with talk and task-oriented activities was roughly 1 to 4. Nurses were busy persons; they gave the smaller amount of time to conversation. During most of their interaction with patients they were working and talking at the same time. Work included giving the patient a treatment, performing a housekeeping function associated with daily care such as bathing, or a miscellaneous activity such as smoothing the sheets. (Activities categorized as treatments include the administration of medications or intravenous fluids, assistance with ambula-

TABLE 31. UTILIZATION OF NURSE-PATIENT INTERACTION TIME, BY ACCOMMODATION*

Interaction	Time with Patients by Accommodation		
	Private	Semiprivate	Ward
A. ACTIVITIES			
Treatment†‡	35%	16%	31%
Daily care‡§	23	9	13
Miscellaneous‡§	10	2	2
B. CONVERSATION TOPICS			
Treatment†‡§	36	17	25
Miscellaneous‡§	32	16	18
Daily care‡	21	10	14
Illness‡	19	9	10
All others‡§	26	7	16
Number of observations	(656)	(560)	(424)

* The percentages represent the proportion of all 20-minute observation intervals in which the given activity or conversation occurred.

† Ward compared to semiprivate, p < .05.

‡ Semiprivate compared to private, p < .05.

§ Ward compared to private, p < .05.

tion, and taking and recording vital signs at the bedside.) Treatments connected with the patient's illness were the most frequent activities that brought staff registered nurses to the bedside. Treatment acts occurred in one in three of the observations for ward and private patients and one in six for the semiprivate patients. The semiprivate patients differed significantly from both ward and private groups, but ward and semiprivate patients did not differ from each other on daily care and miscellaneous activities. In all instances, the private patients had more done for them by staff registered nurses than semiprivate or ward patients. It is especially interesting that daily care and miscellaneous activities, things which staff registered nurses were believed by physicians, hospital administrators, and administrators in the Department of Nursing to do infrequently for any patients, were done quite commonly for the private patients. These figures reveal that staff registered nurses were drawn toward the private patients by factors that were not attributable to the illness of the "body in the bed."

In all accommodations the nurse talked most often with patients about the treatment she was providing, but there were significant differences between any accommodation pair. Treatments were discussed least frequently with semiprivate patients and most frequently with private patients. The frequency of appearance of other conversation topics indicated consistent differences between private and semiprivate groups and between ward and private groups. Except for treatment topics, there were no differences between ward and semiprivate groups. In all instances conversations occurred most frequently with private patients. Private patients talked about their illnesses with staff registered nurses twice as often as patients in the semiprivate accommodations. This finding was corroborated in interviews with staff registered nurses who worked on the private accommodations. They reported they had more time to spend with patients for a number of reasons: there were more private-duty nurses; the ancillary staff was better organized, more stable, and had higher morale; and private physicians knew what their patients wanted or needed and gave the staff registered nurses more direction in caring for their patients.

The staff registered nurses cared for and talked with semiprivate patients least often. This finding is consistent with the staff patterns and the less serious illnesses found among these patients. The ward patients required more attention in the way of treatments and monitoring to be certain they were not losing ground or approaching death. Viewed in another way, the ward patients, though sicker and found to suffer physical pain during observations more often than others (34 per cent for ward patients, 21 per cent for private and semiprivate patients), were also less demanding and assertive in their behavior.

The ancillary staff (licensed practical nurses, student nurses, and nurse's aides) were the principal persons who interacted with patients in each accommodation although miscellaneous staff (dietary, housekeeping, and laboratory personnel) also interacted with patients in conversation and task performance. Ancillary staff spent far more time at the bedside of the patients than did the registered nurses. Moreover, they spent significantly more time with ward than with semiprivate or private patients. This is attributed to a combination of conditions: Ward patients were sicker than others, and more ancillary staff were assigned to the ward accommodations than to others. (See Chapter 5, pp. 67–68.) The figures in mean minutes per 20-minute observation that ancillary and miscellaneous staff interacted with patients by accommodation were: private, 1.63; semiprivate, 1.78; ward, 2.39.

The activities of the ancillary staff were divided, in large part, betweeen treatments and daily care. (See Table 32.) Relatively few interactions involved miscellaneous activities even on the private accommodations; however, they were more than twice as frequent on the private as on the semiprivate divisions and almost double what they were on the wards. The treatment activities were significantly different in frequency between the private and the semiprivate divisions only. Daily care and miscellaneous activities were significantly different for all possible pairs.

Conversational topics showed a rather different pattern among the ancillary staff and the patients when compared with the conversations of registered

TABLE 32. UTILIZATION OF ANCILLARY STAFF–PATIENT INTERACTION TIME, BY ACCOMMODATION*

Interaction	Time with Patients by Accommodation		
	Private	Semiprivate	Ward
A. ACTIVITIES			
Treatment†	16%	11%	13%
Daily care†‡§	34	14	28
Miscellaneous†‡§	9	4	5
B. CONVERSATION TOPICS			
Treatment	13	11	12
Miscellaneous†§	5	17	16
Daily care†‡	29	15	24
Illness‡§	5	3	10
All other†	16	10	13
Number of observations	(656)	(560)	(424)

* These percentages represent the proportion of all 20-minute observation intervals in which the given activity or conversation occurred.
† Semiprivate compared to private, p < .05.
‡ Ward compared to semiprivate, p < .05.
§ Ward compared to private, p < .05.

nurses and patients focused on the treatment the nurse was giving to the patient. (See Table 31, p. 234.) Daily care was the subject of most talk between the ancillary staff and the patients. A second difference between the registered nurses and the ancillary staff was that the patients talked less frequently to the latter than to the former. This point is clear from an examination of the frequencies of conversation between patients and nurses in Table 31, section B, and Table 32, section B. Patient-ancillary staff conversation showed the greatest variation from topic to topic among the private patients, centering on daily care and treatments, accompanied by chitchat about weather, recent happenings in the hospital, and news headlines; the ward patients talked about all kinds of topics with the ancillary staff but daily care was the leading one; the semiprivate patients talked less about daily care than the other accommodation groups. Treatment as a topic of conversation between ancillary staff and patients was the only item in which there were no significant differences among the three accommodations.

In addition to staff registered nurses, student nurses, licensed practical nurses, nurse's aides, and ancillary and miscellaneous staff, still another type of nursing personnel—the private-duty nurse—interacted with patients. The role of the private-duty nurse was of concern to some physicians, the hospital administrators, the staff nurses, and, most important, the private-duty nurses themselves. The professional status of the private-duty nurse as a registered nurse who is a specialist in private, personal care implied that she should be a complete nurse in a technical and personal sense. Physicians, however, were unprepared to direct the efforts of the one group of registered nurses with the opportunity, the time, and the training to give high-quality personal care to individuals who could afford to pay their rates while they were in the hospital. Although the physicians expected excellence in carrying out their orders and the patients expected the same, neither patients nor physicians believed that the private-duty nurse should discuss the details of the illness with the patient. This resulted in inadequate direction to the nurse for ideal patient care. Physicians did not even inquire about the patient's condition from the private-duty nurse. As a consequence, she felt ignored and isolated, and her role was filled with strain. The patients knew the doctors were the top authorities who would not yield to the nurse. What was perhaps of greater importance, the patients would not *permit* the physician to yield to the nurse. In turn, the private-duty nurse had to please both physicians and patients if she was to be successful in her business through referrals. Therefore, it was unlikely that anyone involved in this relationship wanted or expected the private-duty nurse to do other than what she was doing.

Private-duty nurses were well aware of the social status of all their patients; this was necessary to their success as entrepreneurs. They did their best work for patients who were of high social status, mentally stable, and had excellent chances of rapid recovery from their illnesses. These patients were popular with private-duty nurses, especially when they were grateful and freely bestowed praise and gifts. The private-duty nurses did least well with low-status patients who faced multiple problems and were not likely to give bonuses. They did poorly also with patients whom they did not like personally or whose medical conditions were distasteful to them. Unpleasant sights and smells were not readily tolerated by the majority of private-duty nurses. Perhaps this was true of all nurses, but the private-duty nurse had the option of refusing to care for a particular patient.

Although the private-duty nurse was technically in the Department of Nursing she was essentially a free-lance agent within the hospital. She provided personal nursing care to the patient who employed her; presumably, the nurse-patient contact was direct, personal, and of benefit to the patient. In all, 47 private-duty nurses were employed for varying lengths of time to care for 20 patients in this study. Fifteen of these patients were in the private accommodations, 4 were semiprivate patients, and one was a ward patient. The three private-duty nurses who cared for the ward patient were employed and paid by the hospital, but the cost was then added to the patient's bill. The other 44 nurses were employed and paid directly by the patients or the patients' families.

During the 20-minute observation intervals, private-duty nurses spent one third of their time outside the patients' rooms. We observed them in the patients' rooms variously knitting, reading, working crossword puzzles, marking little crosses on the bed sheets, or staring into space during one third of their time. The remaining third of their time was spent interacting with the patients. Although private-duty nurses looked after the needs of their patients more than any other group involved in the patient-care process, they anticipated the needs of high-status patients more often than they did those of lower-status patients. In special instances they went out of their way to gain favor with a VIP or a high-status person who might be of possible aid to them. A hospitalized physician who did not need or want private-duty nurses had numerous offers from four private-duty nurses, caring for other patients on his floor, to give him baths and back-rubs, change his bed, and so forth. He accepted several of the offers from the private-duty nurses who sought him out. He remarked to us, "Isn't it peculiar that many patients complain that they can never get a bath in this hospital. I could get several a day either from the hospital nurses or the private-duty nurses of other patients."

We reviewed systematically the relationships between the private-duty nurses and their patients, family members of patients, and other hospital staff.

We classified these relationships into three categories: *harmonious, moderately discordant,* and *severely discordant.*

A harmonious patient-nurse and nurse-other relationship is illustrated by the story of Mrs. Pinna's hospitalization. Mrs. Pinna was admitted to a private room for major abdominal surgery. She was of high social status and well-known in the community for her church and club activities. She was personally acquainted with many prominent business and political leaders in the city, the state, and beyond. Her surgeon recommended that she obtain private-duty nurses and he helped her select three "good nurses" before she was admitted. The nurses viewed Mrs. Pinna as a very pleasant, cooperative, and cheerful person. One nurse told us:

> I give her back rubs, a bath, and help her change her clothing, assist her in walking and going to the toilet, answer the telephone, give her the necessary medications, and listen a lot about her church and club activities. She talks about everything except her illness. Now the doctor has told her special nurses are no longer necessary and that she would be better off without them. I tried to show her how to push herself around to get out of bed and take care of herself so she won't need someone around all the time. She wants me to come back tomorrow but I told her I couldn't because I don't have anyone to care for my baby.
>
> She takes all of my time. Even if I'm not doing something for her, I'm just talking to her. I'm always in the room. I keep busy except when her visitors are there. Then I just stand and she talks to them. It's pleasant caring for her. The family is very friendly and nice to me. Sometimes I have a lot of trouble with relatives, more trouble with them than with the patients, but these people are very nice and I get a lot of satisfaction in caring for her.

Mrs. Pinna's other private-duty nurses performed and felt similarly. Following their departure, Mrs. Pinna accepted floor care. There was no evidence of discord between the private nurses and the hospital staff. We found that these "good nurses" did not know precisely what the nature of Mrs. Pinna's illness was. They had difficulty reading the doctors' notes, and they had very little inclination to do so. The internist and the surgeons responsible for her diagnosis and treatment did not discuss their plans and findings with the private-duty nurses caring for her.

Moderate discord between private-duty nurses and the patient, as well as other persons in the hospital, is shown in the case of Mr. Thatus, a semiprivate patient admitted to the hospital with a question of a coronary thrombosis. His physician ordered private-duty nurses for Mr. Thatus after he expressed fear of the other patients in his room. One suffering from a brain tumor was noisy, abusive, threatening, and hallucinating most of the time. Another was a minister who preached repentance and salvation between the hours of 3 and 5 in the morning. Unaccustomed to these experiences and fearful that the other patients would harm him because they were ambulatory and he was not, Mr. Thatus thought private-duty nurses were necessary to protect him. However, he felt guilty since he believed he was probably the least ill man in his room and the only one to have private-duty nurses. He was very critical of his nurses for their "yakking" and their overbearing, domineering ways of giving him orders to keep him from moving about, but he felt concerned and thought he had no other choice. One nurse, who shielded him from all other patients, the hospital staff, family members, and our data collectors, especially irritated Mr. Thatus. She informed the doctor that neither Mr. Thatus nor his wife wanted to participate in this research. (This statement was not true.) She told Mrs. Thatus that the doctor did not want us to include Mr. Thatus in this study for fear of provocation of his illness, perhaps even causing "severe complications." (This was pure prevarication.) This nurse was partially successful in her manipulations because the doctor and his patient never discussed their participation in this research with each other. The data collector, realizing what was involved, reported:

> We have met up with a formidable watchdog and spouse-surrogate in a private-duty nurse. She does not want us near her or her patient. Mr. Thatus wants to see me but he is scared of her and dependent upon her. Neither he nor I can do anything about it. She has won the first round.

Reverberations about this relationship reached the nursing supervisor and were, in turn, transmitted to an assistant director of the Department of Nursing. The latter, recognizing the nature of the manipulations, reported to us:

> You can expect this kind of thing from this hostile little nurse, but you can deal with it better than we can. We have little control over private-duty nurses, and we are very dependent upon them. The private-duty nurses are a kind of special group deserving of special attention as a part of your project.

We won the second "round" through persistence and a private communication with the physician and Mrs. Thatus.

Severe discord (between patient and private-duty nurse) was most marked when the patients' social status and the nurses' working arrangements were not pleasing to them. This is illustrated in the story of Mrs. Tessa, the one ward patient who had private-duty nurses. There was trouble from the outset in the relationships of Mrs. Tessa with the private-duty nurses. Mrs. Tessa required special nursing following cardiac surgery. The private-duty nurses performed the tasks necessary in the technical care of Mrs. Tessa but they were not happy. One nurse, in particular, revealed her displeasure:

Mrs. Tessa seemed to think she wasn't getting the best attention. She complained a lot—just general complaints. She complained about the needle; you had to force it on her because she wouldn't take it otherwise. She was very uncooperative. She's not a very good patient to ask about, I'm afraid. She expressed her needs poorly and understood her illness poorly. I don't think she had any conception of what she had wrong with her. I tried to explain things to her but after a few words her interest just wandered. I think she enjoys being ill and doesn't want to get well. All the other nurses feel the same as I do about her. I think she is one they should have left alone because she couldn't accept this operation. She's a very difficult patient. She knew little about being admitted to this hospital or how the [private-duty] nurses were to be paid. I think these patients must know that special nurses are going to be caring for them because they have to put down so much money before they are admitted. This is to ensure that the nurses will be paid.

She was most difficult after the operation. When I asked her why, she said she didn't like me. She said she'd talked with some friends who told her she wouldn't be any better after the operation and that she felt terrible. That's about all I can say about this case.

The relationship of Mrs. Tessa's three private-duty nurses with the hospital personnel was harmonious. The nurses had little interest in protecting Mrs. Tessa from anyone. There was no shielding of the patient from our research interests or from the interests of any of the teaching activities carried on in the ward accommodations.

Both harmony and severe discord between a patient and private-duty nurses are illustrated by the experiences of Mr. Gordon. In the month prior to admission he underwent two major calamities. First, a diagnosis of inoperable cancer of the lung was made. Second, he was seriously injured at work and was admitted to the hospital as an emergency case. Because of the severity of his injuries, abdominal surgery was required and a colostomy performed. The fact that he had been injured on the job involved possible negligence on the part of his employer so he was admitted to a private accommodation, and private-duty nurses were requested.

Mr. Gordon was a low-status construction-gang worker. One private-duty nurse said:

Everyone on the floor speaks to him. He's very jolly and friendly with coworkers who seem to enjoy him. He has a large, close family. He seems to get along well with his wife. They all seem to like him a lot. [In fact, family relationships were strained and chaotic.] He's ideal in terms of cooperation. He turns, coughs, and so forth. He never stalls or refuses. He is very grateful for the care and sorry when he has to bother you with a pain.

She went on to tell us: "He is a man who enjoys life. [The patient was a heavy drinker.] I don't think he has any idea of not going on for years."

(The nurses knew that he had terminal cancer but they thought he did not know; they were wrong.) This nurse was given a rating of harmonious in her relationships with Mr. Gordon. However, she was ignorant of his inner feelings and concerns.

He complained that his other private-duty nurses would not read to him and would care only for his colostomy. While these nurses were supposed to be "specializing him" he told the data collector his eyes "weren't so good" and he asked "if my girls are around these days anymore." One of these private-duty nurses reported:

> He doesn't want to go home and would like to stay for six weeks until the colostomy is closed. I think he feels that we are being paid for what we're doing and that's sufficient. He's a joy to care for, he thinks! Too bad he doesn't know. If he really appreciated his nurses he'd bring in a box of candy or something. Other people are more interesting and make more sense. He adds no interest to any conversation. His wisecracks are boring. I can't understand what his wife would see in such a man. He wouldn't do for you or me, but I guess she's happy with him.

Several weeks later when she was on another case this private-duty nurse was still angry that she had been "stuck" with Mr. Gordon. She told us:

> He was ugly, unattractive, and displeasing. He was vulgar in his talking and behaving. He made no effort to avoid exposing himself [his genitals] to me. He had no sense of shame and I was infuriated. The insurance was paying for his care. I guess he expected me to stay but I didn't. By the way, I'm taking care of the mother-in-law of Dr.—— now.

(The private-duty nurse smiled and left the data collector at this point.)

Mr. Gordon's private-duty nurses did not understand what he knew or felt about his illness or its prognosis. They also knew nothing about his disastrous family relationships. (This family is discussed in further detail in Chapter 16, pp. 344–45.) Beneath his superficial manner Mr. Gordon was a frightened, depressed, and lonely man who knew he was approaching death. His crude ways led the nurses to misinterpret his feelings and his need for understanding. He was disappointed that his nurses gave him minimal attention and that they left him before he felt prepared to face his convalescence without them. He knew the insurance company was paying the bill, and he felt he was deserving of "the very finest care money could buy." However, he got little beyond minimal nursing care. Two of his private-duty nurses frankly despised him and made no effort to hide it from him.

We found several causes for discord in relationships between the private-duty nurses and their patients: Mrs. Davis had major abdominal surgery and hired private-duty nurses for postoperative care. She was a high-status person and her nurses pestered her for more things to do to please her. Two days after surgery Mrs. Davis, an independent woman, chose to be left alone. When her private-duty nurses told her that floor care was unsatisfactory for postoperative patients, she became annoyed and told two of them to leave. However, she was poorly prepared for the transition to the care of staff nurses. Accordingly, she was persuaded to call back her nurses and she had to endure the enforced dependency. A source of irritation for Mrs. Davis was the foul odors of her dressings. The private-duty nurses did not help when they indicated how repelled they were themselves. One nurse began the day with the comment, "Well, if you think you smelled bad yesterday, you stink today." Mrs. Davis fired this nurse at the end of her eight-hour shift. The evening private-duty nurse told Mrs. Davis that a nurse had been raped recently on her return home late at night from working in the hospital. This nurse emphasized the risks she was taking to care for patients during the evenings.

Mrs. Kastard was another high-status person who was accustomed to having private-duty nurses whenever she was hospitalized. Her nurses cared for her adequately but annoyed her with their gossip about staff nurses and other nurses and patients. The personal life of one patient, also included in this study, was reviewed in detail by a private-duty nurse who had cared for him. She told Mrs. Kastard about his divorce and remarriage to a younger woman who had fired the nurse because of jealousy. While this gossip was annoying to Mrs. Kastard, the most anxiety-provoking incident occurred when the private-duty nurse told her as she was being wheeled to the operating room that the residents in Anesthesiology were "wrong" in not reviewing her medical history more carefully prior to the administration of anesthesia. Mrs. Kastard became very anxious and retained her suspicions of medical incompetence for as long as we knew her.

The private-duty nurse faced open conflict in her relations with some patients—for example, Mr. Mennan who had elective gall bladder surgery. Private-duty nurses were engaged to give him postoperative care and he demanded all the comforts they could supply. They gave him medications which kept him sleeping most of the time. He was reluctant to follow the doctor's orders for early ambulation. He fought with his private-duty nurses, one of whom requested he sign a statement that he would follow neither the doctor's nor the nurses' orders. He refused to sign this statement and the nurses continued to give narcotics and barbiturates to keep him quiet. Four days after surgery he developed a cough and three hours later he died suddenly from pulmonary embolism. The nurses' notes document the administration of drugs, but they give no hint of the turmoil between themselves and Mr. Mennan. The notes indicate satisfactory ambulation of a cooperative patient, but our data indicate (1) that Mr. Mennan mostly slept under the influence of heavy medication and (2) the doctors were uninformed about the relationships of the private-duty nurses with the patient and their attendant problems. We cannot answer a question which may be raised here: *Was his death from pulmonary embolism brought about by excessive use of narcotics combined with failure to ambulate?*

There was greater stir, but less disaster, surrounding the postoperative care of Mrs. Sexton, a high-status person who recruited her private-duty nurses through friends. The doctors were anxious to ambulate Mrs. Sexton early, but she resisted and the private-duty nurses were reluctant to risk offending her; they also gave her freely the narcotics which she demanded. The conflict between the patient and the private-duty nurses was perceived by the assistant resident who insisted that the use of narcotics be reduced. This angered Mrs. Sexton who then reported the resident's "mistreatment" to her private surgeon. The private surgeon took the side of his patient against the assistant resident. This young man became very anxious that a "black mark" might appear on his record. He, therefore, allowed further drugs to be given. The private-duty nurses, meanwhile, were not assertive in their handling of Mrs. Sexton. She was not ambulated as ordered because it caused her discomfort. The nurses, who were personally involved, were embarrassed to handle her body, especially her buttocks and genital areas. Her perineal area was not cleansed for three days after surgery. During this time, the stench of residual urine, stool, and even a menstrual flow progressed. At this point the private-duty nurses Mrs. Sexton had obtained through her social contacts left for personal reasons, and others were obtained through regular channels. The replacements had no ties of any kind to Mrs. Sexton or her friends. They proceeded immediately, and with great skill, to clean and ambulate her in spite of her protests.

The interpretation of the patients' illness presented difficulties for private-duty nurses: They often were asked questions which they were unable or unwilling to answer, and they were exposed to information the patient might not wish to have them hear. In general, they chose not to discuss the illness with their patients. Several told us they remained ignorant of the details of the illness so they could answer the patient's questions by saying honestly that they did not know. One said, "I find it best to leave all such matters to the doctor. It avoids trouble for me." In so choosing, the nurse maintained better relations with the doctor, but she was ignorant of the patient's illness. The private-duty nurse also avoided close contact with patients in order not to offend physicians who might make referrals to her; this protected her business. (This problem rarely arose for staff nurses; they had no business interests to protect since they worked for the hospital.)

TABLE 33. RELATIONSHIPS OF PRIVATE-DUTY NURSES WITH PATIENTS AND STAFF

Relationship	Per Cent	Weighted Score
A. PRIVATE-DUTY NURSE/PATIENT		
Harmonious	45	63
Moderate discord	38	36
Severe discord	17	8
Total		107
N = 47		
Mean score = 2.3		
B. PRIVATE-DUTY NURSE/STAFF		
Harmonious	30	42
Moderate discord	55	52
Severe discord	15	7
Total		101
N = 47		
Mean score = 2.1		

The performance of each private-duty nurse in relation to each patient and to the hospital was rated on a scale from 1 through 3. A rating of 1 represents severe discord; a rating of 2, moderate discord; and a rating of 3, a harmonious relationship. These relationships are summarized in Table 33. Harmony prevailed in relationships between private-duty nurses and both patients and staff in only three instances out of twenty patients cared for by private-duty nurses.

We conclude that the concern expressed by physicians, hospital nurses, and administrators about the role of the private-duty nurse was justified. Her services were extremely varied and always expensive. She performed in the manner described partly as a result of her isolation in the hospital setting, her fear of being unappreciated, and her realization that she was losing her position because of the introduction of intensive-care units. However, part of her performance was determined by her directing authorities, the patient and the physician. In order for her to perform well, either she had to be an independent professional, which she often was not, or the doctor and the patient had to be competent, vocal, and consistent. We did not generally find these in a combination that produced optimal results. Even among patients who had committed physician sponsorships and private-duty nurses, the performance of the private-duty nurse was less than satisfactory. The physicians and private-duty nurses rarely communicated with one another. The nurse, therefore, often floundered. Although most of their patients enjoyed luxurious hospital accommodations, the private-duty nurses generally believed their patients were dissatisfied with these accommodations (90 per cent of these patients told us they were satisfied). We suggest that the private-duty nurse was reflecting her own dissatisfactions more than those of her patients—she had many complaints about the institution in which she was working. These problems may be viewed as the failure of private-duty nurses to professionalize their role as free, fee-for-service entrepreneurs in the modern hospital. However, that the private-duty nurse failed so miserably at times may mean that she was the one who tried while others did not. She may not have been a failure as much as she was a victim of the medical-care system of which she was a part.

Summary

The physician assigned to the nurse the role of assistant to carry out his orders and deal with housekeeping tasks, while retaining for himself the role of diagnostician and therapist. Nurses acted as liaison for physicians and kept an extensive set of records for patients and the hospital. Discussions by the nursing staff with patients about hospital or home care, the illness, and feelings in general were limited and discontinuous. This was found to be so even in those situations in which patients had private-duty nurses. The nursing staff, then, was committed primarily to the feeding and cleaning of patients and assisting in the diagnostic and treatment procedures.

Registered nurses were primarily administrators of the technology of medicine as ordered by physicians within the framework of the hospital's policies. The nursing staff was task oriented and, by and large, not patient oriented.

Involvement with patients on a personal basis was rare, with the exception of high-status patients in the private accommodations. There was a reasonably harmonious team of physicians, registered nurses, licensed practical nurses, and aides in the private accommodations. Members of this team were generally pleased with their work. The private patients attracted more time and attention than others. They had a much more influential contact with registered nurses than did other patients. They were better understood but not a great deal more so.

In the ward accommodations, the staff had mixed feelings toward the work they were doing and toward the patients. While some of the nursing staff enjoyed the close association with the doctors and the efforts they were making to "save lives," others, especially the student nurses, were dissatisfied, feeling socially distant from the patients and unable to carry out what they considered to be good nursing practices.

From our observations and the comments of young physicians, patients, and nurses, we reached the conclusion that in the ward accommodations registered nurses were "the big executives," looming large in social position and authority in contrast to their low-status patients. The nurses were close in status to the lowest professionals in the medical hierarchy and sometimes superseded them. This was satisfying to the nurses although it created problems in recognizing the limitations of their role and that of the doctors. These role satisfactions were expressed by the head nurses rather consistently. The bonds between the doctors and nurses were stronger in the ward accommodations than elsewhere. Moreover, bonds between the doctors and the nurses were stronger than the bonds between the patients and the nurses. The nurses also showed distinct interest in the social outlets which developed with interns and medical students.

Ancillary staff spent more time with patients than any other group. They spent more time with ward patients than with those in the other accommodations.

Private-duty nurses were *in* the hospital but not *of* the hospital. They represented a partial monopoly, delivering their services primarily to private patients who could pay their charges. Private-duty nurses had ample time and sufficient reason, considering their relationships with patients, the hospital, and the doctors, to engage in manipulative practices to support their own cause. They were occupied in the care of patients only about one third of their time; even then, some patients wished their private-duty nurses would do less for them. The private-duty nurses felt unwanted and unused. To this extent they exhibited guilt in their performances. While their contacts with a small proportion of patients was far more extensive than that of any other group, their involvement with patients was far more problematic. More time was available for nurse-patient relationships, but the use of that time in the interest of patient care was rarely excellent, usually mediocre, and sometimes chaotic.

Each sick person in the study was involved in a network of family relationships which may have influenced the course of his illness. In Chapter 9 we examined the illnesses of the patients from the viewpoint of their possible etiologies. Now, we return to this problem and examine the illness from the perspective of family relationships in order to answer the question: *Did family relationships have a bearing on the development of the patient's symptoms?*

After examining systematically all the data on each family, we made an assessment of evidence on the contribution of the patient's involvement in family relationships to the development of the illness. We found that 47 per cent of the patients' illnesses were linked definitely to family relationships and 53 per cent were not. When we compared our assessments by accommodation, service, and sex, we found no significant differences from one group to another on this question. Therefore, the data are presented without differentiation among these several groups.

When we examined the data on the 47 per cent of the patients whose illnesses were linked definitely to unsatisfactory family relationships we found that only about one physician in three had some awareness of this interconnection. The data on this point are: awareness by the physician of patient involvement in family relationships, 21 per cent; partial awareness, 15 per cent; no awareness, 64 per cent. Stated otherwise, in one out of five cases the physician had a reasonably cogent awareness of the patient's family problems and in one family out of seven the physician had a partial awareness of such problems, but in approximately two cases out of three the physician had no awareness of the relationship between family problems and his patient's illness. This generalization applies only to the patients for whom there was clear evidence of an etiological connection between the illness and unsatisfactory family relationships.

TABLE 34. RELATIONSHIPS BETWEEN PREHOSPITAL MENTAL
STATUS AND MALADJUSTMENTS IN THE FAMILY

	Family Maladjustment		
Prehospital Mental Status	None or slight	Moderate	Severe
Healthy	59%	7%	1%
Moderately disturbed	41	60	8
Severely disturbed	—	33	67
Psychotic	—	—	24
N =	(17)	(55)	(89)
p < .05; $\overline{C}$ = .83.			

In Chapter 10 we demonstrated a link between the mental status of the patient and the problems with which the physician was asked to deal. We now call attention to the interaction between the mental status of patients and the amount of maladjustment in families. The data presented in Table 34 demonstrate that the mental status of the patients was linked very strongly with the amount of family maladjustment. In brief, the patients who were mentally healthy belonged, in very large part, to families in which there was little or no maladjustment. At the other end of the scale, all the psychotic patients belonged to severely maladjusted families. The moderately disturbed patients were members of families that were, for the most part, either adjusted to one another or only moderately maladjusted. The corrected coefficient of contingency of .83 indicates the high order of correlation between mental status and family maladjustment.

The association between the influence of the patient's usual, or prehospital, mental status on this illness and family maladjustment is shown in Table 35. The difference between the data in Table 34 and those in Table 35 is that in Table 34 we present the linkage between the patient's usual mental status and family maladjustment whereas in Table 35 we focus attention upon the

TABLE 35. RELATIONSHIPS BETWEEN MALADJUSTMENT IN
FAMILY AND INFLUENCE OF PREHOSPITAL MENTAL STATUS
ON THIS ILLNESS

	Family Maladjustment		
Influence on Illness	None or slight	Moderate	Severe
None or little	35%	38%	12%
Moderate	35	30	40
Largely determined by mental status	30	30	30
Identical	—	2	18
N =	(17)	(55)	(89)
p < .05; $\overline{C}$ = .45.			

influence we believe the patient's usual mental status had on this illness and how this was related to family maladjustment. Theoretically, a patient's present illness could have been completely isolated from the amount of maladjustment in his family. For example, Mr. Cuffstat who was psychotic belonged to a severely disturbed family of orientation as well as of procreation. However, he was hospitalized for a high fever and an infectious disease. As far as we were able to determine there was no connection between either his usual mental status or his family maladjustment and the contraction of an infectious disease. In this instance, Mr. Cuffstat was recorded in the top right-hand cell of Table 35 (severe family maladjustment had little or no influence on illness). On the other hand, Mrs. Leadon who was psychotic and a member of a severely disturbed family was recorded in the bottom right-hand cell (severe family maladjustment was identical with influence of mental status on this illness). She somatized her difficulties and hoped to find lumps in her breast so she would have an excuse to see her physician upon whom she had an emotional fixation. The corrected coefficient of contingency of .45 in Table 35 indicates a moderate relationship between family maladjustment and the influence of the usual mental status on the illness.

In all but the most urgent of hospital admissions there was some choice available to the patient and his family in the timing of the admission. This gave the family the opportunity to think about the implications of the impending hospitalization: the cost, ways of paying the bills, and the assumption by others of the essential roles of the sick person during the hospitalization and afterwards. When the patient was the sole or principal source of support, hospitalization was a major threat to the family's economic stability. When the patient was the family manager and housekeeper, as most wives were, the other members of the family faced a series of crucial issues: the care of the home, preparation of meals, supervision of the children, and so on through the multitude of large and small tasks housewives performed daily without much attention from other members of the family.

Speaking generally, the members either drew together to cope with the change in family functioning or they withdrew from participation in the problems created by the crisis in the family's affairs. The drawing together to keep the family functioning may be viewed as a *centripetal* force which led to the mobilization of the family's resources to meet the threat to its integrity. However, the crisis of the hospitalization of a principal member could give rise to sharp changes in the social relations that knit the family together into a meaningful quasi-independent social unit within the larger society. Members of the family could seek to move away from the nuclear group and function independently of it. This type of action may be viewed as a *centrifugal* force which isolated some members of the family from others.

We measured the centrifugal and centripetal tendencies in families by assessing the presence or absence of empathy between the spouses, one of whom was a patient, and between the patient and family members other than the spouse. *Empathy,* the ability to understand and identify with another person, is an important element in family relations, especially during an illness. To put oneself in the position of the sick member and help him solve his problems are integral to the social support associated with family life. Ideally, husbands and wives should be empathic in their relationships with one another. In reality, some three husbands and wives out of five exhibited empathy in their relationships; the remainder did to a certain extent, but there were a number of families in which empathy between the spouses was nonexistent.

Mr. and Mrs. Marsh are an example of a couple who demonstrated empathy in attempting to understand the serious problems which they faced. Mrs. Marsh who suffered from optic neuritis was going blind; there was no hope that her vision would return. Mr. Marsh and his children from an earlier marriage were sympathetic toward Mrs. Marsh; they consistently tried to understand the physical and emotional problems she faced as her vision faded. All members of the family realized she was agitated and depressed. The most critical time for the relationships in this family was during and following the hospitalization when Mrs. Marsh was told that there was no treatment available to restore her sight. She could not reconcile herself to the loss of vision and, in desperation, she turned to the hope of a miracle. Mr. Marsh took her to a famous religious shrine in Canada where she prayed and left an offering. This pilgrimage was to no avail, but she returned home more accepting of her handicap and reconciled to her blindness as God's will. The Marsh family then worked as a unit to help Mrs. Marsh cope with the housework and daily problems. Relatives visited regularly and talked with her, doing all they could to help her live in her frightening new environment.

The Cochran family presented no evidence of empathy between the husband and wife and very little between the wife and the sons. Mrs. Cochran described herself as withdrawn from people and liking to keep things to herself. She thought her husband who was outgoing and friendly knew less about her thoughts than "the man down the street." She said he was "thick and stubborn." Mr. Cochran's conception of his role as husband and father was to work hard to support his family. He supplemented his income from his job with a trucking company by taking on extra jobs such as paperhanging and painting on weekends or periods of lay-off. He described his wife as brighter and better educated than he and a dominant force in the family.

Mrs. Cochran had made herself a martyr to her children, but she felt lonely and distant from them and from her husband. Her adjustment to her illnesses and her emotional separation from her family included episodes when she stared out the window and felt alone in the world. When she became too agitated to contain her feelings she rearranged the furniture. (This may have represented a symbolic attempt to rearrange her life to her liking.) The furniture was moved so frequently that it became a family joke; they said no one was quite sure where he would sleep on any given night.

Mrs. Cochran had major physical maladies which could lead to an early death. This was her eleventh hospitalization in either this or the Catholic hospital. Following her first child's death from meningitis she developed mastoiditis and became deaf in one ear. A few months later she began to have symptoms of gall bladder disease. She saw many doctors through the years but no surgery was performed. About seven months prior to the present admission she was admitted to this hospital with a diagnosis of cancer of the lower colon. At that time a malignant tumor was removed. The present admission was for the removal of the gall bladder which, during the earlier operation, was discovered to have stones. Mrs. Cochran was afraid she would not recover from this surgery. Perhaps she wished not to recover, but she told us she had no right to complain since "there's always someone worse off than me."

While Mrs. Cochran was in the hospital, Mr. Cochran took on a job painting a house to earn money for the expenses of his wife's illness. He fell from a ladder, sustaining a compound fracture of the femur of his left leg, and had to be hospitalized. At this time the physicians discovered he had severe ulcers of the stomach. (Mr. Cochran told us that when he fell from the ladder he had been in great pain.)

Although Mrs. Cochran was isolated from her husband and four sons by her illness and emotional state, the family was not socially disorganized. Mr. Cochran fulfilled his economic role as head of the household to the best of his ability. The sons helped around the home with the chores and ran errands. They tolerated Mrs. Cochran's furniture-moving frenzies without understanding them. There appeared to be some empathy between Mr. Cochran and his sons, but there was a social gulf between the husband and the wife and between the mother and the sons.

In several families, we observed severe maladjustment combined with a lack of empathy between the members. Mr. and Mrs. Wallick came from maladjusted families of orientation and they have procreated another. Mrs. Wallick left school after repeating the ninth grade. She was employed in a local factory for several years. After a radical mastectomy she could no longer do the lifting that was required in that work and she then was employed part time as a sewing-machine operator in a shirt factory. Mrs. Wallick was married at 18 to Joe, the father of her two daughters and a son who died in infancy. (The daughters are now involved in deviant behavior, repeating the errors of the parents.) Life with Joe was a "merry-go-round." They had many friends, but he would not settle down enough to acquire the security Mrs. Wallick wanted, such as a home, and he drank heavily. She started going with other men, though still married to Joe, and eventually she started going with her present husband, Sam, who was married to another woman. She later thought Joe should have stopped her, but she divorced him after fourteen years of marriage and married Sam seven years ago. Joe went on occasion to see Mrs. Wallick and his daughters, one of whom lived in a flat above Mrs. Wallick's. He lived sometimes with their elder daughter and sometimes in a boardinghouse for divorced men and widowers. He drank heavily and coughed constantly as he was in an advanced stage of tuberculosis.

Although Sam was a better provider than Joe, he was not the provider Mrs. Wallick had always wanted. He bought her a house and a car, but she had to work part time to earn money for clothing and personal needs. The daughters disliked Sam and tended to lean toward their father. This created problems in Mrs. Wallick's relationship with her daughters as well as with Sam.

The elder daughter completed three years of high school. During the senior year she "got herself into trouble" and had to be married. She had three childern in three years with this man before he left her. As she had no source of financial support she had to live on state aid for some time. She became pregnant by another man, divorced the first one, and immediately married the second man. This husband adopted the three children and they had two children of their own. Although he was steadily employed in a factory and was good with the children, this daughter began to have "an affair with another man." The younger daughter completed high school but, as she had been "knocked up" by the time she was graduated, she married a few weeks later.

Mrs. Wallick's medical history was long and complicated. In order to prevent pregnancy she had a tubal ligation twenty years ago. At that time it was discovered that she had a heart murmur, and the question of rheumatic fever was raised. Five years ago a hysterectomy and an appendectomy were performed at the same time. She told us, "When they open you up, they find other things." Two years ago Mrs. Wallick was admitted to this hospital for a breast mass which was malignant. One breast was removed and it was believed that all of the cancer was excised. Approximately one month prior to this admission, Mrs. Wallick began to have chest and upper-gastrointestinal pains; there were also changes in her stools. The doctors, suspecting gall bladder disease, took X rays and found a stone. Although it was unknown to Mrs. Wallick or to the general practitioner who sponsored her admission, she was in mild congestive heart failure.

Mrs. Wallick was one of the few semiprivate patients who was not accompanied to the hospital by a member of the family or a friend. She came to the hospital alone for the elective removal of the gall bladder. She told us she did not know where her husband was and when she called home no one answered the telephone. She had entered the hospital after a vicious family fight so that she was not surprised when no one came to visit her for over a week. Then her husband came and cheerfully imparted the latest family news: He had burned a hole in the mattress of their bed; he was planning to get another woman and move her into their flat; the daughter who lived upstairs was having an affair with a trucker (she was afraid she would have to care for her mother so she was planning to go to South Carolina with her new "boyfriend" and leave her two children for Mrs. Wallick to care for). After these disclosures Mr. Wallick left the hospital. Mrs. Wallick became violently nauseated and vomited over the bed and on the floor. She seemed rather pleased with her performance and with the attention it commanded.

During the home visit Mrs. Wallick told us about her husband's "girl friends." He was then drinking more, carrying on openly with other women, and contributing little to her support, but she had decided to abide by the situation and not leave him. (Nine months after she left the hospital the hospital bill was still unpaid.) When she became too upset at Sam she invited Joe to visit her because she knew Sam hated Joe. Her younger daughter had moved away, and as Mrs. Wallick's illnesses became more handicapping she became more isolated from all human associations. She was at odds with everybody. Her belligerency, which had become provocative, had led to economic destitution as well as to social isolation.

The Marsh, Cochran, and Wallick families demonstrate the background materials influencing our judgments of empathic relationships or lack of understanding between the patients and their spouses and other family members. We found empathy between the patient and other members of the family, exclusive of the spouse, more frequently in the semiprivate and private accommodations than in the wards. There was relatively little difference among the three accommodation groups when partial empathy was considered. Lack of empathy in the family was concentrated in the ward group. In this respect the ward patients differed significantly from the semiprivate and private patients.

Some sick persons used their illness to gain personal ends within the family; others were the objects of action by the well members of the family to gain control over the sick person. We call the use of illness to gain personal or group objectives *manipulation*. We now present some details on three families to illustrate different facets of the process of manipulation.

The Cascos were a high-status family. Mrs. Casco's medical history was free of serious illnesses and accidents until about eighteen months before she was admitted to the hospital for a hysterectomy. Her appendix was removed at the same time but gall stones which were discovered were not removed. She was put on a diet and had no serious difficulties from the stones. Her current problem began about five months prior to this admission. At a routine checkup her gynecologist found a small lump in her breast. This was checked by another gynecologist who referred her to a surgeon. The three physicians were convinced that the mass was benign, but Mrs. Casco thought it was malignant. She demanded that the surgeon hospitalize her for a biopsy.

Before she came to the hospital Mrs. Casco ordered a private room and private-duty nurses. The private room was available but her request for private-duty nurses was not honored. The surgeon's and the hospital's refusal to locate special nurses for her brought on a series of tantrums. She complained about the registered nurses, the LPNs, and the aides from the beginning to the end of her hospital stay. She fussed about the care she received and the food she was served. She insisted that her husband call the director of the hospital so she would get better treatment.

Mr. Casco spent a large part of every day with his wife during her hospitalization, but she was annoyed that he could not leave his work to be with her from morning to night. One day when he had to go out of town on business, he was in such a rush to get back to her quickly that he was stopped by the state police for speeding.

Mrs. Casco had convinced her parents, her brothers and sisters, her in-laws, and her husband that she was to be pitied because she had a "small uterus" and could never have a child. This was the fulcrum upon which she based pressure in order to control the several members of the different family groups even though she had undergone a hysterectomy some eighteen months before this admission. She was 40 years old but she still used endearing childish terms in talking with her mother and husband, both of whom reciprocated. Her gynecologist referred to her as "a good girl." After discharge the surgeon recalled her as "a nice little girl."

While Mrs. Casco was in the hospital all of the members of her and her husband's immediate families visited her, prayed for her, called her on the telephone, and accepted her many telephone calls to them. Mr. Casco had lunch with her daily. Mrs. Casco tried to rearrange the hospital procedures to suit her needs just as she had restructured the family relationships to fit her need to be pitied, waited upon, and admired. However, the interns and the surgeon did not view her needs as serious. Since her breast biopsy was negative, it was simply a routine procedure. They felt she did not need social support, but Mrs. Casco was a woman who had a need for the support of others. She attempted to carry into the hospital her habit of controlling her family.

Mr. Krames was the son of Russian immigrants. As a child he helped his father, who had no formal education, to collect and sort the old clothes he bought and sold for a living. He completed high school, attended a local college for two years, and then sold clothing, shoes, real estate, and general merchandise. For the fifteen years before his admission to the hospital he owned a retail store in a local slum.

Mrs. Krames came from the same social background. She was trying very hard to escape the humiliation of poverty. She was embarrassed by the small-ness and the location of the store they owned, and she had never been satisfied with their income or their social status. They had two children, an unmarried daughter and a teen-age son. The daughter had graduated from the public schools and the state teachers' college and she taught in a local elementary school. She was unhappy with her work and the slum neighborhood in which they lived. As she was obese, had a greasy-looking complexion, and was much like her mother in her domineering attitude, she had not been able to attract desirable suitors. The son was ashamed of his father and the location of the store. Mrs. Krames made the decisions for all members of the family; they were annoyed by her dominance but were powerless to do anything about it. Once her husband's health began to fail she was particularly unhappy as she realized she never would attain the status she had desired since childhood.

Mr. Krames suffered from high blood pressure and questionable angina for over twenty years. For much of this time he took proprietary and prescription drugs obtained one way or another. His admission to the hospital resulted from a fainting spell while visiting a friend in this hospital. The doctors, fearing a heart attack, rushed him to the emergency service and admitted him to a private accommodation shortly thereafter. Mrs. Krames was pleased with the hospitalization, for she realized she could now get the support of the doctors to replace his self-dosing with a physician's prescribed drug. She also seized upon his illness as an excuse to realize a lifelong ambition—a trip to Florida.

If Mr. Krames had any thoughts of his own he was not allowed to voice them when his wife was present. She blocked his ideas, interpreted them, or changed them. She talked for him, withheld information, and even told the doctors where the pain was. The physician in charge soon became disgusted with her interference.

Mr. Krames' fainting spell in the hospital was caused partly by fear on seeing his sick friend and partly from overmedication of self-administered drugs. He was more concerned about his economic failure than about his health, but this was never admitted. Just before he was discharged, during one of Mrs. Krames' rare absences from the hospital room, he told us that he wondered who was better off—"the man who stays on the bottom without a struggle or the man who tries to get to the top but can't." However, this understanding of his illness in relation to his social position appeared to be Mr. Krames' and his alone.

Mr. Krames did not use his illness to control members of the family, because his wife would not allow this. He was pushed into the hospital and pushed out of the hospital and on to Miami, just as he had been pushed before he was ill. He was too fearful and too firm in his retreat from his manipulative wife to fight back. During his hospitalization the family members showed little or no feeling for Mr. Krames as a person. They viewed him as a failure in the single social role that was important to them, the role of the provider of income and social position.

At the time of the follow-up visit, there was no substantial change in the pattern of interpersonal relationships between the members of the Krames family. The wife and daughter and son were openly hostile and disparaging of Mr. Krames and his efforts to meet the family's financial needs. He sat hunched in a chair while his wife answered our questions precipitously. In sum, Mr. Krames was a man so overwhelmed by the domination of his wife that he could not have used his illness to manipulate his family. Mrs. Krames, in turn, made use of her husband's illness to control his medication and to take the desired trip to Florida.

The Waters family represents a third type of manipulation associated with illness. In this family, illness is used by both the husband and the wife to gain social and personal objectives. The search for favorable social status is deeply involved in the emotional and medical problems of both Mr. and Mrs. Waters. Mr. Waters was an Old Yankee whose family had lived in New England for three centuries. His ancestors were small farmers, craftsmen, and tradespeople. He was born on a farm, attended public schools, eventually worked his way through the state university, and obtained a salaried position in a minor professional occupation. His income had never been large and, in all likelihood, would never be, but this was of no consequence to Mrs. Waters; she inherited a considerable fortune from her father who had come to this country from Eastern Europe as a small child.

Mrs. Waters married her first husband at the insistence of her parents because he was a member of her ethnic and religious group. After her parents' deaths she divorced him in her search for social status in the Yankee segment of the community. Shortly after the divorce, she married her present husband in whom she found the social attributes she craved—a good English name, a university degree, and a profession. Each partner had something to contribute to the marriage that the other desired: His social status was a favorable one (in comparison with hers), and she had the large income that he was not likely to achieve. They lived on a suburban estate, employed servants, and drove expensive air-conditioned cars. There were no children. The couple focused their energies on sophisticated living with the objective of acceptance within the elite core group of the community.

As the years passed, they developed emotional and somatic complaints linked to these efforts. Six months before Mr. Waters' hospitalization (the case we studied), Mrs. Waters had enough prestige and determination to force a prominent surgeon to perform a cosmetic operation on her although it was against his better professional judgment. After her return from the hospital she moped about the house, cared for by housekeepers and nurses. She became more domineering than before. Mr. Waters indicated to us that even a "kept man" can stand only so much. When he developed abdominal pain in the lower right quadrant Mrs. Waters insisted that he be hospitalized. The internist who was their family physician was out of the city and a sub-stitute physician was caring for his patients. This physician complied with Mrs. Waters' demands, as he realized that he should take no chances with this obviously powerful couple, the private patients of a leading specialist whose practice consisted largely of high-status people.

Mr. Waters was embarrassed when he told us about his wife's social ambi-tions. He implied that his hospitalization for an illness, real or imagined, allowed him to get away from his wife's nagging. Throughout the data col-lection he was passive and dependent while his wife was aggressive and manipulative. The physician who knew the family best told us that the relations between the husband and the wife were "the damndest thing you ever saw." This was a marriage in which each spouse manipulated the other, and the husband may have retreated into psychosomatic illness to gain his need for a measure of personal autonomy.

We classified into three categories the use of the illness as a manipulative device to control members of the family: *use of illness by the patient to gain personal ends; use of illness primarily by a family member to bring the patient to terms with his desires;* and *nonuse of illness to gain personal objec-tives.* When the data on manipulation were classified in terms of these three categories, we found no differences among the three accommodation groups. Within the total study group the percentage of distribution was as follows: use of illness as a manipulative device by the patient on his family, 33 per cent; by the family on the patient, 29 per cent; and nonuse by either party, 38 per cent.

While the use of the illness as a manipulative device by the patient, the

TABLE 36.   USE OF ILLNESS AS A MANIPULATIVE DEVICE TO GAIN ENDS
WITHIN THE FAMILY, BY SERVICE AND SEX

| Manipulation of Illness | Patients by Service and Sex* | | | |
	Medicine	Surgery	Female	Male
By patient on family	35%	31%	49%	16%
By family on patient	39	20	16	41
Nonuse by either party	26	49	35	43
N =	(74)	(87)	(81)	(80)

* $p < .05$ for service; $p < .05$ for sex.

family, or a combination of the two was not related to accommodation it was linked significantly to the service in which the patient was treated and to sex. These associations are summarized in Table 36. Viewed from the perspective of service, the manipulation of the family by the patient was dissimilar on the two services. The family manipulated the patient twice as often among medical patients as among surgical patients; almost one half of the surgical patients (49 per cent) did not show any evidence of manipulation either by the patient or the family. From the viewpoint of sex, when the patient was a female, the family tended to be manipulated; when the patient was a male, the family—usually the wife—did the manipulating.

Some patients denied their illness to family members for personal reasons. For example, Mrs. Davis and her husband appeared to be devoted to one another. There was little or no maladjustment in the family, yet Mrs. Davis could not bring herself to tell her husband that she feared she was afflicted with cancer. Four years prior to admission Mrs. Davis had a cancer removed from her lip. The surgery was done during a two-day hospitalization in this hospital. She recovered soon and was free of symptoms until four months prior to this admission. Then she felt a mass in her rectum which did not cause her pain, bleeding, or trouble in passing stools. When she saw her internist, he reported that the mass had probably been there for several months. He was astounded that she would delay so long after the previous experience with cancer.

Mrs. Davis' delay in seeking the medical care was related to her previous experiences with death. She had been very close to her mother but distant from her father. The most traumatic experience in her life occurred when she was 19 years old and her mother was 44 years of age. At that time her mother told her that she had cancer of the uterus and would die soon. No other member of the family was told. During the last four weeks of her mother's life Mrs. Davis was the only person except the physician who knew she had cancer and that it was terminal. Mrs. Davis remembered that period and her mother's death with horror. Some years later, her father died after a coronary

TABLE 37. VISITORS TO PATIENTS DURING HOSPITALIZATION

| Type of Visitor* | Patients by Accommodation | | |
	Private	Semiprivate	Ward
Spouse	100%	93%	74%
Member of nuclear family	77	71	62
Member of extended family	30	39	55
Friend	73	63	18
Clergyman	27	18	3
N =	(65)	(54)	(42)

Private compared with semiprivate, $p > .05$; private compared with ward, $p < .05$; semiprivate compared with ward, $p < .05$.

* The percentages in each column total more than 100 because most patients were visited by more than one type of visitor.

thrombosis. Again, Mrs. Davis was on the death watch, as no one else in the family was available. Now, Mrs. Davis feared telling her husband that she had cancer and she attempted to elicit the doctor's support in "my little game." Mrs. Davis did not lie to her husband; she simply did not tell him the truth about her illness.

All of the patients in our study were visited during their stay in the hospital by at least one person. The most frequent visitor, as seen in Table 37, was the spouse; the next most frequent visitors were members of the nuclear family; members of the extended family—in-laws, cousins, aunts, uncles, nephews, nieces—visited less frequently. When the data in Table 37 are examined from the perspective of accommodation we see that ward patients differed significantly from the other accommodation groups. Friends outnumbered relatives among the semiprivate and private patients, but few friends visited ward patients. The least frequent visitors in all accommodations were clergymen. When clergymen did visit they concentrated among the private patients, with a minor clustering among the semiprivate patients. One ward patient was visited once by a clergyman at the family's request to administer last rites. The private patients differed most markedly from the ward patients in the kinds of persons who visited them. All of the private patients were visited by their spouses; some three out of four were visited by members of the nuclear family as well as by friends; and one out of four was visited by a clergyman. Ward patients had fewer visits from spouses, nuclear family members, friends, and clergymen than the semiprivate and private patients but more visits from members of the extended family.

During each 20-minute observation period we recorded conversations between the patient and any visitors present. In Table 38 we summarize the topics of conversation between the patient and a visiting family member. There were relatively few differences among the three accommodation groups

TABLE 38. TOPICS OF CONVERSATION BETWEEN PATIENT AND VISITING FAMILY MEMBERS, BY ACCOMMODATION

| | Patients by Accommodation | | |
Topics of Conversation*	Private	Semiprivate	Ward
Chitchat of topical interest	72%	67%	56%
Illness of other family members	40	45	35
Illness of patient	42	28	33
Staff of hospital	32	29	25
Daily care of patient	17	17	13
Diagnosis and treatment of patient	14	17	13
Leisure activities, going home, etc.	16	25	17
This research	14	13	8
Number of visitors observed	(494)	(391)	(288)

* The percentages in each column total more than 100 because more than one topic of conversation occurred during a period of observation.

in the topics discussed; moreover, when we corrected for the number of patients involved, we found that there were no meaningful differences in the number of family members who were observed. The mean number of visiting family members observed by accommodation was: private, 7.6; semiprivate, 7.2; and ward, 6.9.

The most common topic of conversation between patients and visiting family members was small talk about the weather, the news, and so on. Our research was not an important topic of conversation, but it was discussed by some patients and visitors; the ward patients gave us the least attention.

The length of a specific conversation differed significantly from one accommodation to another. The conversations between patients and visiting family members were shortest on the wards and longest on the private accommodations. The mean length of spoken conversation on a topic by one person during a 20-minute period of observation which involved the patient and a member of his family in each accommodation was: private, 45 seconds; semiprivate, 34 seconds; and ward, 21 seconds. In general, the private patients talked longest and the ward patients least on a particular topic of conversation.

The differences in length of each person's discussion of a topic in the three accommodations may be attributable to the circumstances surrounding the patients. The ward patients were in three- and four-bed rooms; there was crowding, confusion, and traffic in and out of the room. The semiprivate patients were also in multiple-bed rooms, but there was less noise, more space between the beds, and greater privacy from other patients. The private patients were in single-bed rooms, with little noise and in-and-out-of-the-room traffic. The length of conversations between patient and visitor may have been influenced by these conditions or may be traceable to the different habits of communication within the different socioeconomic groups. In all cases the project observer was present, so there was no variation regarding the effects of her presence.

The families viewed the hospital with mixed feelings. To some it was the principal source of support for the diagnosis, treatment, and cure of diseases: It was a "fine place." "You receive the best of care there." "The doctors know their stuff." To many other families the hospital was a dreaded institution: It was "the place where they cut you up." "It's the butcher shop." "The last stop before you take your last ride." "My mother and father died in that place." "I had two babies die in there." "The wards are terrible; they treat you like a guinea pig in there." Such comments, both positive and negative, reflect the mixed feelings of dread and hope that family members had about the hospital; but when illness struck a loved one there was no other recourse. Those who looked upon a principal member's entry into the hospital with favor were buoyed up by the hope that the physicians and the hospital would be able to solve their health problems so they could carry on their usual activities free from the burden of illness.

The anticipated expense of the hospitalization was upsetting for almost all families but they viewed the hospitalization as a necessity; its costs had to be faced and paid in some way. To postpone care for the illness might bring about greater threats to the family's well-being than the anticipated burden of the hospital bill and (among the semiprivate and private patients) the physician's fees.

The patient usually was accompanied to the hospital by a member of the nuclear family—the spouse being the most common companion in each accommodation. However, among ward admissions only two out of three were accompanied by a spouse. In the semiprivate accommodations six out of seven patients and in the private accommodations eleven out of twelve patients were accompanied by their spouses; the 13 per cent of the semiprivate patients who were not accompanied by a spouse were brought by some other member of their family. Very few private patients (actually only 3 per cent) came to the hospital without a spouse: Mrs. Glass came to the hospital out of pique with her husband and her surgeon, not expecting to be admitted, but the surgeon took the decision out of her hands; Mr. Gordon who was injured severely on the job was rushed to the hospital in an ambulance; and Mrs. Davis was brought to the hospital by her son while her husband was out of the city on a business trip. Viewed statistically, the person accompanying the patient to the hospital at the time of admission was significantly different for each accommodation group. There were no meaningful differences by service or sex.

Death was a real possibility to each member of the spouse pair. All of the husbands and wives were mature persons in middle age or older; some were approaching the time when they were viewed by society and themselves as senior citizens. Each patient and spouse had experienced the death of a parent, a brother, or sister in the family of orientation or a child in the family of procreation. Death had a personal meaning to each one. The patient had been told he was ill and needed to go to the hospital; a considerable proportion of the patients realized they were seriously ill, and admission to the hospital reinforced this knowledge. This realization brought the possibility of death closer than before. Those who were seriously ill came to the hospital menaced by the thought that their worst fears might be confirmed, that they would die in the hospital or afterwards from the effects of the illness or its treatment.

Experience of death in the family, either in the present or an earlier generation, was similar in each accommodation, sex, and service: 36 per cent had experienced death of one or two family members; 39 per cent, the death of three or four family members; and 25 per cent, the death of five or more family members. The present disease was identified with a disease which resulted in the death of some member of their family by 49 per cent of the patients.

Identification with a family member who died from a given disease was real to a person who was convinced that he, too, would die from the same disease. Such identifications were not related to accommodation, sex, or service. Whether or not the family member actually died from the disease was a matter of hearsay, but the person who identified with this family member was convinced of the cause of death of his father, mother, brother, or sister. From this conviction it was only a small step to the inference that the particular disease—cancer, diabetes, heart ailments—was "in the family." Belief in the existence of the feared disease became a part of the family heritage. If a mother, father, brother, or sister was believed to have died from the feared disease, then the patient's thoughts that he also would die from it became a certainty.

The father of Mr. James died of leukemia. About a year prior to his present admission Mr. James developed a swelling on the side of his face next to the ear. The swelling was obvious, and the fear of cancer was great on the part of the patient and his family and the doctors as well. Surgery and a biopsy soon demonstrated that Mr. James had an infectious process of the parotid gland, but Mr. James thought he was marked for death. He told us, "Satan has placed the evil sign on me." The doctors did not recognize his fears and he left the hospital unconvinced by their statements that he would be cured.

Mr. Whalen had cysts excised from his thighs and some rectal polyps removed two years before the present admission. A year later his father died from an embolism associated with gall bladder surgery. For six months before this hospitalization Mr. Whalen noticed blood in his stools, although he was without symptoms otherwise. He was admitted to the surgical service for the removal of a polyp through the sigmoidoscope, if possible, or by abdominal surgery if necessary. Mr. Whalen was convinced he would die from complications of surgery just as his father had. Fortunately, his fears were unrealized, but he told us upon leaving the hospital that he had "two strikes" against him.

Mr. Sykus and his surviving brothers and sisters identified with their father who is reported to have died of cancer. About six months before admission for this illness, Mr. Sykus had an abdominal operation in another hospital because of bowel obstruction arising from a growth on the colon. Although the growth was malignant and its removal locally relieved the obstruction, it had spread beyond the bowel so the procedure was not considered curative. A brother became very worried about the adequacy of Mr. Sykus' care in that hospital; he arranged for admission to this hospital for further diagnostic studies and perhaps treatment, but Mr. Sykus was found to have a metastatic, incurable cancer. He was discharged to await at home the death he and his brothers and sisters were sure would be their fate.

Several men who identified their illnesses with that of a father and/or a brother feared death from heart disease. Mr. Bari, for example, believed nature had marked him for an early, quick death from a coronary seizure. After the death of his mother in his adolescence, he suffered from enuresis and life-long headaches. The later death of a sister and of his first wife also created fears. When he witnessed his brother's death from heart disease four years later, he became convinced that he, too, would die from heart disease. During his hospitalization for a tonsillectomy the doctors, by exaggerating his illness, attempted to persuade him to undergo cardiac surgery. His fears were magnified when his roommate in the multiple-bed semiprivate room had a heart seizure and died with only Mr. Bari present in the room.

Having been exposed to several illnesses, both mental and physical, in his family over the years, Mr. Bari had come to distrust the competence and honesty of doctors and hospitals. He resisted admission to the Catholic hospital, he told us, because he had more confidence in science than in religious ceremonies and magic words. Although he was Italian and his physicians were Italians, some members of his family advised him to get specialists who were not Italian. Mr. Bari felt that he was "caught" between the "scientific" hospital and the "religious" hospital, between physicians of his own ethnic group and others who might have been better, between fear of heart surgery and death from the "family weakness." In this dilemma, he chose to live a little longer with his "diseased heart."

Many women were convinced that they had the same malady which claimed their mother and/or sister. Mrs. Riley had had a coronary thrombosis two or three years before this admission, as well as some upper gastrointestinal difficulties. She was overweight and enjoyed eating. The evening of her present admission she and her husband had gone to a dinner dance in an effort to forget the loss of her sister, dead of heart disease, who had been buried that day. While dancing, Mrs. Riley developed chest pains. Her physician attributed the symptoms to cardiac ischemia. There was no evidence of a heart attack. Eventually, Mr. and Mrs. Riley were convinced by the doctor that her symptoms arose from fears of heart disease but her fears had led her to a hospital admission for a suspected coronary thrombosis.

Mrs. Bear had been in this hospital on several previous occasions. Her mother, a sister-in-law, and a daughter's husband had died from heart disease. Mrs. Bear identified with these people and she was convinced that she was going to die from heart disease. In her case the fear of death from heart disease was realistic, and she later died in this hospital.

Several women were sure that "cancer runs in the family." When one or both parents, a brother, or sister died of cancer, the conclusion was reached that "I, too, will be a victim" of this dreaded malady. Mrs. Schniff's mother died of cancer of the intestine when she was 55 years old. At age 54, Mrs. Schniff was morbidly fearful that she too would die when she was 55. She was aware of the fact that she had had cancer five years before when a radical mastectomy had been performed. She knew during this hospitalization, as she had a second radical mastectomy, that she had cancer. Although the surgeon told her that he "got it all," he recommended radiation therapy at the same time. Mrs. Schniff believed God was punishing her because in past years she had resented her large, pendulous breasts. Her identification was with her mother and "the fate" that took her to the grave. Mrs. Schniff was sure it was her turn to walk down the "dark corridor all alone." She was convinced the "evil eye" had been cast upon her and she could not avoid its consequences.

Cancer and heart disease were the two most frequently fatal maladies in the family with which patients identified, but other disorders were feared intensely by some persons who thought they "ran in the family." These maladies included diabetes, vascular disease, renal disease, and tuberculosis. Mrs. Margillo's mother died from diabetes. Mrs. Margillo had advanced diabetes, vascular disease, urinary tract problems, and heart disease. She knew she had the first two disorders but was not aware that she suffered from the other diseases as well. She was admitted to the hospital for the treatment of gangrene in one toe. She was approaching the age at which her mother died and she was very frightened that she would die in the same way.

Mrs. Hatt had been in reasonably good health until four years prior to admission when she began to develop high blood pressure and other symptoms suggesting renal disease. She told us this malady "runs in my family," and she believed she had progressive kidney disease. She told us that it would kill her just as it had her father and an older brother. Her conviction was so strong that it ruled out any help she might receive from her physician and from medical treatment.

Mr. Jones lost his father from pulmonary congestion which he attributed to working in coal mines in West Virginia and Pennsylvania. Mr. Jones himself worked in the coal mines from the time he was 14 years of age until he moved to this state five years ago. In addition, Mrs. Jones' father and two brothers had died of "miners' consumption" from the same type of work. Both Mr. and Mrs. Jones were sure he would die as their fathers had—from the "curse of the mines." A month after discharge from this hospitalization, Mr. Jones died.

Summary

When comparing the influence of patients' involvement in family relationships to the development of illness, we found no significant difference in accommodation, service, or sex. However, the mental status of the patient was strongly linked with maladjustment in the family and the influence of the patient's usual mental status on the illness. There was a significant difference in the degree of family empathy by accommodation, often in combination with severe maladjustment. There was no difference in any of the three accommodation groups in manipulation of illness to control family members, but there was a significant difference by sex and service: in one half of the surgical patients there was no evidence of manipulation by either patient or family member; in three quarters of medical patients either the patient or a family member used the illness to manipulate the family, but when the patient was a male his spouse usually did the manipulation. These dimensions of the patients' illnesses were rarely understood or dealt with by the professionals.

Ward patients had the fewest visitors and fewer visits from spouses, nuclear family members, and friends than patients on the other two accommodations. There was little difference among patients by accommodation in topics of conversation discussed by visitors. The difference found in the length of discussion of any one topic may have been attributable to the lack of privacy and different habits of communication among ward patients.

A question is raised here that cannot be answered through our research— whether or not the types of diseases discussed in this chapter actually occur significantly more often in some families than in others. Later research may give a definitive answer. Here, we are concerned only with pointing out that in approximately one patient out of two there was a firm belief that a dreaded disease recurs in the patient's family. Psychologically and socially, the disease *was* in the family, and the patient was burdened by the fear that he would "get" the disease. Identification with the dead relative, almost always a person of the same sex as the patient, was a meaningful dimension of the illness. It was overlooked almost entirely by the physician.

Reactions to the hospitalization were shaped by the patient's illness, his prognosis, the accommodation in which he was housed, and, most of all, by his image of the institution. Although the hospital was especially equipped to deal with disease in a positive way, there were many persons who assigned negative connotations to it: the hospital is a place where suffering is concentrated, bodies are mutilated, people are taken to die. When a person was admitted to the hospital as a patient, the negative and positive functions of the institution became confused in his thoughts and in those of other family members. Reactions to the hospitalization were expressed in numerous ways: Some patients verbalized their feelings to those who were willing to listen to their stories—family members, other patients, hospital staff, or, in the instance of this study, the data collectors. Some patients attempted to repress their anxieties by playing an assumed role of bravery (all is well), but their behavior and visage conveyed the opposite message.

During the first interview after we gained the patients' permission to include them in the study, we made a systematic attempt to elicit their thoughts about coming to the hospital. In general, the hospital was viewed as the lesser of two evils. Very few persons came to the hospital anticipating a pleasant experience, but the typical feeling was that if one is "sick enough" it may be the only place where the sickness can be treated properly. The dilemma for the patient was expressed by one man, "Many go in head first—but come out feet first—dead!" This is the cutting edge of the razor: go and/or take the consequences.

We summarized into three categories—*apprehensive, anxious,* and *fearful* —the answers patients gave to our questions about their feelings at the time they came to the hospital. Patients assigned to the apprehensive category had qualms about their illnesses but they did not focus their mental anguish on the hospital. They viewed the hospital positively: it was a place of refuge and treatment; here one could be healed of infirmities. Those in the anxious category had mixed feelings about the hospital and their illnesses: the hospital was the proper place for the treatment of disease, but people suffered here; some people died here; some people were treated badly. Patients categorized as fearful were afraid of the hospital. On admission to the hospital fear was their predominant reaction; some were in a near-panic state. The distribution of the patients' verbalized responses to our questions on reaction to hospitalization is given in Table 39.

TABLE 39. REACTIONS TO HOSPITALIZATION, BY ACCOMMODATION

| Reaction as Verbalized | Total | Patients by Accommodation | | |
		Private	Semiprivate	Ward
Apprehension	27%	25%	24%	36%
Anxiety	21	20	11	36
Fear	52	55	65	29
N =	(161)	(65)	(54)	(42)

Private compared with semiprivate, $p > .05$; private compared with ward, $p < .05$; semiprivate compared with ward, $p < .05$.

Patients less ill were more fearful of the hospital than those who were desperately ill. Thus, ward patients whose admissions were more urgent than those in other accommodations tended to view the hospital as a refuge from their troubles; the illness by comparison was the greater threat. Only 20 per cent of the ward patients whose admission was urgent voiced either anxiety or fear of hospitalization. Overall, one half of all the patients were fearful of admission to the hospital. When we combine the anxious and fearful we see that some three persons out of four were worried about their entry into the hospital.

The general hospital possessed many of the characteristics of total institutions.[1] Between admission to and discharge from the hospital, the patients were subject to the orders of the staff. They were separated from their families. Their street clothes were shed. They were assigned to beds, given numbers, and dressed in bedroom apparel. They had to permit strangers access to the most intimate parts of their bodies. Their diet was controlled, as were the hours of their days and nights, the people they saw, and the times they saw them. They were bathed, fed, and questioned; they were ordered or forbidden to do specified things. As long as they were in the hospital they were not considered self-sufficient adults.

Unless the newly admitted patient had been hospitalized before, he had little knowledge of the hospital's bureaucracy. He was not oriented as to what his behavior in the hospital should be or what he should expect of the hospital. He did not know that the physician controlled most information about his condition and that communications between patients and nurses, aides, and other staff members were rigidly controlled. He had little idea of the way diseases were diagnosed and treated. However, he was cautious in accepting what he was told about his illness because he came to the hospital suspecting that physicians lie to patients, and his experiences in the hospital reinforced this suspicion.

Except in the instance of a committed sponsor willing to take the time, few patients received instructions about the hospital from their physicians; semiprivate and private patients with casual sponsors very rarely received such instruction, and ward patients never got information on the subject. The orientation of patients to hospital routines was left to nurses who were usually so rushed that they took little time to do this. Only the patient in the private accommodation whom they spotted as a "VIP" was briefed about room services, diet, diagnosis, treatment, and personal care. On the wards and the semiprivate accommodations where the patient was assigned to a multiple-bed room, there was little orientation by any member of the staff. The neophyte patient was usually instructed by a "veteran" in the next bed. In these accommodations the interaction of patient with patient was far more common and intense than interaction between the staff and the patient.

Patients saw themselves as sojourners in a strange institution dominated by physicians, nurses, aides, orderlies, technicians, and administrators. Their illness forced them to submit to the orders and manipulations of the functionaries who ran the hospital. The patients realized they were reduced to dependency in this situation and had to adapt to the demands of those who controlled it. They often objected to hospital routine. A common complaint was, "The nurse wakes me up to give me a sleeping pill." Such behavior disturbed the patients, but they knew they could do nothing about it. They made remarks indicative of their awareness of the differences between the staff and themselves: "They're all dressed up in green like men from Mars." "They have a right to joke—they're pushing the wagon." "He can talk—he's not the one who's sick."

Private patients were separated from one another. Each private room was a little home. The patients in these accommodations usually desired privacy and could afford to pay for it. They did not associate with their fellow patients except on their own terms. The semiprivate and ward patients usually could not claim a whole room; they were assigned to a bed in a specific area of a room. These patients soon learned to identify with other patients. They talked to one another. They observed that each had his turn in the hospital routine—each went to the laboratory, the X-ray room, the operating room, physical therapy, and so on, according to orders. When a patient was discharged and a new patient added to a room, a small crisis took place as the group reconstituted itself.

While the patient lay in bed, thinking about the activities surrounding him, he observed and listened to what went on in his room and other rooms. Within a short time he became keenly aware of his own position in a strictly controlled and restricted situation. Generally, each patient sensed when he was "in a bad way" and when other patients were facing the same fateful issue. Mrs. Caputo, for example, told us she was dying of heart failure, and she said a woman in her four-bed room was also dying. The next evening the woman died, and two weeks later Mrs. Caputo died.

Patients in multiple-bed rooms were acutely aware of suffering and death. They were sobered by the discovery of a person missing from their room, especially late at night or early in the morning. They made such comments as: "Now I know what was going on last night; she didn't make it." "Mr.—— was right; he didn't pull through." Many patients for the first time in their lives began to read the obituary columns in the local newspaper. Then we heard such remarks as: "Mine will be there soon." "I wouldn't be surprised to see my own in tomorrow's paper."

Patients were often desperate. Their anguish was aggravated by their awareness that other patients were equally, if not more, frenzied. Those who were disconsolate shared their woes with those around them. In their hours of extreme need the forlorn turned for help to the miserable. Generally, the seeker of help found it in a fellow sufferer who gave him reassurance at the same time he was seeking it himself. They instructed one another on being a "good patient" and on ways to cope with anxiety and fear.

The despair of patients was revealed by their frequent references to the hospital as a jail and themselves as its prisoners. For the panic-stricken patient there was no way out of the dilemma that enmeshed him—he was a prisoner of his illness and under the complete control of others. Women often prayed for relief from pain and suffering while men were more likely to joke about mechanical things, particularly about escape; some talked about jumping out the window. Some spoke openly of suicide while others had fantasies of escape so detailed as to discuss what action the police might take in apprehending and returning them to "jail." One physician also voiced the judgment that the hospital was like a jail. In discussing a patient he said, "She doesn't get along well with the other patients in her room. They, in turn, don't appreciate a vociferous cell-mate."

Anxiety and fear about coming to the hospital were linked with a more generic fear, that of the illness. The threat of the illness to one's normal activities and to life itself was connected to uncertainties about the treatment the physician would prescribe and carry out in the hospital. Treatment was viewed with mixed feelings: There was pain and risk, but these negative responses were countered by the hope that the treatment would result in a cure or at least in the alleviation of pain. Sometimes the treatment was feared more than the disease. Among cancer sufferers the two reinforced each other. Cancer was "the dreaded disease," but the mutilation and pain of surgery exacerbated the victim's fears. When surgery failed or could not be used, there was the final threat of chemotherapy—"those bullets." In either treatment modality, the patient was threatened with mutilation of his body. We found no patient who was wholly free of anxiety when he came to the hospital for diagnosis and treatment. We made an assessment of the level of manifest fear of his illness shown by each patient. All assessments were summarized into three categories: *minor, moderate,* and *severe.* We illustrate each category by a brief statement of a typical patient in the category.

Mr. Church's fear of his illness was minor. He did not anticipate any uncomfortable diagnostic studies or painful treatment in the hospital although he was concerned that he was "in a place where people die." He told us, "The admitting officer must have the information he asks for. If someone dies then he can call in the right one to bring in the box." Mr. Church's wife characterized him as "a great hypochondriac who enjoys reciting his symptoms." His anxieties were generalized, becoming more specific when he talked about relatives and friends who had died of cancer or heart disease. His conversation varied from banter to the possibility that he might be suffering from the early symptoms of cancer. He underwent the diagnostic studies more or less as a ritual and he accepted the prescriptions for his treatment in a similar manner.

Mr. Cheki's fears were rated as moderate. He was admitted to the hospital for surgical repair of an inguinal hernia. He was wary because he realized that the swelling from his hernia could be the tumor of a cancer and he had lost his father and his first wife from cancer. He was suspicious that his physician, a general practitioner, was withholding information from him. However, he thought it best not to ask physicians in the hospital if his fears had any specific basis in his history or the examination. The hours before he was scheduled to go to surgery marked the peak of his agitation. He fingered the bedrail and the sheets between frequent rollings from side to side. When he was informed that spinal anesthesia would be used he became very upset. He told us a friend had become "paralyzed" after spinal anesthesia in preparation for surgery. As he was rolled into the operating room he was wide-eyed and rigid and his fists were clenched tightly. After the surgery he asked for information about his disease. The surgeon told him it was "only a hernia," and he calmed down. From then until his release from the hospital, he was able to control his uneasiness.

We rated Mrs. Potofski's fears as severe. For several years she had been obsessed with the notion that she would die of cancer. When she found a lump in her breast she became panic-stricken. The day we first saw her she told us she was afraid she would die in "this jail." She said, "What a terrible place this." She imagined her breast would be grasped by "metal tongs and cut off like a slice of meat in a butcher shop"; she thought blood would then gush out of her heart, the bleeding would be uncontrollable, and she would soon die. Prior to surgery, she was preoccupied day and night with these fears. She was fearful especially that spinal anesthesia would be used. She thought this might cause paralysis or painful headaches which would not go away. She told us her fears of her illness and how it would be treated, then added, "I think I am going to lose my mind." On her way to the operating room she shut her eyes and repeatedly told herself to be calm. Then she would say to no one in particular, "Oh, I'm so scared. I am so scared." When she was being given the anesthesia she inquired, "How will you know when I'm asleep?" Then she warned the staff, "Don't do it when I'm still awake."

No significant differences by accommodation or sex were found in the extent of the patients' fears of their illnesses. Therefore, we present only the distribution for all patients: 10 per cent showed minor fears; 30 per cent moderate fears; and 60 per cent severe fears. These figures indicate that fear of illness among patients was general. Surgical patients, however, were far more fearful than medical patients. A corrected coefficient of contingency of .68 reveals that the degree of fear of the illness was associated strongly with the surgical service.

The foregoing analyses of the patients' fears of their illnesses present the data solely from the perspective of the patient. When we compared the patient's fears of his illness in relation to the prognosis his physician had made for the illness, we found that the patients' fears were linked significantly to the physicians' prognoses. The figures summarized in Table 40 demonstrate that it was unusual for a patient to have a poor or very poor prognosis and not be fearful of his illness. When we combined those patients who were moderately or severely fearful about their illnesses with those who had poor or very poor prognoses, we found that they represented 94 per cent of all the patients in this grouping. At the same time it was rather common for a patient to have a good prognosis and yet to be burdened by oppressive fears of his illness.

Anxiety was a characteristic response from the time a person learned he had to be hospitalized until he was discharged. Even when he returned

TABLE 40. PATIENTS' FEARS OF ILLNESS, BY PROGNOSIS

Prognosis by Physician	Extent of Patients' Fears of Illness		
	Minor*	Moderate*	Severe
Good	63%	61%	24%
Fair	31	20	21
Poor	—	16	31
Very poor	6	2	25
N =	(16)	(49)	(96)
$p < .05$; $\overline{C} = .56$.			

* These columns were combined in chi-square testing.

home, he might still be fearful. In our close questioning of patients and the systematic observation of their behavior we soon learned to distinguish their worries by their behavior, both verbal and gestural. (We recorded their words and described their actions as soon as possible after they occurred.)

Attempts in the hospital to cope with the mental anguish created by the illness is illustrated by Mrs. Grant, age 44, a surgical patient. Mrs. Grant was a demanding woman from an unstable background who believed that the best defense was to attack. When her anxieties mounted she made unreasonable demands on those around her; when her anxieties lessened she became more reasonable and was able to get along with other persons. Over the years Mrs. Grant had been treated for various diseases in the clinics of this hospital. Weeks before her emergency admission she had been told she should be hospitalized to have the veins in her legs stripped. However, she had no money to pay the hospital for an elective surgical procedure and no one to take care of her nine children while she was in the hospital. Eventually, she came to the Emergency Room with an acute episode of bleeding veins in her legs. At this point hospitalization was no longer elective.

A gulf of misunderstanding and hostility soon opened between Mrs. Grant and the intern in charge. He scolded her for neglecting herself and said she had "no excuse" for allowing herself "to get into such a condition." She became angry and demanded that he treat her "like a lady." As the intern left the room she told the data collector:

This room stinks. I felt like kicking one woman in here out of bed last night because she moaned and groaned and kept everybody awake all night.

Mrs. Grant even made demands of the data collector, saying, "I deserve to be waited on because I'm suffering so much." Her early belligerence intensified markedly as she had to undergo the discomforts of postoperative pain.

Typically, the nurses endured Mrs. Grant's demands, criticisms, and insults for a time and then turned on her. The head nurse told us:

> It's awfully hard to accept this woman with her complaints and demands when the teen-ager in the next bed is dying but not complaining. Last night while another patient in her room screamed with pain Mrs. Grant kept demanding that I adjust her window.

This nurse was observed making unusual efforts to please Mrs. Grant but to no avail. Finally she lost her temper and screamed at Mrs. Grant, "You expect me to be God or something."

Before long, physicians, medical students, nurses, nursing students, aides, and other patients in Mrs. Grant's room were involved in a collective disturbance of her making. The other patients adopted her demanding ways and competed with her for attention from the nurses, physicians, students, visitors, and the data collector. The nurses decided not to move any of them to other rooms for fear of spreading the disturbance. A few days after the surgery when the pain in her legs lessened, Mrs. Grant's fear subsided and her generally disturbed behavior abated. The other patients also settled down.

Some patients faced their fears alone because of lack of understanding on the part of their spouses. Mrs. Grant, discussed above, told us her husband would not understand her problems because he had never understood her suffering during pregnancy and childbirth. Some spouses were too preoccupied with their own problems to be of any help to their mates. Mrs. Panter, age 53, was admitted to the ward surgical service for a hernia. Her husband had been ill for five years. First he had been involved in a disastrous automobile accident, and more recently he had developed inoperable cancer of the prostate gland. With the onset of the cancer he began to drink heavily, became severely depressed, and deteriorated rapidly. Before Mrs. Panter's hospitalization she had begun to find his sexual advances repugnant. He, in turn, became sexually seductive with women in the neighborhood. The struggle with their illnesses and personal problems created a separation between the spouses. Their children, affected by the deteriorating family relationship, also got into difficulties and left home.

Mrs. Panter had been hospitalized several times before for the repair of hernias, prolapse of the uterus, and urinary incontinence. On this occasion her hope for relief was mixed with despair. She trembled as she described her earlier operations and told us about the anticipated surgery. However, the surgical service could not agree with the gynecological service as to which repairs to attempt. Finally, they decided to postpone the surgery until a later time and discharged her with a prescription for medication to take for her urinary tract infection. Mrs. Panter told us, "It took me three months to brace myself for this. Now I have to do it all over again when they're ready." She went home convinced that she had cancer and the physicians were withholding the truth from her. She could not discuss her fears with any family member. Each was encased in his own problems; each could offer only more problems. Obsessed by her fear of cancer, Mrs. Panter sought out her "favorite doctor"—a medical student on her committee. He referred her to the intern who passed her on to the assistant resident. No one understood her fears, and she was rebuffed each time. Mrs. Panter had to face her problems alone.

Speaking generally, ward patients had the fewest opportunities to share the burdens of their fears with physicians, nurses, or ancillary personnel. These patients shared their hospital rooms; privacy was impossible because of the close physical presence of other sick persons who also were attempting to cope with anxieties and fears. The staff members were busy; they moved from bed to bed rapidly; the students rotated from service to service as an essential part of their learning process. Under these circumstances ward patients either kept their fears to themselves or, what was more common, shared them with one another.

Semiprivate patients faced many of the same circumstances as the ward patients, but their rooms were larger and there was greater physical distance between the beds. Moreover, they were less ill than the ward patients, but they also turned to one another for support while facing the crisis of their illnesses. Mrs. Polofski, discussed earlier, illustrates this process.

Through a misunderstanding on the part of the surgeon, Mrs. Polofski was placed in a mixed accommodation—she was a semiprivate patient housed with ward patients. The surgeon left her case and all communications with her family to the house staff. Mrs. Polofski complained to her son about the way the surgeon acted to her, but the son, who had secured the services of the surgeon through an acquaintance on the faculty of the university, assured her that he was a very competent man. Humiliated and isolated emotionally, she resolved to make the best of the situation. She soon became the center of attention of the other three women in her room. She poured out her fears to them until she exhausted herself and her audience. When they could no longer listen to her anxieties about "the metal tongs," "gushing blood," and "my condition," she crept out to the lavatory and spent the night there reading the Bible, crying, and praying. Before she was wheeled up to the operating room, one patient said, "Remember, if your mind gets jumpy, just say a prayer." Another started humming, "God Be With You Till We Meet Again." The others joined in and they all sang "The Old Rugged Cross" as she was taken out of the room.

Among private patients, fears of the hospital, the illness, and treatment were just as great, but families, physicians, and nurses were more often in a position to support the private patient, share his fears, and isolate him from the disturbing troubles of other patients. The story of Mr. Ward, a 57-year-old businessman, illustrates this point. Following the discovery of a tumor in the colon, Mr. Ward discussed his fears with his family and a few friends. He came to believe that he was fortunate to have the tumor discovered early. He was admitted to a private room and arranged for private-duty nurses for postsurgery care. The day before surgery, relatives and friends including two physicians visited to wish him well and offer their assistance if needed. His surgeon came also and went over the details of the surgery, the anesthesia, and the outlook. Mr. Ward who had been fantasizing escape from the hospital was considerably relieved by these assurances. He said, "People tell you that they're not afraid of hospitals but they don't like doctors. The first is not true. They are very very afraid. The second *is* true. They don't like doctors but what they really fear is illness."

For the most part, the anguish and fears of the patients were outside the interests of the physicians and nurses. No ward patient thought there was a physician to whom he could talk about his fears of hospitalization, illness, or treatment. (This is hardly surprising since ward patients, in large part, were cared for by house staff and medical students under the supervision of faculty. As we demonstrated in Chapter 11, Table 30, p. 234, faculty in the School of Medicine had very limited contacts with ward patients.) It may be surprising that six out of seven semiprivate and four out of five private patients believed they could not discuss their anxieties with their physicians. However, when we recall that the attending private physician spent less than one half-minute, on the average, with his patient in the private accommodations and one fifth of a minute in the semiprivate accommodations during a 20-minute period of observation, the proportion of patients who did not think they could share their fears with their physicians is not startling. We infer that social distance characterized the physician-patient relationship among the vast majority of hospitalized patients whether the nexus between them was learning or a fee. Visitors and data collectors who watched the desperate behavior of the patients and listened to their conversations were swept along in the current of intense, sincere, emotionally painful yet awe-inspiring, and tragic efforts of the sick to cope with their fears. These efforts were almost entirely ignored by the physicians, nurses, and other members of the hospital staff.

We turn now to the outcome of the patients' fears following their discharge from the hospital. In the subsequent analyses, the data are limited to the 155 persons who were discharged from the hospital alive. The data summarized in Table 41, demonstrate that the outcome of the sick person's

TABLE 41. OUTCOME OF FEARS OF ILLNESS IN CONVALESCENT
PERIOD, BY PROGNOSIS

| | Outcome of Fears | | |
Prognosis	Reduced	No change	Increased
Good	59%	36%	20%
Fair	26	36	6
Poor/very poor	15	28	75
N =	(68)	(36)	(51)

p < .05; $\overline{C}$ = .60.

anxieties concerning his illness was linked to prognosis. Individuals with
favorable prognoses tended to have their fears reduced. Those with a poor or
very poor outlook exhibited increased misgivings over the state of their
health.

The fears of persons housed on the wards had a significantly different
outcome than those of persons who used semiprivate and private accommodations. Among ward patients, 55 per cent exhibited increased misgivings
over their illnesses in contrast to 27 per cent on the other accommodations;
51 per cent of the private patients showed reduced dread of their illnesses,
while the comparable percentage for the ward patients was 34. We thought
these differences might be attributable to the poorer prognoses among ward
patients. Therefore, we controlled for poor and very poor prognosis in the
three accommodations. Nevertheless, the significant difference between the
wards and the other accommodations reappeared. In the following analysis
we combine the semiprivate and the private patients since they exhibited a
similar outcome of the fears of illness. The data to demonstrate this finding
are summarized in Table 42. Approximately nine out of ten ward patients
with poor and very poor prognoses had increased fears of illness after
hospitalization. The corresponding ratio for semiprivate and private patients combined is about one out of two. A similar trend was found when
patients' good and fair prognoses were compared by accommodation. In this

TABLE 42. OUTCOME OF FEARS OF ILLNESS AMONG THOSE WITH
POOR AND VERY POOR PROGNOSES, BY ACCOMMODATION

| | Patients by Accommodation | |
Outcome of Fears of Illness	Private/Semiprivate	Ward
Reduced	20%	11%
No change	25	—
Increased	55	89
N =	(40)	(18)

p < .05; $\overline{C}$ = .57.

TABLE 43. OUTCOME OF FEARS OF TREATMENT AMONG THOSE
WITH POOR AND VERY POOR PROGNOSES

Outcome of Fears of Treatment	Patients by Accommodation	
	Private/Semiprivate	Ward
Reduced	20%	28%
No change	63	22
Increased	17	50
N =	(40)	(18)
p < .05; $\overline{C}$ = .49.		

analysis one ward patient in four with a good or fair prognosis had increased fears of illness after hospitalization. The corresponding ratio for semiprivate and private patients combined was one in ten.

The outcome of the fears of treatment was significantly different among ward patients in comparison with semiprivate and private patients. A glance at the bottom row of percentages in Table 43 shows that half of the ward patients with poor and very poor prognoses, but only 17 per cent of the private and semiprivate patients, exhibited increased fears over their treatment for this illness during convalescence. The corrected coefficient of contingency of .49 reveals that the relationship between accommodation and the outcome of fears of treatment was not as strong as the association between accommodation and the outcome of fear of the illness demonstrated in Table 42. The preceding analyses indicate that when prognosis was controlled, ward patients had more apprehensions about their illnesses and the treatment they received than either semiprivate or private patients during the convalescent period.

We elicited information from each person about his satisfaction with his medical care separately from his satisfaction with his hospital accommodations and services. In our evaluation of the patient's satisfaction we did not attempt to impose any standard upon the patient; we relied upon the patient's ideas to judge what he expected during the hospitalization. Conceivably, there could have been 155 different standards of evaluation, but we were able to place each person's answers into one of three categories: *fully satisfied, satisfied in some ways and dissatisfied in others* (partially satisfied), or *dissatisfied*. The patient's statements of what was done for him, how it was done, and to what end are summarized in the detailed figures on satisfaction by accommodation, service, and sex in Table 44. Only among the private patients was the level of satisfaction markedly different for females than for males. In the semiprivate accommodations more males were emphatically dissatisfied on the medical service than females, and the reverse was true on the surgical service. No ward female medical pa-

TABLE 44. PATIENT SATISFACTION WITH MEDICAL CARE, BY ACCOMMODATION, SERVICE, AND SEX*

		Service and Sex				
		Medicine			Surgery	
Level of Satisfaction	Total	Females	Males	Total	Females	Males
A. PRIVATE PATIENTS						
Fully satisfied	37%	15%	57%	56%	40%	75%
Partially satisfied	22	31	21	33	50	13
Dissatisfied	41	54	21	11	10	12
N =	(27)	(13)	(14)	(36)	(20)	(16)
B. SEMIPRIVATE PATIENTS						
Fully satisfied	27%	25%	29%	46%	46%	47%
Partially satisfied	27	22	14	36	31	40
Dissatisfied	46	53	57	18	23	13
N =	(26)	(12)	(14)	(28)	(13)	(15)
C. WARD PATIENTS						
Fully satisfied	24%	—	57%	28%	30%	36%
Partially satisfied	11	30%	—	48	50	36
Dissatisfied	65	70	43	24	20	27
N =	(17)	(10)	(7)	(21)	(10)	(11)

* Because of the small numbers in each cell of this table no statement is made regarding significance.

tient was satisfied with her medical care. The males on ward Medicine were approximately divided between the satisfied and the dissatisfied. On the surgical service, ward females and males were proportionately divided among the three groups.

When the percentages for each service by level of satisfaction (the Total columns in Table 44) are studied, gradients appear by accommodation in the proportion of patients fully satisfied with their medical care:

Fully Satisfied	Medicine	Surgery
Private	37%	56%
Semiprivate	27	46
Ward	24	28

At the other end of the scale the complementary percentages are:

Dissatisfied	Medicine	Surgery
Private	41%	11%
Semiprivate	46	18
Ward	65	24

TABLE 45. PATIENT SATISFACTION WITH HOSPITAL FACILITIES, BY
ACCOMMODATION, SERVICE, AND SEX*

| | Service and Sex | | | |
| | Medicine | | Surgery | |
Level of Satisfaction	Females	Males	Females	Males
A. PRIVATE PATIENTS				
Fully satisfied	46%	79%	75%	75%
Partially satisfied	15	7	20	19
Dissatisfied	38	14	5	6
N =	(13)	(14)	(20)	(16)
B. SEMIPRIVATE PATIENTS				
Fully satisfied	25%	50%	39%	73%
Partially satisfied	50	29	46	27
Dissatisfied	25	21	15	—
N =	(12)	(14)	(13)	(15)
C. WARD PATIENTS				
Fully satisfied	40%	57%	40%	64%
Partially satisfied	40	43	30	9
Dissatisfied	20	—	30	27
N =	(10)	(7)	(10)	(11)

* Because of the small numbers in each cell of this table no statement of
significance is made.

This point leads us to the more general question of the patients' reaction
to the accommodations on which they were housed and the care they received while in the hospital. To answer this question we present data on
the patients' reactions to their beds, rooms, food served, fellow patients,
and their visitors, and related matters. Here again, we did not attempt to
impose a standard upon the respondent. During the home visits each patient
was given an opportunity to tell us what he thought of the little segment of
the hospital in which he lived for a time. The distribution of patient
satisfaction with the hospital by accommodation, service, and sex is given
in Table 45. Private patients, female and male, were more often satisfied
with the hospital than the patients in the other accommodations. These
findings reflect the extra effort the staff made to meet the expectations of
private patients. Many private patients realized they were given greater consideration than other patients, but they expected this; if it was not forthcoming
they made demands on the staff for more attention, and the staff responded to
their requests in positive ways. If a staff member did not act as a private
patient desired, the patient usually understood how to make his request known
to the person most able to correct the alleged fault. Even so, one private
patient in three was dissatisfied in one way or another with the hospital's
services. Overall, 17 per cent of the patients were thoroughly dissatisfied with

the hospital whereas 26 per cent were dissatisfied in some way, and 57 per cent were satisfied.

The hospital routinely gave each patient at the time of discharge a questionnaire with his name on it. The patient was asked to indicate his level of satisfaction with his reception, meals, room, nursing care, and treatment while in the hospital. A final question specifically invited criticisms by asking for suggestions for "changes or improvements." At the bottom, a place for signature and date was indicated, and a stamped, addressed envelope was supplied.

Twenty-four patients (15 per cent) returned their questionnaires to the hospital. These questionnaires were then made available to us. We found that returning a questionnaire was not related to service or sex. However, it was related to accommodation: more than twice as many semiprivate and private patients as ward patients returned their questionnaires. Some of the patients failed to report their dissatisfaction even though they returned questionnaires to the hospital and were dissatisfied. Thus, while four of the patients who returned the questionnaires told us they were dissatisfied with their nursing care, three of them reported on their questionnaires that their nursing care was "good." Similarly, eleven of the twenty-four reported to us that they were dissatisfied with their medical care but none made any reference whatever to this in the questionnaire. Nine of the twenty-four stated to us that they were dissatisfied with their hospital care and accommodations, but only four of the nine made any reference to their dissatisfaction on the questionnaire. No patient who was satisfied according to our data reported dissatisfaction in the comment card.

A further analysis was made to learn if returning a questionnaire was related to patient satisfaction with nursing, medical, or hospital care. In no instance was a meaningful relationship found. The discrepancy between what the patients expressed to us and what they wrote over their signatures for the hospital's perusal may be attributed to the fact that we had gained their confidence and they trusted us not to identify them with a particular complaint.

On our assessment schedule we asked this question: *Did anything happen during the hospitalization which raised the patient's anxieties or fears regarding the practice of medicine in this hospital?* To answer this question we re-examined the entire dossier we had accumulated on each patient and family. In 61 cases the patient, the spouse, and other family members reported no anxiety-provoking incident or event. In the remaining 100 cases the patients, alone or in coordination with a spouse or other family member, told us about one or more happenings while they were in the hospital which raised their anxieties about the practice of medicine in this hospital. We made a content analysis of each event or experience in terms of the principal source of the complaint. Six categories were used for this purpose: (1) *technical competence of the physician was in question*; (2) *physician failed to communicate appropriately with the patient about his illness and its treatment;* (3) *technical competence of the nurse was questioned*; (4) *nurse failed to communicate appropriately with the patient about his illness and its treatment*; (5) *patient experienced a lack of coordination in the organization of the hospital*; (6) *presence of sickness and death was upsetting to the patient*. We illustrate each type of anxiety-provoking incident before presenting the statistical summaries.

1. *Physician's competence was questioned.* Mrs. Cochran, a semiprivate patient with a casual sponsorship, had had a malignant tumor of the large intestine removed surgically in this hospital seven months prior to her current admission. During that operation gall stones were found. She was readmitted to have her gall bladder removed. After surgery Mrs. Cochran developed back pains suggesting kidney complications. This was investigated by X-ray studies and consultations with a urologist. During this admission, a second operation was then carried out by a general surgeon and the urologist, during which a suture was found obstructing the ureter. Although Mrs. Cochran was never told the truth about the surgical error, she guessed that something had gone wrong because of what "the doctor did at the operation." Her suspicions had been aroused when she found her surgeon reluctant to discuss details with her. She questioned the need for the urologist "unless someone goofed." She said, "I never had kidney trouble before in my life. I finally asked him [the surgeon] what happened. He just looked at me and didn't answer."

2. *Physician failed to communicate adequately.* Mr. Mundy, a ward patient, told us he was ill-informed about his condition. Although many studies were done he was given little information before or after the tests. He was very anxious, but he felt he could not ask the physicians questions because of his lack of education. The assistant resident told us:

> We try to work up the patient thoroughly and to apprise him of a minimum amount of knowledge so we can accomplish the study without alarming him greatly. I would say this patient understood his illness very poorly. I mean the causes for what he has could be life-threatening but there is no need to bring these things up. While we think of them ourselves, we usually tell the patient very little about what is going on. I don't know if it's right or wrong but that's the way we do it.

Mr. Mundy was upset by the lack of communication. He felt he was being used as a guinea pig for the doctors "to learn on."

3. *Technical competence of the nurse was questioned.* Mrs. Adler was

admitted to the private accommodation for some diagnostic studies as a convenience to her internist. The physician ordered castor oil in preparation for X rays. The floor nurse gave the castor oil to a woman in another room who had the expected results while Mrs. Adler had to remain in the hospital an extra day because of the error. In the middle of the second night, Mrs. Adler was awakened from a comfortable sleep by a nurse with a hypodermic needle in hand pulling the bedcovers aside. Mrs. Adler was very fearful of injections because she believed a friend of hers had died suddenly after an injection given in a hospital. She told the nurse her doctor had assured her no injections would be given. The nurse felt certain of her orders but when Mrs. Adler continued to object, the nurse asked her name. Mrs. Adler told us, "When I gave her my name, the nurse then said she was in the wrong room and left. I didn't sleep any more that night."

4. *Nurse failed in communications.* Mr. Bickford was worried about becoming a victim of nurse-error in the administration of medications, especially those given by injection. He asked the nurses what they were giving and how much. They refused to discuss his questions. He believed patients deserved to have their questions answered. He told us specifically that nurse-error in administering medications could be avoided by the alert patient. While the nurses' ways of dealing with him were understandable in terms of their responsibilities to other patients, the communications failure resulted in marked increases of Mr. Bickford's fear about his care in the hospital.

5. *Lack of coordination in organization.* Mrs. Rose spent 75 minutes in the corridor outside the operating room strapped to a stretcher cart waiting to have her breast removed. She noticed another woman being pushed from the operating room with a blood-stained bandage on her chest, and she became very fearful. The telephones rang constantly and the nurses, busy in other rooms, delayed answering them. Mrs. Rose overheard two nurses conversing as they worked. One said, "This place ran all weekend. They're still doing an aortic aneurysm in Room 5. We have delays and instrument problems this morning." The other nurse said, "Yes, and I see the secretary is sick too."

When Mrs. Rose was finally pushed to the operating room and placed on the table under the light, the surgeon said, "The record seems to be missing. We should have an internal examination. How long have you had this?" Mrs. Rose responded, "About two years." The anesthesiologist asked, "Which side?" Mrs. Rose told him, "Left side." The physician doing the surgical preparation observed an abdominal scar and asked, "Who operated on your gall bladder?" Mrs. Rose said, "It wasn't my gall bladder. It was my ulcers."

6. *Exposure to sickness and death.* Patients in multiple-bed rooms are forced by circumstances to endure the pain and fears of their roommates. Earlier in this chapter we referred to Mrs. Caputo's realization that one of

her fellow patients was dying. While this small drama was being enacted, a third seriously ill woman moaned throughout the night, "Oh Jesus, take me. Oh, Jesus, come to me." Between these calls for divine intervention in her illness she prayed loudly for surcease from her travail. Earlier, we called attention (Chapter 11, p. 239) to the problems of Mr. Thatus in a multiple-bed room on the semiprivate accommodation of the medical service. For present purposes it is enough to point out that he was hospitalized with a supposed heart attack. His roommates were a disturbed minister who preached salvation before dawn each morning, an hallucinating patient who made violent threats against an imaginary enemy, and a man suffering from a brain tumor. These fellow patients were all ambulatory and Mr. Thatus was not. He was told to lie still and rest his heart. In desperation he hired private-duty nurses and eventually requested transfer to a private room to avoid the disturbing environment created by his roommates.

The 100 persons who reported one or more anxiety-provoking incidents while they were in the hospital cited a total of 164 such events. From the viewpoint of physicians, nurses, and hospital administrators, these complaints may not have been justified, but when a patient reported misgivings over some experience he usually had a good and sufficient reason to be uneasy. We observed a number of events that were anxiety-provoking when they occurred but which the patients *did not report* then or at a later time. For example, we saw two nurses and an orderly drop one of our patients from a mobile stretcher onto the floor, but the patient did not complain about this.

Although those who reported anxiety-provoking incidents were scattered throughout each accommodation and both services and sexes, when we compared the number of reported events by accommodation, we found significantly more such events reported from the wards than from either the private or semiprivate accommodations. The distribution of the 164 complaints made by 100 patients is presented in the following tabulation:

Subject of Complaint	Distribution of Complaints
Physician	
Technical performance	18%
Communication with patient	45
Nurse	
Technical performance	4
Communication with patient	3
Hospital	
Incoordination of activity	22
Exposure to sickness and death	8
Number of complaints	(164)

There were relatively few complaints about nurses. Complaints regarding the incoordination of activities in the hospital were concentrated in the ward accommodations, as were the strong reactions to exposure to sickness and death, with a smaller number of complaints from the semiprivate patients. Nearly one half of all complaints were about communications of physicians. In the light of other findings in this research, such as the amount of time physicians spent with patients and the pattern of communications between patients and doctors, this is not surprising. Nor is it surprising to find that complaints about the technical performance of the physician and the lack of coordination of the hospital staff are traceable frequently to physician-patient communication failure.

Summary

Patients' fears in the hospital were related to the prognosis of the illness and the treatment anticipated. The accommodation in which the patient was housed set the conditions for coping with fear. In the private accommodations, patients had some advantages: more access to knowledge about their condition and comparative isolation from the despair of their fellow patients. In the semiprivate accommodations, patients had less access to knowledge about their condition, less control of their environment, and more exposure to the raw experiences of other patients. However, they did have substantial trust in others. Generally, at least one person cared enough for them to show concern and understanding.

The ward accommodations were outstanding in several ways in the matter of the fears of patients: Ward patients were the poorest, sickest, and most crowded in the hospital. They were cared for by a rushed group of physicians and nurses, who, under the circumstances, showed little concern for them beyond care for the physical condition. These patients were generally deprived socially. Their hospital care reflected and extended that deprivation. More than patients in other accommodations, they harbored terrifying memories and suspicions which were then added to their long list of life's adversities. While fears of illness and treatment and life misfortunes were found in all groups, the situation of the ward patients was most trying. Accustomed as they were to adversity, ward patients found their accommodations oppressive.

Physicians rarely showed consideration in matters dealing directly with the emotions of the patients. Few of the hospital staff recognized the high anxiety level which patients and family members exhibited. Defective communications with physicians were the most prevalent basis for anxiety-provoking events. Ambiguities, evasions, and, most of all, simple absence of communication about matters of vital concern to patients were the source of many complaints. The lack of organization in the flow of work was upsetting, especially on the wards where physicians, nurses, and medical and nursing students combined learning and demonstrations with the care of the patients. Finally, anxiety-provoking events which revolved around communication failures of physicians with patients and lack of coordination in hospital activities were concentrated among ward patients.

Satisfaction and dissatisfaction with medical care were linked to accommodation and sex on each service. In all accommodations and on both services, women reported the least satisfaction with the hospital or were more vocal in their complaints than men. The level of satisfaction fell off and the level of dissatisfaction rose on both the medical and surgical services from the private to the semiprivate and the ward accommodations. Overall, only 17 per cent of the patients were thoroughly dissatisfied with hospital services; semiprivate and ward patients were more dissatisfied with hospital services than private patients.

NOTE

1. Erving Goffman, *Asylums: Essays on the Social Situation of Mental Patients and other Inmates,* Aldine, Chicago, 1961.

PART V IMPACT OF THE ILLNESS

The IMPACT OF A PHYSICAL ILLNESS UPON A GIVEN individual depends, broadly speaking, upon a number of factors—the nature of the illness, the treatment received, and the character of the person. The illness may be acute or chronic, disabling or not disabling. The prognosis may be good, clouded with uncertainty, or poor. Treatment may be successful, ineffective, or harmful. The sick person may be well-adjusted or mentally disturbed. Each of these factors alone or in combination may affect the ways an afflicted individual reacts to an illness experience. Recognizing multiple variables that may influence the effects an illness has upon a person, we limit this chapter to three areas of impact: (1) the probable prognosis, (2) the outcome of the treatment each patient received, and (3) the individual's feelings about his illness as he related them to his work and his family.

As medical knowledge has increased, the ancient practice of forecasting the outcome of an illness, known in medical circles as *prognosis*, has become refined. However, it is still an art, and the problematics of the effect of a disease on a given individual are calculable only within broad, poorly defined limits. We are aware of these limits as well as of the amount of indeterminacy within them. Nevertheless, at the time of each patient's discharge from the hospital we made an assessment of the likely outcome of his illness. Our estimate was based upon the diagnosis of the disease, the demonstrated course of the illness, and the patient's condition up to that time.

We used three prognostic categories: *good, fair,* and *poor*. Patients whose illnesses did not reduce their life expectancy were given a prognosis of good; included in this category were patients with such disorders as hernias, curable infectious diseases, and uncomplicated gall bladder diseases. A prognosis of fair was given to patients whole life expectancy was reduced, in our judgment, from a slight to a moderate amount; this category included a wide range of conditions such as high blood pressure, heart attack uncomplicated by congestive heart failure, diabetes, and so forth. Persons who had marked reduction in life expectancy, were faced with an early death, or had died in the hospital were given a prognosis of poor; patients with advanced heart disease, metastatic cancer, and the complications of such disorders were included in this category.

We compared the prognoses of the patients by sex, but no meaningful differences appeared. Although there were no significant differences in prognosis by accommodation, the ward patients had a larger percentage of poor prognoses than either the semiprivate or private patients. Prognosis *was* linked, however, to the service in which the patient was treated: Surgical patients had a good prognosis twice as frequently as medical patients. On the other hand, the proportion of medical patients with a fair prognosis was three times higher than that of surgical patients. Approximately two out of five medical and surgical patients had a poor prognosis. These differences were traceable to the existence of numerous chronic diseases among medical patients, while surgical patients tended to have correctable conditions which did not lead to a disabling life-threatening complication.

All the patients entered the hospital for the diagnosis and treatment of a presumably physical problem. We found that 98 per cent were treated for the illness or condition which gave rise to their admission to the hospital. Speaking generally, when an individual was afflicted with a disease his bodily processes were usually altered so that he was placed at a disadvantage in comparison with a healthy person. The objective of treatment was to check or reverse the natural course of the disease or the physical condition which handicapped the sick individual. Ideally, treatment for a disease should reduce the disadvantage under which an afflicted person suffered in comparison with a healthy person of the same age and sex. At a minimum, the treatment administered should not obstruct the application of whatever residual capacity the sick person possessed to adjust to any handicap he may have had as a consequence of being diseased.

Success of treatment depended upon the following of several steps: early recognition of symptoms, evaluation by physicians, accurate diagnosis, application of prescribed treatment, and the availability of an effective remedy. The failure of the treatment administered may be attributed to faults in any one of the steps in the diagnosis and the treatment of the disease, or it may be attributed to lack of an effective therapy. In evaluating the outcome of the treatment each patient received, we utilized the medical record and the responsible physician's statement of the patient's condition and probable prognosis, combined with the patient's demonstrated performance in his family and/or on the job after he had convalesced from his hospitalization.

We decided upon four categories for evaluating the outcome of treatment:

cure, substantial improvement, limited improvement, and *no improvement or treatment harmful.* The first category, *cure,* includes patients who recovered fully from such diseases as pneumonia, acute cholecystitis, hernia, and appendicitis. Persons in this category were diagnosed and treated correctly and cooperated with those who cared for them. An effective remedy was available and was applied, and they did not have disabling or complicating emotional disorders.

In the category *substantial improvement,* the illnesses consisted primarily of gastrointestinal and cardiovascular diseases and selected early malignancies. The patients received definite benefit from their treatment; disabling emotional problems were infrequent.

In the *limited improvement* category, the patients suffered from chronic diseases, usually a physical malady but occasionally from an emotional disorder. Often there was a combination of physical and mental disorders. In any case, regardless of the nature of the illness, the therapy offered in the hospital resulted in little improvement in their condition.

In the last group, *no improvement or treatment harmful,* the patients suffered from advanced physical diseases, emotional disorders, or a combination of the two. This category included patients with advanced heart, malignant, and metabolic diseases for which treatment was not available or was unsatisfactory. Also patients with *ad hoc* diagnoses (10 per cent of all patients) were included in this category. In general, these patients were not diagnosed accurately, and their treatment reflected this fault. Patients who received *ad hoc* diagnoses and those who exhibited psychic symptoms that were not recognized as such by the responsible physician presented a series of difficulties for the assessment of the success or failure of treatment. In these patients we discerned a pattern of failure of communications between patients and physicians and often between the patient and the family. This failure resulted in the commitment to misleading diagnoses and corresponding treatments which no one involved, especially the physician, felt free to abandon if he were "to save face." The treatment administered resulted in failure in every instance. This is, perhaps, understandable since a disorder that was primarily emotional was brought to the attention of practitioners whose orientation was organic and technical. These practitioners did not undertake the diagnosis and treatment of emotional disorders whether or not they were associated with physical disorders. To illustrate this process, we refer again to the case of Mrs. Helms whose story is told in Chapter 9, pp. 162–63.

Mrs. Helms was admitted to the hospital for study of "fainting" episodes which she had reported to several physicians. While in the hospital she indicated to us her apprehension that she might be mentally ill, but she did not communicate this concern to the doctors, nor did they reveal to her their growing suspicion that a psychiatric diagnosis was the most fitting one. Both private physicians and house staff told us at first that Mrs. Helms could not possibly be "a crock"; she was "too pleasant, sweet, and kind for that." Later they changed their minds but, as she was a private patient, they chose not to risk offense. They told her she was suffering from a "vascular insufficiency" of the brain which might be caused by a defective heart valve or "the narrowing of a blood vessel at the base of the brain." Frightened by this diagnosis, Mrs. Helms left the hospital troubled not only by her personal and family problems but also about the possibility of heart or brain disease. Her fears mounted enormously. Although she was angry at the physicians for offering her no treatment, she had to live with the consequences which were partly of her own doing.

In her manipulations Mrs. Helms misled her husband deliberately; she wanted more attention from him and, above all, she wanted her daughter to come home. In addition to the tales she told her family, Mrs. Helms communicated selectively with the doctors. She led them away from a psychiatric diagnosis by exaggerating her physical symptoms while avoiding any discussion about her emotions. Caught up initially in a network of faulty communications the physicians were not permitted to help; later, when they became aware of the *ad hoc* diagnosis, they would not help. They felt they had done their job and wanted Mrs. Helms to stop pestering them like a dissatisfied customer. In making her rounds from one doctor to another Mrs. Helms was offered different medications, all of which were ineffective. The physicians found themselves allied with the pathological forces in the family. Eventually, Mrs. Helms became an invalid cared for by her daughter. In short, this patient exhibited marked ambivalence toward her disease as well as toward her husband and the physicians. Because of this, the performance of the physicians was altered in significant ways.

For the 157 patients who were given treatments of one kind or another the outcome of treatment was unrelated to either accommodation or sex, but

TABLE 46. OUTCOME OF TREATMENT, BY SERVICE

Outcome of Treatment	Total	Patients by Service Medicine	Surgery
Cure	17%	4%	28%
Substantial improvement	30	27	32
Limited improvement	31	34	29
No improvement or treatment harmful	22	35	11
N =	(157)	(71)	(86)
p < .05			

it was associated significantly with service, as shown in Table 46. Patients who were rated as cured were concentrated heavily on the surgical service, while those in the substantial improvement and limited improvement categories were divided about equally between the two services. Three times as many patients in the *no improvement* or *treatment harmful* category were found on the medical service as on the surgical service.

To determine if the 155 persons who survived hospitalization had a handicap or disadvantage with which they had to cope, we directed our attention to the following question: *Was the person able to resume his usual social roles as the breadwinner or homemaker subsequent to his convalescence?* Our answers to this query involved two related but essentially different assessments of the data: (1) the *source* of the handicap, if any, and (2) *its extent* in limiting the performance of social roles in the home, on the job, or a combination of the two. To determine if the person was handicapped we looked to the source of his disability, if any. We attributed disability to one of three conditions: (1) *physical impairment* clearly linked to disease processes (the source was primarily organic in nature); (2) *personality disturbance* primarily (principally a socioemotional problem with which the patient was attempting to cope through somatization processes); and (3) *any combination of physical and socioemotional disturbances.*

A person could be impaired by physical handicaps in varying degrees while his performance at work and in family roles could be unrelated within wide limits to physical impairments. When physical handicaps were present and clear in their disabling influence, the source of the impairment was attributed to this condition. Conversely, even though a person had a capable body he might be handicapped in his role relations and functions by nonphysical factors in his character structure. Therefore, a person could be handicapped both physically and emotionally, and each of the conditions might interact to limit his ability to perform as a member of the family and work groups.

Concomitant with the assessment of the source of a patient's handicap, we categorized its extent. Three levels of disability were recognized in the performance of social roles: *slight impairment, moderate impairment,* and *severe impairment.* We illustrate how we combined the source of the person's handicap and its extent by sketching briefly some case histories. Mr. Petaro, a barber, was admitted to the surgical service because of pulmonary emboli. Ligation of the inferior vena cava prevented further embolization and Mr. Petaro recovered satisfactorily. Because he had residual difficulties with edema of the lower extremities, he had to reduce his hours of work. He cooperated in the use of elastic stockings and the limitation of his standing so that he could still work and produce income while preserving his health. He continued to make a satisfactory living as a barber and performed effectively as a father in his family. We categorize him as a person with a physical handicap and a slight impairment of the work role.

A physical handicap with a moderate performance disability in work roles is illustrated by Mr. Melara, a factory worker who suffered from paralysis caused by a disease of the central nervous system. Following two years of progressive weakness, he lost his job. He was unable to return to his job after discharge from the hospital because there was no effective treatment for his disease. This problem was discussed in the family, and it was decided that Mr. Melara would remain at home and manage the house and children from a wheelchair while Mrs. Melara went to work to support the family. Although this adjustment was a painful one for all concerned, it was evident that a maximal utilization of residual capacities was achieved. Thus, although the physical handicap was severe, the performance disability was moderate. Mr. Melara performed satisfactorily as a parent even though he could not take the father's usual position of breadwinner.

A physical handicap with a severe performance disability is illustrated by Mr. Shirmen. This man had abdominal cancer and liver metastases; he became jaundiced and was wasting rapidly. Unable to work or carry on his former tasks, he spent most of his days in bed, wholly dependent upon his family as his illness progressed and death approached.

Mrs. Neilson is an example of moderate performance disability attributable to a personality disturbance. As a child Mrs. Neilson had been reared in the "strict life of a good Catholic home," in which sex was never discussed. Courtship was avoided until her late twenties when she married a Protestant with whom she was in conflict over religious matters. She talked to us about her "nervousness" which began after her last pregnancy five years before her hospitalization. Although the biopsy for a breast mass proved the condition to be benign, her "nervousness" became much worse. She told us that "dirt," particularly on herself, was upsetting and she found it very important to keep the two children and her home immaculately clean:

> When I don't feel well and especially when I'm feeling nervous I take a bath, dress up, fix my hair, fly around the house, clean things up, and get it in order. Then I go out with my girl friends or go shopping or do something that is fun.

Mrs. Neilson rarely went out with her husband, but she was often out of the house taking care of "my nervousness" when her children needed her. Mr. Neilson usually came home from work, had supper, watched television, and went to bed. They rarely had intercourse because, as Mrs. Neilson told us, she was always "so exhausted." She told us that her husband was understanding of this. However, while Mr. Neilson and the children tolerated the unreliability of her impaired performance as wife and mother, Mrs. Neilson was, nonetheless, handicapped as a homemaker.

Mrs. Pellbro was a patient whose personality disturbance gave rise to severe performance disability. For ten years Mrs. Pellbro suffered from periodic vomiting by which she controlled family situations. She had been hospitalized three times in another hospital for a gastrointestinal disorder similar to that which resulted in her present hospitalization. On this occasion as before, a family argument was followed by uncontrolled vomiting. She vomited continuously for five days until she was brought to this hospital. Once admitted, Mrs. Pellbro continued the same pattern of behavior. She was the instigator of arguments with the doctors who would not recommend the surgery she desired, and she indulged in shouting fits when she couldn't get her way. She had to be cared for like a child. She refused to follow the advice of her physician and demanded to be discharged. After her return home, Mr. Pellbro was obliged to assist her in the simplest of household tasks in order to get them done. Family members complained about her behavior, but they were powerless to stop the cycle of an angry mother who vomited when she didn't get her way. Mrs. Pellbro told us she felt "like a martyr" to the family. When she made them feel guilty about the "hard work" she did, she thought she was "justifying" her illness. Regardless of family compliance with her wishes, she believed she would never get well until she had an "operation" on her "stomach."

Mr. Natrio illustrated the combination of physical and socioemotional conditions accompanied by severe performance disability. (Other details of this case are discussed in Chapter 11, pp. 222–23.) Following surgery for basal cell skin tumors, Mr. Natrio's position in the family, which had been troublesome for several years, became worse. He retired prematurely from his job and spent most of his days reminiscing with drifters in a local park. He could not meet mortgage payments on his home, so his son, after much arguing, took over the house and the payments. Mr. Natrio argued continuously with his son, daughter-in-law, and wife. He no longer functioned in his former occupational role, and his family role performance was reduced to a problematic level.

Twenty-one persons who had recovered from uncomplicated restorative surgery or acute infectious diseases (13 per cent of all patients) showed no disabilities in the performance of their usual social roles. These individuals were mainly males who had been housed on the private and semiprivate accommodations. They were eliminated from further analysis. Thus, there remained 134 survivors of hospitalization who had a physical or psychosocial handicap: 13 per cent were disabled for physical reasons, 15 per cent were disabled by primarily organic factors, 51 per cent by conditions attributable primarily to psychosocial factors, and 21 per cent by a combination of physical and psychosocial factors. There were no significant differences by accommodation, service, or sex among these persons. Moreover, there was no significant relationship between the source of the handicap and the extent of the disability. Approximately one person out of four had a handicap traceable primarily to organic disease, while one person out of five had a disability traceable to both his organic condition and his personality structure. It is interesting to note that although 51 per cent of the handicapped persons were afflicted primarily with psychosocial factors, they were not treated for their psychological difficulties.

The next analysis answered a question pertinent to these observations— *Were the medical problems which gave rise to the hospitalization the same as those which caused the performance disability?* To answer this question, we re-examined the records of the 134 persons with some performance disability. Then, we categorized our answers into three groups: *related, partially related,* and *not related.* Although we found no accommodation or sex differences, there were clear-cut service differences, as the data summarized in Table 47 demonstrate. These differences result from the fact that more medical than surgical patients were troubled by emotional problems which brought them to the hospital. While medical and surgical patients had the same amount of disability attributable to psychosocial disturbances following convalescence, these disturbances were influential in bringing about hospitalization for 91 per cent of these medical patients but only 18 per cent of the corresponding surgical patients. The relevant data to support this conclusion are presented in Table 48. When we consider the diseases and problems discussed in Chapter 10, the findings in Tables 47 and 48 should not be a surprise.

We carried this analysis one step further to learn if the posthospital disability of persons, whose handicap was attributed primarily to psychosocial factors or a combination of psychosocial and organic factors, was linked to their prehospital mental status. The 21 persons without a handicap and 17

TABLE 47. RELATIONSHIP OF REASON FOR HOSPITALIZATION TO
PERFORMANCE DISABILITY, BY SERVICE

Reason for Hospitalization and Disability	Total	Patients by Service Medicine	Surgery
Related	58%	72%	45%
Partially related	19	25	12
Not related	23	3	43
N =	(134)	(67)	(67)
$p < .05$			

TABLE 48. RELATIONSHIP OF PSYCHOSOCIAL DISABILITY TO
CAUSE OF HOSPITALIZATION, BY SERVICE

Psychosocial Disability and Cause of Hospitalization	Total	Patients by Service Medicine	Surgery
Related ·	29%	50%	9%
Partially related	25	41	9
Not related	46	9	83
N =	(69)	(35)	(34)
p < .05			

persons whose handicaps were clearly traceable to physical factors were eliminated from the analysis under discussion. This left 117 persons who were
coping with a disability of one kind or another, the origin of which had a
marked psychosocial component. The data on the interaction of prehospital
mental status and posthospital disability are summarized in Table 49. An
examination of the figures in this table shows that as one moves from the
"Healthy" column to the "disturbed" columns the impact of mental status
on performance disability becomes heavier: Two out of three severely disturbed persons suffered from moderate disabilities that were largely psychosocial in origin; among the psychotic persons, three out of four were severely
disabled in the performance of their social roles.

In preceding paragraphs we have been concerned with handicaps which
disabled the sick person in one way or another to perform work and family
roles. We turn now to the meaning the illness had to the patient. In centering
attention on the subjective feelings the patient expressed to us about his ability
to perform his usual work and home roles, we look at the data from the
perspective of the patient so that we can answer the general question: *What
was the impact of the illness upon the person's feelings toward his work and
family?* The patients' answers are grouped into five categories which are

TABLE 49. PREHOSPITAL MENTAL STATUS AND POSTHOSPITAL PERFORM-
ANCE DISABILITY OF PSYCHOSOCIAL ORIGIN

Degree of Performance Disability	Patients by Prehospital Mental Status			
	Healthy	Moderately disturbed	Severely disturbed	Psychotic
None or mild	100%*	52	4	—
Moderate	—	36	67	25
Severe	—	12	29	75
N =	(5)	(25)	(67)	(20)
p < .05				

* The five persons in this cell of the table were combined with those in the
moderately neurotic category in the chi-square analysis.

discussed below: (1) *improved,* (2) *did not change,* (3) *became worse,* (4) *became much worse,* and (5) *deteriorated catastrophically.*

1. *Improved.* Six patients (4 per cent) were placed in this category: five were private patients, one a semiprivate patient; three were men and three women; four were surgical and two were medical patients. Each of these persons suffered from a disease that was curable. The four surgical patients were operated upon and their difficulties were corrected. Specific therapies were available for the diseases of the two medical patients. At the time of the home visit, all of them had resumed their usual roles in the home and on the job. The treatment had relieved them of their symptoms and their worries over the illness.

Mr. Tischler was typical of patients in this category. At the age of 59 he suffered progressive discomfort from a growing lump in his groin. He did not discuss it with his wife or anyone else until six weeks prior to his admission to the hospital when he began to fear that it was cancer. When Mrs. Tischler heard about it, she too was fearful of cancer but she did not mention this to her husband. She did, however, discuss his condition with a close friend who was the secretary of a local surgeon. Through this friend, Mr. Tischler was introduced to the surgeon, who examined him, made a diagnosis of a hernia, and recommended hospitalization for repair of the hernia. Both Mr. and Mrs. Tischler thought the surgeon was trying to be kind to them since Mr. Tischler, in their fearful fantasies, was afflicted with cancer. The surgeon scheduled admission to the hospital for elective repair of the hernia.

After the surgery the hernia disappeared, the incision healed normally, and there were no complications. Mr. Tischler then realized that the surgeon had been accurate in his diagnosis and prognosis. He returned to work in three weeks, free from pain and all disability. He resumed his usual functions at home. He was free also of the anxiety that the lump in his groin might be cancer. His state of mind improved just as the condition of his body did. He was pleased with the outcome and grateful for the services of his surgeon. Worry free, he approached his work with added vigor.

2. *No change.* Twenty-six per cent of the patients were placed in this category. They had illnesses prior to hospitalization that were of short duration though sometimes very troubling. Recovery from the acute episode of the illness was accompanied by improvement in their states of mind as well as the restoration of their health. Overall, these individuals exhibited little change in their feelings toward their work and families as a result of their illness.

Mr. Bickford, a 51-year-old salesman, developed abdominal pain suddenly. He telephoned his regular physician who arranged to meet him immediately at the emergency service of the hospital. Mr. Bickford was taken to the operating room, and a Meckel's diverticulum, which had caused inflammation and bleeding, was found and removed. He convalesced rapidly. After his return to work his view of his illness was that it had caused temporary inconvenience, a moderate amount of suffering for a limited time, and a minimal economic loss as his colleagues and friends had carried on his business during his brief hospitalization. He thought his recovery was complete and he probably would have no complications from the illness or the treatment. Mr. Bickford's life changed very little from the onset of the illness to the time of his recovery and return to work. He felt that the illness was an episode which had passed and would not return. He was not burdened by any unusual fears about the strength of his body, his ability to carry on his work, his home life, or his usual recreational activities.

3. *Became worse.* Twenty-three per cent of the patients were placed in this category. These individuals felt worse after than before the illness. The bodies of some persons in this category were damaged by disease or treatment. Whether their bodies were less whole or not, they felt disabled in various ways. Often the chief handicap was traceable to the belief that they were peculiarly vulnerable to illness. They believed they had been weakened by the illness, the treatment, or both, and they feared they might suffer more in the future from the same disease or a different one. These patients invariably exhibited symptoms of anxiety and depression concerning their work and family.

Mrs. Dahlia illustrates this type of patient. At age 41 she was admitted to the hospital with congestive heart failure. Over the years she had suffered from hypertension, diabetes, obesity, and toxemia of pregnancies but she had never been so severely ill and disabled before. Mrs. Dahlia had known she suffered from diabetes for ten years although she denied its significance until the present hospitalization. Now, she had begun to think she would soon die of diabetes as her mother had.

For complications of her various maladies Mrs. Dahlia had been to numerous general practitioners; one finally referred her to a specialist who then admitted her to the hospital. During the interviews Mrs. Dahlia belittled the severity of her condition by emphasizing that she was being treated as "queen for a day." She responded satisfactorily to treatment for diabetes and soon was discharged from the hospital. She resumed her usual family activities, encouraged by her response to treatment and pleased with the new physician whom she viewed as more competent than her previous ones. She was, nevertheless, uneasy about the relentless progress of her symptoms. She approached her household tasks and the supervision of her children with much less vigor. During her convalescence she referred repeatedly to her body "falling apart." She told and retold the story of her mother's illness and compared that story with her own unfolding experience with illness. She recalled also that several family members who had suffered from diabetes had died in their forties or fifties. She said, "Time is running out. Diabetes gets you sooner or later, but in my family it gets you early." In brief, Mrs. Dahlia was not destitute either physically or emotionally, but her feelings toward her family and her work were worse after her hospitalization than they were before.

4. *Became much worse.* Twenty-seven per cent of the patients were placed in this category. These persons had strong feelings concerning their handicaps, their future, and their ability to carry on their work and family lives. Sometimes it was physical disability that resulted in discouragement and depression; sometimes it was the fear of illness, such as heart disease or malignancy, which made them feel much worse than before their illness experience. As their illnesses progressed their handicaps became greater. The impact of increasing disability was an overriding consideration in their efforts to cope with all family and work situations. The burdens of life were closing in on them, and the weakening person often anticipated death with mixed feelings.

Mr. Stauffer was a typical patient whose feelings toward family and work became much worse after the illness than before. As a child Mr. Stauffer had felt that he was compared unfavorably with his brothers and sisters. He entered college hoping to study engineering, but he did poorly and left. He then went to technical school, successfully passed the courses, became a draftsman, and worked for different firms. However, he never succeeded in his ambition to develop his own business.

He then married and had three children. The burden of family expenses over the years was so great that he was not able to meet them even though the family income was supplemented by Mrs. Stauffer's salary for clerking in a local store. While the family achieved some degree of success as the years passed, Mr. Stauffer came to view himself as a failure; his wife and children concurred in this view. The Stauffers' daughter married successfully. The sons led difficult lives: The older son failed in college as his father had done, and the younger son developed chronic osteomyelitis and had to leave school in the tenth grade.

At age 45, Mr. Stauffer was saving money to make the necessary down payment on his own business when he suddenly developed acute chest pains. He recognized immediately the symptoms of a heart attack and called the doctor who diagnosed coronary thrombosis. He recovered after the hospitalization but his illness experience confirmed his conception of himself as an inferior person and a "failure." He realized that his illness had ended any possibility that his career ambitions would be achieved. He viewed the illness as heralding the end of youth and the beginning of old age and, perhaps, an early death. He had, for years, seen himself as inferior mentally; now he felt inferior physically also. He thought his sons were failures too and that he had accomplished nothing he had set out to do. Mrs. Stauffer, who had always dominated her husband and family, belittled him even more and over-powered him with her criticism. Mr. Stauffer became preoccupied with the fear that another heart attack might occur and kill him. In brief, Mr. Stauffer's attitude toward himself predisposed him to interpret the illness in this way. Regardless of his actual recovery from the heart attack, he felt he would never be the same again.

5. *Deteriorated catastrophically.* The 20 per cent of patients who were placed in this category were severely disabled by disease and each had a poor prognosis. All were unable to work; sometimes they had been wrenched from their families and placed in institutions for custodial care with the expectation that they would be there for the rest of their lives. They were devastated personally and severely depressed. A lingering death often con-tributed to the catastrophe for both the individual and the family. Enmeshed in the destruction of their lives by illness and powerless to alter the situation, the patients were convinced that they were a burden to their families and to all those who cared for them. This is illustrated by the story of Mr. Deo.

Mr. Deo's first episode of tuberculosis began when he was 38 years of age. At that time, the illness was controlled after a brief sanitorium stay and he had been able to work until recently. At age 51, the illness recurred but drugs, which had successfully controlled the infection, were no longer effective. He was admitted to this hospital for evaluation of surgical treatment for pulmo-nary tuberculosis. The surgeons decided that removal of the infected lung would be the treatment of choice; however, removal of the diseased tissue would be accompanied by the loss of some functioning lung tissue. This might result in such severe pulmonary insufficiency as to cause death. The surgeons, there-fore, viewing him as a "poor operative risk," declined to operate. Following the hospitalization, Mr. Deo went back to the private sanitorium where differ-ent drug combinations were tried with little success. After a few months he was sent home on drug therapy. Shortly after his return home he requested transfer to a public clinic for follow-up care since the drugs there cost less than those at the private clinic.

The transfer soon resulted in recommendation for hospitalization in a public tuberculosis sanitorium. Mr. Deo found it difficult to endure the institutional controls and began to view the sanitorium as a prison. After 18 months he signed out, against medical advice. He had resolved for better or worse to take his chances at home.

From the onset of tuberculosis Mr. Deo suffered from many social and economic problems. His first wife committed suicide shortly after he first be-came ill, leaving him with two young children. His second wife remained with him as his children grew up, married, and left home. He was able to support them and provide for their education through high school. During the course of his second hospital stay and sanitorium care, he gradually came to realize he would never work again. He could not return to work partly because he was an infectious risk and partly because, since he had so little functioning tissue remaining, he was incapable of working. This was very upsetting to him. He felt discouraged and depressed and talked a great deal about wanting to get back to his job. Although he had been assured that his job was waiting for him, he felt this might not be so. He told us, "It all depends on whether the factory wants to make it easy or hard for me. They may just want to get rid of me."

After his return home, Mr. Deo found life there much like that in the public hospital. He could no longer spend any amount of time with his family. He was told not to sleep with Mrs. Deo and he was separated from his children and grandchildren because of the fear of spreading the tuberculosis organisms. Mr. Deo saw himself as an "outcast" from his family and an "untouchable" in society. In brief, this man moved from the role of family head and wage earner to the point at which he was socially and physically isolated, stripped of his savings, and fully dependent economically on other people. He became an invalid who had only his wife to shield him from life as an "untouchable" in a public sanitorium. He dealt with his illness by expressions of anger, grief, depression, and marked anxiety. For him, there was nothing left.

Viewed statistically, there were no significant differences in the patients' reactions to their illness experiences by accommodation, service, or sex. The person's subjective reactions to the effect of the illness on his work and family life were linked to the type of disease he had, its duration, and the degree of his disablement rather than to his sex, the type of treatment he received, or the area of the hospital in which he was housed. The widest difference in the reaction of the patients to their illnesses was by the service in which they were treated. Patients with minor correctable ailments had only a mild reaction to their illnesses; these were found more often on Surgery than on Medicine. Of the patients on Medicine, 10 per cent were improved or unchanged, while 26 per cent faced catastrophic consequences from their illness. Surgical patients in the latter category totaled 18 per cent.

The feelings a patient had regarding his illness were linked to the degree of physical handicap he had suffered from his illness. To determine this, we cross-tabulated the physical disability of the 155 patients who survived to the time of the home visit with their subjective reaction to the illness. This tabulation produced a corrected coefficient of contingency of .71; this is a strong association. We infer that the physical effects of the disease process were the primary source of the sick person's feelings about his inability to perform his usual roles in the family. As the disease process went on, one's capacity to function decreased and the sick person's anxieties rose until he was completely incapacitated. In the words of Mr. Deo, "I am just a little bit alive."

Summary

This chapter measures the impact of the illness on the patient, based upon the probable prognosis, the success of treatment, and the person's subjective feelings toward work and family roles. We found that both prognosis and success of treatment were unrelated to hospital accommodation or sex, but they were linked significantly to the hospital service on which the patient was treated. In discussing the person's subjective feelings toward work and family roles, we analyzed the type of disability, its source, and its extent in performance of work roles. We found no significant differences by accommodation, service, or sex in any of these relationships. We found no accommodation or sex differences in the relationship between problems which gave rise to hospitalization and those which caused the performance disability, but there were clear-cut differences by service. In judging the person's subjective feelings about illness, we demonstrate a link with the type of disease, its duration, and degree of disablement, but not with sex, the type of treatment received, or hospital accommodation. Prehospital mental status was related to the person's ability to perform family and work roles at the end of convalescence, but it was not linked to the person's subjective feelings about his illness. Our findings suggest that the inability to perform an accustomed role after hospitalization was attributable in part to the person's mental status; however, subjective reaction to the physical illness was traceable to the degree of physical handicap resulting from the illness. We conclude that life problems tended to disable a person with or without organic disease, but with physical disease the existing problems were exacerbated and the focus of the patient was on his physical condition, not his emotional state, for he thought it was the former which threatened his life.

CHAPTER 15 DYING AND DEATH

A PATIENT WHO WAS TERMINALLY ILL CREATED CRISES IN human relations for those who were caring for him. One dilemma arose from the fact that not every member of the group involved—the sick person, the spouse, the responsible physician, nurses, and other family members—realized the illness was a fatal one. It may have been in the interests of some persons to mislead other members of the group. Evasions, silences, half-truths, and deliberate lies then became elements in the social realities that tied the group together and, in turn, influenced the communications of one person with another. A second dilemma arose from the lack of explicit norms in our culture to guide the day-to-day relations of the group as death approached. A third revolved around the uncertainty of when death would occur. The physician had clearer definitions governing his relations with the patient than the patient and the family had in their relations with the physician, but even in the former relationship the physician had to make crucial decisions regarding his interaction with the patient and the family, guided largely by "the rule of thumb," "my judgment," "the physician-patient relationship."

When the physician became aware that treatment had failed, the canons of professional self-respect did not provide for a way to tell the patient that the mortician would shortly take over. The patient, himself, may have given up, but because of therapy used or failure of the disease to stop a vital function, life lingered on in the moribund body. The physician then had to ask himself if the patient and his family should be told. Neither the professionals —physicians and nurses—nor the family had a list of socially defined rules to help them answer such vexing questions as: *To what extent should misrepresentations, evasions, half-truths, or untruths be used to "protect" the patient and the family? How far should the disease be treated?* The patient, too, was in a quandary: Should he assume that the physician would tell him everything pertinent about his illness and its probable outcome, or *should he ask the physician to explain the meaning of his symptoms? If he did not ask, would the physician tell him? If he did ask, should he expose his family to the fears raised by the physician's evaluation of his illness? Should the patient insist that the physician withhold disturbing information from his family?* Such questions were puzzling to patients, family members, physicians, nurses, and others in the drama of a terminal illness. (While we cannot answer these questions, we do call attention to them and show their pertinence to the behavior of persons we observed when they faced the reality of impending death.) Each member of the group functioned within a network of ambiguous definitions of what *might* be done, what *should* be done, what *must* be done.

Between the time we selected a patient for study and the end of data collection, 25 per cent of the 161 patients had died. Of the 40 persons who did not survive, 22 died in this hospital during either the hospitalization in which they were selected for study or a subsequent one; 3 additional patients died in another hospital, and 15 died either in their homes or in a nursing home. Thirty-nine succumbed from a chronic disease—2 unexpectedly from complications associated with their disease and its care during the hospitalization in which they were selected for study. The death of only one person was unrelated to the illness for which he had been hospitalized when he entered the study; this person experienced a massive cerebral hemorrhage at work and died a few hours later.

The median length of elapsed time between the known onset of the illness and death was 29 months, but severe disability afflicted almost every person for varying lengths of time. The 37 chronically ill patients whose deaths were expected were so disabled during the final weeks of life that the end was only a matter of time; for 84 per cent, the physicians and nurses, usually the family as well, knew in the last seven days that treatment had failed and death was imminent.

At the time of death 40 per cent of the deceased persons were less than 55 years of age and 60 per cent were over 55. Death was unrelated to either the sex of the patients or to the service upon which they were treated. Death was related, however, to accommodation: those who died comprised 26 per cent of the private patients, 15 per cent of the semiprivate, and 37 per cent of the ward patients. The higher proportion of deaths among the private and ward patients compared to the semiprivate patients, was linked, we believe, to the urgency for admission discussed in Chapter 9, p. 151. This, in turn, was a reflection of the patient's illness and the way the hospital is used by physicians.

Communication between the members of the group involved in the care of terminally ill patients was associated with the nature of the patient's illness and the role each person played in his care. The physician exercised responsibility for making the diagnosis, estimating the prognosis, and prescribing the treatment. The patient placed his life and future well-being in the hands of the physician. The spouse also relied on the physician. However, the way the doctor related to the patient was linked with sponsorship. This, in turn, as we demonstrated in Chapter 8, p. 124, was associated significantly with both the socioeconomic status of patients and the accommodations in which they were housed.

The amount of information communicated to the patient was associated with the physician's diagnosis of the disease. Heart disease was feared among patients and their families, but it was not dreaded as was cancer. A senior surgeon in private practice told us, "Cancer is a dirty word. I never use it in talking with a patient." This surgeon was not alone in his evasion of a discussion of cancer with a patient. A diagnosis of cancer evoked a response of horror in patients and their families. As a consequence, when cancer was diagnosed evasions regarding diagnosis, probable prognosis, and the value of therapy were the rule in communications between members of the group involved rather than the exception. If the physician decided the symptoms were benign, the patient was told. If the physician concluded the symptoms indicated the presence of a probable malignancy, the patient was not told the real diagnosis unless he made a determined effort to learn it. When the physician made a diagnosis of heart disease, private and semiprivate but not ward patients were likely to be told the truth. The relationship between diagnosis and the use of evasion in discussing it is tabulated below:

Diagnosis	Evasion Used	Evasion Not Used
Cancer	75%	19%
Heart and other diseases	25	81
N =	(24)	(16)
p < .05		

The rationale for informing the patient of his diagnosis is that treatment can be more "dignified." The patient and family can understand what therapeutic alternatives are available and they can help in the selection of the most appropriate treatment. Although this model is an ideal one, it was not followed in practice. Physicians in the study believed generally that well-educated persons did not need to be told they had a serious disease. The physicians thought these patients drew a more or less accurate conclusion of what their disease was from their symptoms. If the patient decided he was suffering from cancer, and he was, the physicians believed they should not try to evade the truth; at the same time, however, they tried not to stress the probable grave prognosis. They believed a patient who realized what was wrong with him and desired to utilize the information to enable him and his family to plan realistically should be encouraged to handle the situation by hearing the facts of the eventual outcome as far as medical experience indicated them.

Two executives who had major business as well as family responsibilties demanded full disclosure of their diagnoses, and their physicians realized it was practically impossible to evade the issue. One of these men, Mr. Wellin, developed symptoms of pain in his abdomen for which an internist could find no abnormalities for about six months before he was referred to this medical center for diagnostic studies. In this hospital he was seen by several physicians including a psychiatrist who thought his symptoms were not attributable to psychological problems. After a few days the physicians decided on exploratory surgery. Mr. and Mrs. Wellin discussed the fact that it might be cancer. Mr. Wellin insisted, in spite of wife's advice, that he be told the truth about his illness. Prior to the surgery he made a "binding pact" with the surgeon that, regardless of his physical or emotional condition, he be told the diagnosis. After surgery, Mr. Wellin was informed he had a malignancy which could not be removed. He was given hope for some extension of his life through radiation or chemotherapy, but he was aware of the limitations of this treatment and that his doctor was emphasizing the successes of the treatment rather than the failures. He was not buoyed up, except temporarily, by the hope of palliation of the malignancy. He accepted the radiation therapy, feeling it would be of little value, but he refused offers of chemotherapy because he had even less confidence in it. He went home, accepting only symptomatic treatment for his disease. He put his affairs in order and died at home about four months after his discharge from the hospital.

The third private patient to whom full disclosure of the diagnosis and probable prognosis was made was told of the surgical findings in a startling way. Mr. Donner first saw a neighborhood general practitioner who knew little about him personally or socially. The surgeon to whom this physician referred Mr. Donner telephoned the general practitioner and discussed the symptoms. In the course of the conversation the surgeon asked the general practitioner about Mr. Donner's financial status. (This surgeon usually accepted as patients only well-to-do persons.) The general practitioner told the surgeon he thought Mr. Donner had a good job as "he drives a new Chrysler." (Mr. Donner actually worked in a factory and was a man of very moderate means.) The surgeon indicated to us that when he accepted the responsibility of operating on this man he had been misled about his finances by the general practitioner.

Mr. Donner's diagnosis was metastatic abdominal cancer. A colostomy was performed and radiation recommended. The day after surgery Mr. Donner asked about his condition. The surgeon told him he had widespread cancer and there was no hope for him. Between broken, body-racking sobs, Mr. Donner told us about the encounter: "He gave it to me straight." Such a direct, blunt disclosure probably would not have occurred except for the special circumstances of the physician-patient relationship in this instance. The surgeon told us he thought the referral was an improper one and he did not plan to care for the patient in the future. Further medical care, including an additional hospitalization and surgery, was arranged by another physician.

Information regarding the probable prognosis of severe disease, whether it was cancer, heart disease, or some other malady, was guarded even more carefully by the professionals than was the diagnosis. Questions about the likely outcome of the disease were ignored, glossed over, or evaded. Patients, and family members, were confused by the evasions and fictions circulated by physicians and concurred in by nurses concerning the probable outcome of the illness.

In 73 per cent of the 37 expected deaths, a mutual decision was made by the physician and the family to avoid letting the sick person know the truth about his condition and its expected outcome. In 36 per cent of these cases the physician was instructed by the spouse or other family member not to disclose the truth to the patient. If the physician or the spouse believed the patient should be "protected" from the diagnosis and prognosis of his illness, elaborate stratagems were created to see that the sick person was deceived.

One type of evasion with such stratagems is illustrated in the story of Mrs. Steissen who had had a morbid fear of cancer since her mother's death from this disease. After many years of complaints Mrs. Steissen's general practitioner decided she was giving voice to neurotic feelings. (She had been the central figure in family turmoil for a long time.) Mrs. Steissen's daughter thought that her mother should see a specialist. The internist who then saw her and took X rays made a diagnosis of stomach cancer. An operation was performed to determine the extent of the disease and to treat it if possible, but nothing could be done because metastases were widespread. When Mr. Steissen was told of his wife's condition by the family physician, he asked this physician not to tell his wife. The family doctor, for his own personal and professional reasons, agreed to this deception. Mr. Steissen then informed some family members and intimate friends of the true diagnosis and probable prognosis and explained that other persons would be told a "fairy tale." The general practitioner told nurses, house staff, and three consulting specialists from Surgery, Internal Medicine, and Radiology that the diagnosis was not to be revealed to Mrs. Steissen. The general practitioner reported to us, "Mrs. Steissen has cancer all over the place but she believes, now that so many have told her the same story, that she has a slowly healing inflammation of her stomach. She is an open-and-shut case." (By this he meant that Mrs. Steissen's malignancy was inoperable. Her abdomen had been opened and the incision closed without further surgery.)

Following the surgery, cancer chemotherapy was administered. The general practitioner, who could not endure facing Mrs. Steissen and her family under the circumstances he had created partly with his "failure" to recognize the "real" cause of her symptoms and partly with his cooperation in the pretense, withdrew his services and asked a colleague to take responsibility for Mrs. Steissen's care.

This pretense was upheld for a number of reasons: First, the family doctor believed he had missed a diagnosis until it was too late; it was difficult for him to face Mrs. Steissen with the news that she was suffering from cancer when for so long he had told her her complaints were fears and nothing more. Second, Mr. Steissen was afraid that if Mrs. Steissen were told her diagnosis and prognosis she might "go off the deep end completely," or "be even more impossible to live with." His relationship with his wife involved the continued necessity of offering half-truths and lies to explain her deteriorating condition. The family did not want to discuss the situation with us. They did reveal, however, that their lives were a "living hell." After Mrs. Steissen's death, a follow-up interview with a family member was denied; the reason given was that any further reference to the terminal illness was just a reminder of that "hell."

Uncertainties of early diagnosis sometimes led to a tentative diagnosis of the condition as benign which was communicated to the patient. Then, when the fatal diagnosis became known, the problem arose of withdrawing the early diagnosis and offering the true diagnosis in its place. We found when this problem confronted the physician in his relationship to the patient the true diagnosis, as a rule, was not offered to the patient; the physician usually adhered to his, or another physician's, earlier diagnosis.

Mrs. Steig, for example, died of cancer at the age of 46, following a lengthy terminal illness for eight months of which she was severely disabled. Because of multiple abdominal complaints for about 18 months prior to her death, she had gone to an internist who attributed her symptoms to anxieties. (She was a neurotic person.) However, her symptoms continued and she returned again and again to this internist. After several months of complaints and examinations, an enlarged lymph node was found in her neck and she was referred to a surgeon for a biopsy of the swelling. Cancer cells were found and the decision to operate was made. The internist, realizing he might have missed an early diagnosis, told the surgeon that Mrs. Steig must not be informed she had a malignancy. Although the surgeon became angry at this, he agreed to withhold the information. He performed an abdominal exploration and found a widespread inoperable malignancy. He told Mrs. Steig she would recover quickly from the surgery. He said, "I'll dance a jig with you in a week," but he then vitiated his agreement by informing her that "growths were present." He told her also he was unhappy with the internist's "handling of the situation;" he told us he was "washing his hands of her case."

Mrs. Steig was never informed directly of her diagnosis beyond what the surgeon told her. The internist continued to discuss the symptoms with her in terms of an arthritic condition or abdominal complaint secondary to anxiety. The house staff alternated from optimism to pessimism in their comments about her treatment. Near the end, one of the chemotherapy physicians wrote a note in the medical record indicating "encouraging results." On the same day an intern wrote, "She is going downhill."

Behind the scenes, Mrs. Steig was quite alone in her illness. After the surgeon withdrew from the case she told us:

> I woke up one morning and there were six doctors standing around my bed. One of them came and put a tube down my throat and gave me some pills that are like bullets for my shrinking intestines. I'm in the hands of the chemotherapy boys now. I feel like a statistic for the first time in my life.

Mrs. Steig's husband, who had been mentally ill a few years before, presented himself to the doctors with a dulled effect. Nobody bothered to talk to him. In the end, he was aware that he had been "left outside," and he thought this was "not fair." Moreover, he did not think his wife's treatment had been satisfactory. The suffering she had endured as a result of the treatment made him angry while the impoverishment imposed upon him made him furious. The $7,000 cost of the terminal illness was much beyond his means. In summing up his reactions to his experience, he told us: "I'm mad at all of them [the doctors]. I never knew what the diagnosis was until I saw it on the death certificate in the undertaker's office. It was cancer."

Some physicians told us they believed in informing patients of their diagnosis and probable prognosis, but when we examined the communications of these doctors with their patients we found they employed evasions as frequently as those physicians who were guarded in their statements regarding how much a patient should be told. Mrs. Lottso's case illustrated this aspect of the problem. About five years after a radical mastectomy, the malignancy recurred and became widespread. The responsible physician told us he believed in informing patients frankly of their diagnoses, yet he chose to tell Mrs. Lottso that she was suffering from "arthritis and bursitis." He never discussed treatment alternatives realistically with either Mr. or Mrs. Lottso. However, another physician, while administering cancer chemotherapy in this hospital, gave some hints about "those cells," suggesting to Mrs. Lottso that it might be recurring cancer. She acted as if she knew she had cancer but she would not voice this fear. In her grossly deteriorated state, Mrs. Lottso could say only that she wanted to be better. Accordingly, she accepted palliative treatment recommendations and corrective procedures. Her private physician went ahead with cancer chemotherapy and restorative surgery for pathological fractures. The probable extension of her life was of dubious value, for Mrs. Lottso suffered enormously. Mr. Lottso described to us his view of his wife's treatment:

> She had orthopedic surgery on her hip to remove cancer in the bone in the hope that she could be up on her feet during her remaining days. She decided she wanted the surgery because she thought she had only bursitis and arthritis. But the bone was too brittle to hold a pin. She went back to surgery again but with no success. The third time they operated they removed the pin altogether. A month later she died.

With rare exceptions, the physicians continued, long after death was imminent, to apply treatment measures to combat disease, offering hope to the patient and the family that "in this instance" they might be effective. They did not tell the patients that there was little hope. Only five patients, the three cancer victims we discussed earlier and two heart patients (all men), were told their illnesses were terminal. No ward patient was told that the illness was a terminal one, and no family member of a ward patient was informed that the illness was a fatal one until death was near.

The patient and his family looked to the physician to control the outcome of the illness. The physician was expected to give the patient relief from his symptoms and hopefully to cure the person of his disease. The patient was told to cooperate in therapy in order to get relief from his suffering. The patients cooperated, placing their hopes for the most effective and humane treatment in the hands of physicians and nurses. Common reaction to the prescribed therapy was: "If it has to be done, it has to be done." "What else is there to do? It's his field, not mine." "The doctor went to medical school; I didn't." The physicians placed a strong emphasis on therapeutic alternatives; if one did not work, perhaps another would. The therapeutic possibilities were given more emphasis than experience warranted, but the patients did not realize this. The physician could give the appearance of doing everything possible within the bounds of modern scientific medicine to prolong the life of the patient, but for many illnesses he could not deliver a suitable cure. Above all, the physician could offer hope even though it was largely unfounded and he knew it. Physicians were aware of the dilemmas with which they had to cope in their relationships with terminally ill patients and members of their families. One physician told us:

The situation of the dying patient is problematic. Some patients apparently want everything done and others want nothing done. No matter what the doctor does, the family may later change their minds and accuse the doctor of malpractice. They may see, for example, the dramatics of a television death and feel that the patient should have been given the benefit of all such heroic measures rather than be allowed to die.

While the professionals and the family were "playing games," their deceptions were generally suspected by the dying person. Of the patients whose illnesses were terminal, 45 per cent were convinced they would soon die and an additional 29 per cent were highly suspicious of what they were told. The remainder, 26 per cent, died of some unexpected complication or suffered from brain damage so that their awareness of what was happening to them was impaired. Thus, the level of awareness of three out of four persons who were dying was high, but it was not shared with the physicians or the family because of the evasions—sometimes by the doctors alone, sometimes by the family, and sometimes conspiratorially between them.

Decisions concerning the treatment of the patient were made within a network of pretenses. The treatment chosen by the physician was almost always approved by the patient and the family. A physician in pretending to offer a plausible therapy for malignancy or heart disease may have recommended palliation principally to convey hope and optimism: "It is all we have to offer. Maybe a miracle will happen." Such comments were commonly used to justify action taken. The patient accepted this explanation, at least in the beginning, because he wanted relief from suffering. Neither the patient nor the family realized the treatment decisions reflected the nature of the pretenses more than the reality of the illness. Many treatment decisions were essentially blind because no one had examined the consequences of the pretenses even though the several participants may have suspected they were playing a fanciful game, with death as the sure winner. Death was rejected so completely that almost no one dared to face it as an inevitable concomitant to life. Usually evasions were in the interest of kindness to the patient and to those around him, but they also were used out of concern for the family in a time of crisis, and some doctors and families had other motives.

When a physician made a mistake in diagnosing a patient's illness he faced a question, perhaps a fatal one for the patient, of importance to his self-respect and for his practice: *Should he tell the patient and the patient's family the truth, or should he evade the issue and bluff his way to the end?* The story of Mr. Walters illustrates a facet of this problem. When Mr. Walters' symptoms first developed he sought professional advice from his family doctor, a general practitioner, and was told that he had "nothing to worry about; just a little stomach trouble." He sought no further medical advice until his symptoms became so marked that he began to worry about cancer. He went to a second physician, telling his wife that if he had cancer he would kill himself. This thought was never communicated to either physician or discussed further between the husband and wife. However, when the second physician suggested Mr. Walters come to the hospital Mrs. Walters was careful to keep his collection of guns under her surveillance and the ammunition locked up. Following a series of diagnostic studies in the ward accommodation, exploratory surgery was decided upon. The surgical note reads in part:

> Large carcinoma of the transverse colon seen involving small bowel, stomach, and extending to the retroperitoneal area. This was resected in total. A colocolostomy ileo-ileostomy, subtotal gastrectomy, and gastrojejunoscopy were done. A large lump was palpated in the liver posteriorly but was not seen or biopsied.

The surgical resident wrote a note in the medical record: "I told him [Mr. Walters] he had an abdominal abcess and that it was all removed as far as we could tell." Although Mr. Walters was discharged with the assurance that he would be able to return to work in a few weeks, his symptoms soon became increased and he re-entered the hospital in a semiprivate accommodation under semicommittee sponsorship. The house staff decided that the explanation given by the surgical resident in the preceding hospitalization would serve as a diagnosis for the time being, as they felt an abdominal abcess might actually have been present. To add to the uncertainty, an arthritic complication, though not seriously considered by the several members of the semicommittee, was given considerable weight in their discussions with Mr. Walters when he asked about his failure to recover from the earlier surgery. This time, the physicians decided upon chemotherapy "to stop the infection."

Mr. Walters discussed with us the possibilities of a tumor, infection, and arthritis to explain his readmission to the hospital. The semicommittee praised his stoic performance in the face of mutilative surgery and the "strong treatment" (cancer chemotherapy) which was prescribed and administered. Consistent with his temperament, Mr. Walters was pleased with the doctors' praise. They kept reminding him that a great deal depended upon how vigorously he asserted himself in fighting his disease. He maintained a remarkable keenness of mind in spite of the ravages of cancer, the mutilating surgery, and the use of narcotics.

Mrs. Walters did not intervene in the treatment or inquire about the prognosis. She told us, "These are important men. I can't take up their time." She made practically no demands upon the private physician or the house staff who administered medical care to Mr. Walters during his terminal illness. As death approached, Mr. Walters and his family were buoyed up briefly, then "let down." Near the end Mr. Walters asked repeatedly, "Is this the day for me, doc?" or, "Am I going to die today?" The physicians always responded with evasions. One told us:

> He would lie there in his extremely wasted state, vomiting feces, and with a keen eye stare at me and ask if I thought he would die that day. It was terribly disconcerting, but not one of us had guts enough to tell him he was dying. He had five chemotherapy treatments for cancer and had some diarrhea and some rather severe stomatitis which was extremely uncomfortable. He was a stalwart individual and extremely grateful for everything we could do for him, but it was difficult to say whether he thought we were really doing something for him or that we were just a bunch of bastards.

Mr. Walters' story illustrates the tactics of the semicommittee as well as some of the conflicts around the patient in the hour of death. However, not all patients nor their families were as accepting of what was or was not done for the patient. Some families openly challenged the physicians and attempted to use medical, personal, political, or religious influences to have the patient treated differently. House officers, especially, and medical students had trouble keeping such families under control. The case of Mr. Silvetta was an example of conflict within the family affecting the relationship between the family and the committee caring for a dying ward patient.

The family structure of the Silvettas was an essential part of their relations with one another and with the hospital. Both spouses in this marriage had grown children from a previous marriage but none together. Two of Mrs. Silvetta's children lived with them, but she had nothing to do with Mr. Silvetta's children. She felt she was "justified" since she was "putting up" with their father who turned out to be an unfaithful husband as well as an alcoholic and an habitual gambler.

Mr. Silvetta had been aware of "lung trouble" for a year before this hospitalization but he delayed seeking medical care because he "was afraid of what the doctors might tell me." As the months passed he began to lose weight and soon became disabled. Mrs. Silvetta took him to a general practitioner who examined him briefly and directed him to the emergency service of this hospital for further help. Two days after admission to the ward accommodation an intern told Mr. and Mrs. Silvetta that there were no signs of cancer. However, the surgical resident and his assistants soon diagnosed a case of pulmonary malignancy so far advanced that surgery was useless. They recommended radiation therapy on an outpatient basis.

The intern who had told Mr. and Mrs. Silvetta that there was no cancer then sought out Mrs. Silvetta. He told her her husband had cancer and would probably not live more than two or three months. Mrs. Silvetta said she did not want her husband to know his diagnosis. The intern, thus instructed, told Mr. Silvetta that he had "lung congestion." At this point, Mr. Silvetta's two daughters appeared at the hospital. As Mrs. Silvetta would not talk with them they discussed the situation with the intern. They felt their father had the right to know he was dying and tried to persuade the intern to tell him. The intern, in agreement on this point with the daughters, attempted to change Mrs. Silvetta's mind. Mrs. Silvetta was adamant and left orders that the daughters were not to be allowed to visit Mr. Silvetta. However, she was still concerned about the intentions of the intern who had argued with her. She called a specialist in the community, whom she knew slightly, appealing to him to "go to the highest authority in the hospital" to have the intern silenced. The specialist declined to interfere. She then went to the general practitioner who had seen Mr. Silvetta originally. Although this physician would not intervene, he suggested that Mrs. Silvetta call the Chairman of the Department of Surgery and go through "medical channels" of the hospital. This she did and was referred to the resident on the ward. She called the resident and also persuaded the general practitioner to call him. The three of them then agreed that the intern should be relieved of further responsibility in communications with Mr. Silvetta. The resident took this action without discussing the source of the problem with the intern.

When we interviewed the intern he was angry because he felt he had been abiding by the best principles of patient management and feared there would be a black mark against him after this incident. The resident explained to us, "You have to keep peace with the outside practitioners and with the Great White Father [the Chairman of the Department of Surgery]." In this instance the resident was wrong. To the best of our knowledge, the Chairman's secretary had intercepted the telephone call and the Chairman, himself, never knew anything about the case. Also, Mrs. Silvetta's strenuous efforts to isolate Mr. Silvetta from his daughters were prompted by the fact that before his entry into the hospital she had talked him into naming her sole beneficiary of his small estate. She feared that if the daughters talked to him of his impending death he might change his will.

When terminality was not evident, pretenses on the part of the family and professionals might cause no serious concern. However, as the illness advanced pretenses were not so easy to maintain. Often, the inappropriate presence of family members and friends, especially their kindness and solicitude, convinced the patient that his illness was more threatening than he had been led to believe. His skepticism caused him to ask more and more questions; then evasions were used to an even greater extent. The patient soon tired of trying to get answers and simply lived out the rest of his life without a direct discussion of his impending death with any human being. The pretenses and half-truths served to isolate individuals from one another, and the most isolated person was the patient.

Patients and spouses expected physicians to offer treatment in the hope that the ravages of the disease would be stopped. This expectation was pressed upon the doctors so vigorously that, when possible, they offered hope and even when a patient was dying they offered the *image of hope*. In so doing, almost all doctors discounted the severity of the disease and the grim prognosis while they proceeded to apply therapies which they knew were of little value. The importance of treatment was inflated beyond its true worth (this knowledge was rarely shared with the patient), while the realistic concerns of the family and its dying member were set aside and sometimes ignored. One physician told us: "It gets sticky, sometimes awfully messy. You have to lie because there's no other way." Another said:

> This whole institution [the hospital] treats diseases, not people. I don't know really what we're achieving. Sometimes I think we ought to quit on some of these patients, but even to mention this raises eyebrows around here and people ask you, "What, you aren't going to operate on this cancer?" Others say, "You aren't even going to take a look at it?" Or, "What kind of doctor are you and what kind of hospital is this?"

A few physicians voiced their discontent at the pressure they felt from their colleagues, the hospital, and families of patients to prolong life when death in a short time was inevitable. We quote the position of one of these exceptional physicians:

> The dying patient should be treated with dignity. It has always bothered me that our job as doctors is not to alleviate suffering but to prolong life. We're almost forced to do everything in our power to prolong life. We're doing it in the hope that maybe something will happen, maybe a miracle will occur. We throw people into oxygen tents; we do all sorts of heroic things. We even rip open chests and squeeze hearts of patients who have massive myocardial infarctions or cancer involving their hearts. Everything is justified to save the life of a salvageable patient. But where death is inevitable I wonder if it isn't the best thing to make them comfortable and leave them alone. Usually, we don't. I become impatient with those who think first and foremost of the health of the body and never think about the soundness of moral fortitude and the soul within the golden vessel known as the human body.

Young physicians, particularly house officers, were inclined to view the hospital as a laboratory where research and learning took place and where long-range benefits outweighed the harm that sometimes might be done in the treatment of diseases. They argued that the life of any patient should be extended for as long as possible. Sometimes this practice "paid off" for a patient whose life could be saved dramatically. These eager young physicians maintained that any and all procedures which showed any promise should be tried and evaluated. They would then be adopted, if worthwhile, or discarded, if not.

In general, the families looked for miracles instead of death. The feeling among laymen was that science and research would bring forth the miracles. When a patient was suffering from the pain of the last phases of a disabling chronic illness he wanted relief from his distress so that his suffering would be mitigated, and doctors promoted hope by such statements as: "The solution may be just around the corner;" or "Each patient is different; *you* may respond to this treatment." Physicians chose this course for a variety of reasons: Some believed that families would not tolerate inaction. Others thought there was no "moral justification ever" for withholding any conceivably helpful treatment because "it is wrong to take a life" or "play God." The idea of "giving up," though widely talked of among physicians, was almost nonexistent in practice. Finally, physicians believed the practice of medicine demanded this resolution, for it was the only one which was consistent with the image the public held of the physician as the champion in the combat against disease and a haven of hope for the sick.

To combat disease by supporting the professionals in every way was an obligation of the family and the patient, and they accepted this responsibility by giving freely of their time, energy, and resources. In contemplating death, family members aimed for a "clear conscience." Many said afterwards, "We did all it was possible to do."

A physician who thought that therapy ought to be withdrawn could not withdraw it without other physicians and nurses being aware of his action. This was especially true for patients who were hospitalized. The physician had to "play it safe," and the safest thing to do was to keep doing things. It was evidently intolerable on the part of anyone to avoid pretenses, for to do so was to entertain hopelessness. This the physician could not do without violating the role expectations the patient, the patient's family, and the institution had for him. Regardless of the hopelessness of the patient's condition, there were those who were ready to make attempts of one kind or another to prolong life even though the patient was in great pain and desired nothing more than a long dreamless sleep. Physicians rejected death, but in so doing they ran the risk of violating the rights of the dying. The patient's desires concerning his right to die had little value in the therapeutic alternatives available to the physician.

We found only one instance when "heroic" efforts were stopped before death. The patient, in previous admisions to the hospital, had undergone multiple surgery on the ward service for visceral cancer. During this hospitalization he had been treated with surgery, radiation, and finally chemotherapy. His condition was hopeless, he was in great pain, and his strength was ebbing fast. The resident on the service called for the "old college try," another operation; maybe a miracle would occur! A senior physician who was called examined the patient carefully, checked the record, and said, "Enough is enough." He realized the man was near death and felt that his wish to die at home should be honored. The patient was discharged and died at home two days later.

Interpersonal relations in the group surrounding the dying person were of two kinds: primary and secondary. The patient was tied to his spouse, his children and their spouses, granchildren, and other relatives by primary social and emotional bonds developed over the years. The relationships of the family members with one another were personal, emotional, and all-encompassing. The impending death had a special meaning for each one. When death came, even though it had been expected for days, weeks, or months, it strained relations within the family. A reaction engulfed the group whether it was one of shock, depression, relief, grief, or even hysteria. The intimate relationships of a lifetime were dissolved; a void appeared in the lives of the surviving members.

The relationships of physicians, nurses, technicians, aides, and others involved with the dying patient were secondary and directed toward technical care. When a patient died in the hospital, the nurses, aides, and technicians turned to other patients who needed their attention; the room had to be cleaned and made ready for the next patient. The physician who was responsible for obtaining the postmortem permit turned toward the surviving relatives, particularly to the spouse who had the authority to sign the permit. Family members had to decide quickly whether to allow an autopsy or to deny it, because burial plans had to be made. As a rule, the physician who was responsible for the patient's care or the one who knew him best asked the responsible family member to sign the permit for a postmortem examination. This posed some severely trying moments for all parties—physicians as well as family members.

Within the hospital and the School of Medicine attention was directed in several ways to the matter of autopsies. The *House Staff Manual* called attention to and "highly" recommended a memorandum entitled "Autopsies." This mimeographed memorandum presented legal and religious information supporting the practice of autopsies. It was available to house officers, and its fundamental points commonly were transmitted informally among physicians and student physicians. The memorandum stated: "The autopsy record of a hospital reflects equally on all services, not merely the Department of Pathology, and is the joint responsibility of all members of the medical staff. The annual A.M.A. [American Medical Association] list of hospitals with the highest autopsy percentages is almost exclusively comprised of those hospitals providing the best medical care in the nation." Since the percentage of autopsies performed in the hospital played a part in its evaluation as a patient-care, teaching, and research institution, it was essential to have a high autopsy rate in order to protect its reputation as well as to achieve its objectives.

The memorandum went on to describe a series of steps to help the house officers obtain the responsible relative's signature on a postmortem permit. Rapport with the family was emphasized: Prepare them for death. Settle on the member of the family most likely to be cooperative to "deal with." Choose a quiet room and tell the selected relative, "He passed away quietly." Be firm, clear, and mature, and have a "ready pen." Obtain the signature quickly because "Relatives who leave to discuss the matter with members of the family seldom return." Regarding terminology, "autopsy," "dissection," and "removal of organs" should never be used; use instead "acceptable similies": "examination," "a look inside," "similar to a surgical examination." Tell the families that the procedure "leaves little more than an operative scar," that it is carried out with the same "dignity" and "precautions" as "an operation," and that it is performed by a "single highly trained specialist particularly interested in afflictions," including in order "cancer, heart disease, diabetes, infections, brain diseases." Stress that the postmortem may "bear on their own future well-being." The argument of "helping the next patient" is strategy to impress the "calm, intelligent individual." Reassure the family that *"the service"* is "performed absolutely free of charge."

Even obvious misrepresentations were suggested in this memorandum: "If it had not been for the information we got by performing a postmortem examination last week, a little boy now in the hospital would have died. It is possible that we could have saved your husband had someone not refused permission for an examination." This memorandum was written so forcefully that any house officer with a modicum of sensitivity realized he must get permission for the autopsy no matter what he had to say to get it. It was made clear to the house officer that he was expected to "get that post."

Some house officers followed "the rules of the game" assiduously. One resident told us:

I can usually anticipate the death of a patient and I have always prepared the family for the autopsy request by the time the patient has died. I think the secret of getting autopsies is knowing the family well and having them know you and your attitude about the whole disease entity. I point out what the course of the disease has been. My opening statement is that we would like permission to examine his body, and I tell them what our motives are. The motives are to learn about the course of the disease in this particular patient. About 80 per cent just come across right away. The other 20 per cent require a little more pushing. Then I emphasize we may find out something that the family should know about, and so on and so forth. My own personal autopsy permission rate is 95 per cent.

House officers were troubled often by the expectation that "posts" had to be obtained in the face of family resistance. They believed that they were doing an unpleasant selling task involving misrepresentations. One intern reported:

We are constantly urged to get permissions for postmortem examinations. The hospital is rated by its percentage of posts; there's a rather strong push for us to supply postmortems on every patient. I have never gotten completely used to this. I mean I never feel at ease going in and asking a person to sign a permission for a postmortem examination. I get my share, but it's not a pleasant job. When you ask them for a permit they sometimes jump up and shout, "My God, you're not going to cut up Momma." That's the first reaction, and you more or less expect it because it's normal. Then you find yourself stretching the truth about the postmortem. After all, a postmortem is a messy, dirty, stinking job, and you see these people all hacked up. They yank the insides out, stuff the body, sew it back up, and send it away. And if it has an interesting knee, they yank out the knee or anything else that interests them. The pathologists don't give a rat's ass what happens to the body. You say to the family that these are surgical operations done by trained doctors. Well, God, if the surgeons operated this way it would be hell.

Posts are important enough to make people angry. You have to do it. You try to get them, and you pressure some people very hard. It's really a third degree. I'm sure no New York cop ever beat a confession out of anybody as hard as we beat postmortems out of people sometimes. We get them in a room and surround them with doctors and we don't leave them alone until they sign it. Their father has just died or their wife and they're in a weakened state anyway. You just shove that pen and paper in their hand, and while they're saying "no, no, no" they're signing the thing and you know they didn't want to. You really browbeat people into these things. It's not very likable work.

In spite of the unpleasantness connected with talking the family into signing the postmortem permit, there was a common feeling among house officers that they deserved "the post" as a reward for their hard work in the care of inpatients. One intern told us:

We work hard for these patients and we deserve to have the postmortem. We work very hard to get them. I would say about 50 per cent of the families come across when we simply explain our interest and our request. The others we have to work harder on. Usually they come across if we tell them that their own interests are involved. Reminding them about cancer, infections, or hereditary diseases scares them so that they want to know. For their own selfish reasons they grant the permission.

A second house officer reported:

I always try very hard to get a post, and if I don't get it I feel cheated. This happened to me last week, but the family couldn't be talked into it. You would think after we worked so hard, they'd be willing to grant a post, but they didn't.

Although the house officers sometimes felt guilty for their misrepresentations, they resolved the issue routinely in favor of what they believed to be their learning opportunities. One intern reported his concern for the undue pressure used on ward patients and then described immediately his own variety of pressure. Some house officers relied on the clergy for assistance in getting the postmortem permits. One said:

We feel very strongly about it and do everything we can to get it within the bounds of good sense and reason. There are various devices that are used, and most of them are sort of aimed at convincing the family that it is part of the patient's medical care. Sometimes families will grant permission if they're approached by their priest who says that he understands why it is necessary and agrees it will not be painful. Families seem to be frightened by the thought of their loved ones being mutilated. This is not hard to understand and the clergyman can be very helpful in telling them that they won't suffer any more because of the autopsy. Often the priest can convince them to go along with anything that represents potentially better medical care.

Families often had second thoughts about a postmortem examination after they had signed the permit under stress. They sometimes wondered just what was done and asked the mortician. Sometimes the mortician was put "on the spot" and called the hospital. An administrator reported:

One of the morticians called me the other day and was very disturbed. He said that a house officer had told the wife that this would be just a small incision so they could look at his lung and so on. The mortician said, "You know that's not true. Now she wants me to let her see the body to make sure that's all that was done." He reminded me that this is pretty bad business if the house officer really had told her that, and I have to agree.

There was a strong competitive spirit among the house officers to make points by obtaining a "post." The medical intern who obtained the highest percentage of autopsy permits was rewarded by time off and paid expenses to attend a medical meeting near the end of the year. This prize was awarded by the Department of Medicine, School of Medicine, although the medical house officers were reluctant to discuss it. (Some administrators in the hospital as well as house officers in the other departments of the School of Medicine denied any knowledge of this award.) Some believed it was an inappropriate reward, but all medical house officers understood that it was symbolic of the departmental emphasis placed upon securing all possible postmortem permits. One of the medical interns made some brief, revealing remarks about it:

> It's a plum. It's not the sort of thing that's written about or posted on the bulletin board, and I don't know who puts up the money for it. Most of us find out about it in the first month we're here.

Young physicians on the ward accommodations were motivated both by their identification with the School of Medicine and the expectations of the hospital to get the permission for a postmortem examination from a surviving relative. It was in the interest of the young physician to have a high percentage of autopsies to his credit. The professors in the School of Medicine desired this, and the hospital expected it. On the medical service there was the added incentive of the award.

The expectation for high autopsy rates on the medical service was consistent with the image this service maintained in the hospital. There was a common belief on the medical service that they had the most "complete" work-up of any department, the most adequate diagnostic appraisals, and the most thorough treatments. This approach was believed to be founded mostly upon the research and teaching interests of the faculty and house officers. In addition, the service was viewed as being oriented toward the intern. The patients were, in large part, his responsibility. Responsibility for obtaining postmortem permits also was his. He was young and eager to please. He was ambitious. His aim often was a research and teaching career. Interest in patients appeared to be a secondary matter. The performance of the intern in securing the postmortem permits appeared to reflect these realities in the role.

On the surgical service, the responsibility for the care of patients was oriented more toward the residents than the interns. When a patient died, it was customary for the physician, usually a resident, who performed the surgery to request the postmortem examination. Although an intern might do this, it was more likely to be the surgeon who operated and discussed the care of the patient with the patient himself and the family. The resident's added years of experience, combined with the diminished interest on the surgical service in another "look inside," introduced a tone of moderation in his efforts to gain an autopsy permit.

The hospital showed its interest in autopsies by listing routinely on the agenda of each meeting of the Medical Board the autopsy rate for the previous month. If everyone on the Medical Board was satisfied that the rate was high enough the chairman passed over the item without comment. However, if the rate was lower than expected there was discussion about it. When the rate dropped, renewed pressure was brought to bear to raise it to a satisfactory level.

Terminal illness among ward patients presented special problems. Eight of the 15 ward patients who died during this study succumbed in this hospital. The experiences of these patients with the committee, nurses, aides, and their families during the last days of their lives were fraught with impersonality, evasion, deception, fear, frustration, and general dissatisfaction with the course of events. A special point of tension between surviving family members and the young physicians revolved around the efforts of the house staff to obtain a permit for an autopsy. The ward patient was under the supervision of a committee of residents, interns, and medical students, who were interested in learning. Their attention was on the unusual disease rather than on the dying patient. They were imbued with the values of scientific medicine—use of the latest drugs, techniques, procedures, and machines to keep the patient alive. The "disease in the body in the bed" was the focus of the committee's attention. The desires of the patient and the cost of his care tended to be ignored. The spouse of the patient and other family members were viewed usually as interfering with the treatment. They had to be allowed to see the patient but under terms laid down by the members of the committee. Permission for autopsy was sought from families of ward patients with this same attitude.

The approach to a family member used by a physician in his request for an autopsy was related to accommodation and sponsorship. One house officer reported:

> The private physician is the one who handles the dying patient's family, or he should be the one, and not the house staff. Most of the time the private doctors don't care about the posts. Many times they won't even come into the hospital and speak to the family and help the house staff to get a postmortem permit. They wouldn't be bothered about it. They simply tell us, "You can ask for a post if you want to, boys."

Another reported:

> The house officer when dealing with the private patient is handicapped because he does not have power over the patient. You are personnel in that kind of situation and the private doctor has little interest in the posts.

Private practitioners realized the complexities associated with asking for a postmortem examination permit from a relative who was emotionally overwrought in the hour of death, and they had little interest in pursuing the subject of an autopsy. Spokesmen for the private practitioners on both the medical and surgical services were champions of the kindly "soft sell," but they agreed that the "hard sell" was necessary to boost the percentage of permissions. However, they preferred to leave the pressure of the "hard sell" to the house officers. We found no private practitioner using anything more than a very "soft sell" for postmortem permits.

A series of interrelated problems was associated with the care of patients who were of low status, poorly educated, and accepting of what the committee did or did not do for them. In these cases, neither the family members nor the patient openly questioned the decisions of the committee's members until death had occurred. The first open challenge to the committee often involved the pressure put upon the surviving spouse for a signature on the permit for a postmortem examination. This was illustrated by the death of Mrs. Maselli on the ward surgical service. Mr. and Mrs. Maselli were on city welfare at the time of her last admission to the hospital. They had been welfare recipients for several years. Mrs. Maselli was a long-time user of the emergency, clinic, and ward services of this hospital, having visited the emergency services 28 times (5 times in the year prior to her last hospitalization) and the clinics 476 times (18 in the year before her death). She had been hospitalized 5 times on the wards before her terminal illness. Two of these hospitalizations were in the three months prior to her death; she had had multiple complaints: respiratory disease, injuries of various kinds, and, near the end, abdominal pain. An intern wrote about her admission prior to the terminal one: "My old friend returns. It is pathetic to see this unhappy, sloppy, unattractive woman again. She is a nuisance with her frequent hospital visits."

Mrs. Maselli had had symptoms of abdominal discomfort for two years prior to her death. She was seen by two general practitioners in the community, but since she had no money to pay them they recommended that she return to the hospital's clinic. She came back to the clinic where X rays were taken which failed to disclose any malignancy. When Mrs. Maselli, who was obese and difficult to examine, continued her complaints, the physicians in the outpatient department told her she was anxious. Eventually, she came into the hospital acutely ill with obstruction of the intestine and was admitted to a ward accommodation on the surgical service. Surgery revealed an intestinal tumor. Following a colostomy, Mrs. Maselli was told she had an inflammation and as soon as it healed the surgeon would "hook up" her colon again in a subsequent hospitalization. After recovering from the first operation, she was discharged from the hospital. Two weeks later she was readmitted for removal of the tumor and the colostomy. During this surgery there was sufficient trauma to diseased tissues so that bleeding developed. Although the surgery was halted and the patient returned to her room, the bleeding continued and she soon went into shock. Attempts were made to transfuse her and stop the bleeding by another surgical procedure, but this was unsuccessful and Mrs. Maselli died.

Members of the committee had given Mr. Maselli varying hints concerning the cause of the bleeding. He explained to us that some doctors thought it was a tumor, some that a vein had been damaged, and others that the inflammation was out of control. He said, "The doctors weren't sure. Sometimes they said it was an intestinal obstruction. Sometimes they said it was a vein that broke loose, and some said it was a malignious [sic] tumor." He didn't know what to believe because of the conflicting stories given to him and his wife. He thought he couldn't argue with the doctors or even question their statements because of their superior knowledge. He told us, "I can't ask the doctors questions. They would only say who went to school, me or them, and that would be the end of the questions." Mr. Maselli felt powerless also because he was on welfare and "not a paying customer who is always taken care of better."

At his wife's death Mr. Maselli was left alone. The surgical assistant resident requested permission to do a postmortem examination which Mr. Maselli denied. When the resident persisted, Mr. Maselli said, "If you didn't find out what was wrong with her with all the cutting you did, you won't find out by cutting her up any more."

The death of another patient, Mr. Decker, illustrated multifaceted problems, concluding with pressure and misrepresentation in an attempt to get permission for a postmortem examination. Mr. Decker was 62 years old at the time of his death from heart failure on the medical service. His illness began six years before this admission with a heart attack, from which he recovered rather well so that he was able to go back to work. However, the last two years of his life were miserable because he was disabled, could not be employed, and was a burden to himself and to Mrs. Decker. She grew tired of his complaints, his declining health, his uselessness, and the burden of his care. She feared he would never work again and she would be destitute since their meager savings were being used for medical care and living expenses.

Mr. and Mrs. Decker had some arguments about his need for hospitalization. He resisted going back to "that miserable place," while she felt he would be given better care in the hospital and it would be easier on her. Two days before Christmas Mr. Decker was admitted to the hospital in congestive heart failure. He responded initially to the treatment given but then began to deteriorate. Although he was annoyed with his wife for having brought him to the hospital, he clung to her, wanting her to remain at his bedside. However, the members of the committee in charge of his case limited her visiting to avoid interference with the necessary work of the four-bed room in which he was housed. They never told Mrs. Decker that her husband was terminally ill; they assumed that she knew, but Mrs. Decker did not understand this fact. Mr. Decker believed his condition was worsening day by day. However, in trying to be humorous about the many drugs, the different electronic equipment rolled into his room, the emergency supplies kept at his bedside, and so forth, he led Mrs. Decker to believe that he was getting better. Finally, on New Year's Eve as she was about to go home he gave her his wedding ring. Mrs. Decker became frightened but before she could question him an intern forced her out of the room. She began to suspect that the physicians were going to carry out a "mercy killing" on her husband.

Mrs. Decker felt lost and alone. She did not want to call her son, who lived in the city, because she and Mr. Decker had been estranged from him for several years; she was not sure he even knew his father was in the hospital. She chose not to call any neighbors or friends. The only person she felt she could confide in was our data collector with whom she had established a relationship of trust. She telephoned the data collector, found her at home, and asked her to come to the hospital to help her.

When the data collector arrived Mrs. Decker poured out her concern about the "mercy killing," her guilt for bringing her husband to the hospital against his wishes, and so on for about an hour. She then attempted to enter her husband's room but was not permitted to do so. While Mrs. Decker and the data collector waited outside the room, with its door slightly ajar, they heard one of the young physicians say, "Decker is going to die anyway. He won't make it through the night." As Mrs. Decker faced, for the first time, the fact that her husband might die, her anxieties mounted. By this time members of the committee perceived that she had attached herself to the data collector. They told Mrs. Decker and the data collector to wait in a doctor's office nearby. Shortly after, an intern appeared in the office and asked the data collector to leave the room. A second intern waited outside the room "to see how things would go." This did not escape the attention of either Mrs. Decker or the data collector who also waited outside the half-open door. Without informing Mrs. Decker that her husband had died, the intern requested her to sign the permit for a postmortem examination. The second intern paced up and down the corridor emphasizing to the data collector how important it was to "get this post," while inside the room the first intern explained the importance of the postmortem examination. Mrs. Decker cried out, "Why couldn't I have seen him before he died?" The intern told her it was better to "remember him alive." This didn't comfort Mrs. Decker. She told the intern that her son might not want an autopsy.

When the existence of a son was brought into the conversation, the intern suggested that they ask the son to come to the hospital and talk with his mother. Mrs. Decker agreed to this. The second intern left to try to locate the son by telephone. In about half an hour the son was found at a New Year's Eve party, and he promised to come to the hospital immediately. In the meantime the first intern learned from Mrs. Decker that she had felt guilty about bringing her husband to the hospital against his wishes. He said:

> Oh, I didn't know this was a problem between you two. You shouldn't feel that way at all because Mr. Decker had to be in the hospital. You couldn't have cared for him at home. Had I known you felt this way, I would have told him that he had to be here. There was no question of his being at home. I never knew this was a problem at all.

The first intern then left the room and Mrs. Decker sobbed to the data collector, "They don't care what happens to me." A little later she said, "I know this was a mercy killing. No one could die that quickly. Joe was talking to me before they sent me out of the room."

At this point, although the son had not yet reached the hospital, the first intern returned and said, "Your son is quite willing to have a postmortem done." He leaned over the desk, picked up the postmortem permit attached to a clipboard, took out his pen, knelt down beside her chair and began in a very pleasant voice to say that the paper would just permit the hospital to do the autopsy. Mrs. Decker turned, looked him straight in the eye, and said, "Doctor, I'll wait until my son gets here, if you don't mind." The intern rose, quickly placed the pad and pen on the desk, and left the room.

About five minutes later the son appeared and demanded to talk privately with his mother. Mrs. Decker insisted that the data collector remain in the room. She told the son to inspect his father's body with no one else around and to look for evidence of a mercy killing. This he did, asking that no one accompany him as he went in to look at his father's body. Presently, he returned and informed his mother that there was no evidence of a mercy killing and that an autopsy was not inconsistent with his father's wishes. He encouraged his mother to sign the postmortem permit, which she did. After the permit was signed the son and Mrs. Decker were left sitting in the doctor's office. Presently, they discovered there was no further need for them to remain and so they left the hospital.

Summary

Pretenses and evasions entailed in the care of patients appeared in all accommodations. However, communication problems were most severe in the ward accommodations because the families had been pushed about a great deal not only in their health care but also in life in general. They realized their relative impotence and they were painfully conscious of their ignorance. They were also highly suspicious of the various deceptions that might have been used, and these conditions aggravated an existing sense of distrust.

The performance of respective individuals in the care of a dying patient was consistent with their conception of their roles and themselves. Patients and families expected treatment and hope, and doctors gave hope even though they knew it might be only an image of hope. When a patient was dying, the doctor resolved the dilemma for himself primarily in such terms. Neither patients nor doctors were experts in dying, but the doctors were experts in the treatment of disease. Accordingly, we conclude that the doctors generally chose to treat the disease and set aside the personal and familial consequences of their decisions. By this means the doctor did not have to face a death which he could not prevent; at the same time he avoided having to communicate the disheartening news to distraught patients and could delay discussing it with their families until the very end. In a research and teaching institution, this approach was uniquely fitting because it allowed for a concentration of the energies of physicians upon their learning about disease. This course, however, had clear implications for the choices of patients. Throughout the experience, the doctors concentrated upon the study and the treatment of the disease. They did this even after death occurred, requesting postmortem examinations for further study and securing them most frequently in the ward accommodations.

In the case of "the postmortem game," rules were clear in the three accommodations: In the semiprivate and private accommodations permission for the postmortem examination was requested but there was freedom from undue pressure. In the wards, however, there was a vast difference. In spite of unsatisfactory communications and chaos arising within the families and between the patients and families and hospital staff, the request for the postmortem examination was pressed. The house officers were "on the spot." Though they were uncomfortable about it, they were obliged to meet the expectations of the Medical Center. In so doing, they found themselves, according to their own estimates, using misrepresentations and unusual pressures to secure the permits. Although some house officers resented the necessity, they performed routinely. The situation of the house staff seemed to be summed up in the comment of one house officer: "Treat them kindly and gently if possible, but, if they fail to come across, turn on the pressure."

Each patient was linked to his or her spouse by generational experiences, affectional feelings, shared responsibilities, and years of living in a common home. The forceful withdrawal by hospitalization of one member of the spouse pair created situations which required adjustment within the familial group. The well spouse was most closely involved with the sick person and, therefore, was affected by the illness in numerous ways. In the face of these facts, we wanted to know what emotional impact this illness had upon the spouse. In order to find out we turned to feelings the spouse expressed regarding the illness and the ill person during the hospitalization and the home visits.

We used four categories of emotional impact—*minimal, moderate, extensive,* and *catastrophic*—to summarize the reaction of the spouse to the illness. In the first category, *minimal* impact, the illness was minor or of short duration, perhaps an infectious disease or minor surgery. There were no complications to handicap the patient at the end of convalescence. The family could and did cope successfully with the temporary adversity. For example, the acute infectious illness of Mr. Cuffstat, discussed in Chapters 9 and 12, had little or no impact upon the spouse. Although he was absent for ten days he was hardly missed; he returned to his job in two weeks and there were no aftereffects of the illness. Mrs. Colten, who was hospitalized for psoriasis, is another illustration of this group. Mrs. Colten's illness provided justification for an adjustment which both husband and wife sought but were reluctant to act upon: Mr. Colten was relieved of the annoying ritual of caring for his wife's body, and Mrs. Colten escaped from her husband's sexual advances. Her absence from home was hardly felt because she had prepared meals for her family in advance. The hospital and doctor's bills were paid by insurance companies. "It's a kind of vacation," Mrs. Colten told us, and, following two and a half weeks of treatment in the hospital, her condition improved and she was more cheerful than she had been before.

The second category, *moderate* impact, included families in which one spouse usually had a physical disease and an emotional disorder. Mrs. Roberts, who underwent a radical mastectomy for carcinoma of the breast, was typical of patients in this group. While she had a fair prognosis, the impact upon her husband was marked. From childhood Mrs. Roberts had suffered from exposure to illness and death. Her parents died when she was in her teens. Several other family members and friends had died of cancer. When she discovered a lump in her breast she thought she was doomed. Her fears grew although her physician tried to reassure her by saying, "You saved your life by coming in early for treatment." Mrs. Roberts' fears spread to Mr. Roberts and their son who became very frightened by this development. Considerable time and energy were spent discussing their fears and the prospects of Mrs. Roberts' early death. After the surgery, the family was pleased to hear the surgeon's assurances but they were convinced that "Doctors do not always tell the truth about cancer and you just can't be sure." Mrs. Roberts could not bear to look at her own body and she refused to have sexual intercourse with Mr. Roberts. Thus, following hospitalization life within the family became more tense than before.

Families in the third category, *extensive* impact, were faced with the necessity of adjusting to the disturbing influences of severe forms of physical disease or socioemotional behavior. The occurrence of a heart attack, the existence of chronic alcoholism, advancing malignancy, and so on were very disquieting to the spouse. In all instances, the patients could no longer carry out their usual family roles. They were reduced to dependency; understandably, the impact on the family was extensive.

The Feltons were typical of this category. Mrs. Felton had delayed having children because of her interest in teaching instrumental music. Her work was very satisfying, but when she developed heart failure, loss of vision, and renal difficulties as concomitants of her two-year history of diabetes, she had to give up her music because she was incapacitated physically and emotionally. She became progressively dependent upon her husand. Mr. Felton owned and operated a small business. He had a wide circle of friends and associates, whom he saw often. Although each spouse had developed a satisfying life of his own, they were very close to and dependent upon each other; each was, at the same time, a child and a parent to the other.

After the hospitalization, Mrs. Felton felt better for a short time, but she soon accumulated fluid, had difficulty with leg pains, became short of breath and incontinent of urine, and could not sleep. As she demanded increasing amounts of Mr. Felton's time and attention, he was required to reduce his outside activities and carry on his business in as brief a period of the day as possible. Mrs. Felton saw little hope of ever returning to her music. Mr. Felton was annoyed with the doctors for their undue optimism at the time of his wife's discharge from the hospital and their failure to understand that Mrs. Felton had become dependent upon him night and day. He was able to secure a licensed practical nurse for daytime care, but at night he waited upon her. The Feltons thought often of two close family members who had died just a few months before Mrs. Felton's hospitalization. This experience with death, combined with the illness itself, depressed and frightened the Feltons; at the same time they had to adjust to the problems of physical disability and dependency. Mr. Felton told us, "Life has become hellish."

Another illustration of this category is the Ronco family. In the two years prior to this admission Mr. Ronco had been hospitalized seven times for a total of seventy-five days. He had been a chronic alcoholic for many years and had been treated for bleeding esophageal varices, hepatic coma, meningitis, and renal disease. When he developed liver failure, he stopped drinking and entered therapy in the outpatient department of the hospital where he responded so well he became almost a mascot. His adjustment to treatment was a kind of symbiosis in which he exchanged his body and its diseases in return for limited therapy and the status the clinic physicians and nurses gave him for performing a superior role as a patient.

Although Mr. Ronco had been a social problem to his family, he had always been able to produce an income to support them. When he developed liver failure he and his spouse became dependent upon the meager resources available through social security for total disability and the contributions of their three adult children. Mr. Ronco required special diets, transportation to and from the hospital clinic, and hospital care, all of which drained the family economy. Mrs. Ronco had completed only six grades of school. At age 60 she had no skills with which to earn money outside the home and was needed at home to prepare the diets to maintain the delicate balance of her husband's health. They were not eligible for public welfare as they had some small savings and a house. Financial problems, the daily worry of preparing special meals for Mr. Ronco, and the necessity for his many trips to the hospital created a new way of life that had an extensive impact on Mrs. Ronco.

A *catastrophic* impact occurred invariably when one spouse was severely disabled for any reason or had a poor prognosis and faced an early death. When families in this category confronted untreatable physical or mental disease, family functioning was altered initially because the patient was unable to perform his accustomed roles, but when death occurred the family structure was changed by the dissolution of the spouse pair.

The Lottso family, whose story is told partly in Chapter 15, illustrated the catastrophic impact of an illness upon the spouse. When we first asked their general practitioner for permission to include Mrs. Lottso in the study, he characterized the Lottsos as a "rough-hewn, working-class family." Mr. Lottso was a subforeman in a local factory, earning $115 per week. Although he had been with this plant for fifteen years and had relatively high seniority in his union, he thought his limited education would keep him from advancing further. The Lottsos had three children, a married daughter who was living out of the country at an army post with her husband, and two teen-aged sons.

Mrs. Lottso was suffering from metastatic cancer. During her first admission to this hospital some years earlier, a radical mastectomy had been performed. According to Mrs. Lottso, who had attended school only through the ninth grade, she had "mastitis." She knew it had something to do with her breast, but she wasn't sure just what it was. The surgeon told her, "You're one of the lucky ones. We got it all." She was satisfied and returned home.

Four years later a pain in her hip took her to .the family physician who diagnosed it at first as "arthritis" and then later as "bursitis." A few weeks later her leg gave way and she was brought to the hospital with a "broken leg." Mr. Lottso, informed of his wife's real diagnosis, begged the physicians to keep it from her, and our data collectors were warned within one minute of our first contact with her family physician never to indicate to her that she had cancer. Mr. Lottso told the physicians he wanted to do "everything possible for her." During the six subsequent hospitalizations Mrs. Lottso was treated for her "arthritis and bursitis" by chemotherapy and surgery, to which she consented when the physicians told her it would help to alleviate the pain if it didn't actually make her "better." An orthopedic surgeon put a pin in her leg, repeated this a second time when the "tissues failed to hold," and then had to remove it in a third operation.

During this long and expensive series of treatments and hospitalizations Mr. Lottso attempted to adjust his domestic and economic problems while under intense emotional strain. He decided to sell the family's six-room house in a suburban town to help cut down expenses. He moved with his sons into a flat in a four-family house, owned by Mrs. Lottso's sister, in a residential area near the factory. In this way the sister would be available to assist Mrs. Lottso when she was home from the hospital, and Mr. Lottso would be nearer his place of work and would have more time for the family chores which now became his obligation. He tried to prepare his sons for their mother's death. He told us: "My sons are men all the way." Yet, the sons seldom visited their mother in the hospital. Mrs. Lottso explained their absence to us: "They're busy—one with his girl friend, and the other with his old car."

During the last eighteen months of Mrs. Lottso's life, her husband was frantic with fear that she would learn of her malignancy. His anxiety about her possible suicide was the controlling factor in his relationships with her and with the physician. By entering into a "conspiracy of silence" with the physicians he thought he was prolonging her life. As time passed, Mr. Lottso became increasingly worried about money. In the first year of Mrs. Lottso's terminal illness he nearly exhausted the limits of his Blue Cross, Blue Shield, and major medical insurance coverage, spent an additional $2,500 of his earnings, and owed $1,800 more in medical bills. By early fall of the second year, he had used up all of his benefits. Mrs. Lottso, ignorant of her impending death, worried most about the cost of her illness and its effects upon her husband and sons. She told us, "Doctors charge lots of money. Hospitals and doctors are so expensive these days." However, she did not communicate her fears about the expense to her husband and he did not communicate his fears about her illness to her.

At Mrs. Lottso's final admission to this hospital, Mr. Lottso had an argument with the admissions officer. Mrs. Lottso was brought in by ambulance and, at Mr. Lottso's request, put into a private accommodation. The admissions officer intercepted Mr. Lottso, who had been parking his car, and challenged his ability to pay for the accommodation. Mr. Lottso was furious. Although his wife had been in the semiprivate accommodations previously, he had always been able to pay the bills and he could not understand the hospital's concern now that his wife was so ill. Mr. Lottso had failed to realize that his major medical policy was limited to $10,000 in any one year and the hospital had already collected $9,500 from it in that year. By the third day, Mr. Lottso agreed to have her transferred to semiprivate accommodations, partly to save money and partly because he felt there was less chance of her committing suicide if other patients were in the room with her.

The day before the Lottsos' insurance benefits expired completely, a hospital social worker came to the semiprivate room and told Mrs. Lottso she had better have her husband arrange a transfer to a convalescent home. When Mr. Lottso came to the hospital and heard about it, he questioned the social worker and was told that the hospital had done all it could for Mrs. Lottso. He told us later, "I didn't believe them. I put two and two together and I realized that as long as the money lasted the doctors and the hospital were interested in helping my wife, but my insurance was all gone." He knew, however, that the hospital would not "toss her out." Instead of looking for a convalescent home, he went to the personnel officer in his factory and explained his predicament. The personnel officer telephoned the hospital and made arrangements for Mrs. Lottso to have credit for a month with the assurance that the factory would help pay the bill if necessary. The personnel officer then contacted the Cancer Society. Upon learning of Mr. Lottso's financial problems, the Cancer Society agreed to pay $300 toward Mrs. Lottso's medical expenses. Three weeks later Mrs. Lottso died.

Mr. Lottso was bitter about the way he had been handled by the hospital and toward the long series of physicians who had treated his wife. He had accumulated a total of $6,500 in medical bills after his insurance benefits were exhausted. Although Mrs. Lottso had been cared for by specialists during the last 142 days of her life, which were spent in the hospital, the family practitioner sent a bill for $1,700 for his calls. Mr. Lottso felt there was nothing he could do about this. He told us, "They just drain it out of a working man." However, he felt justified in the lengthy expenditure:

> I wanted the best for her. I can honestly say I tried to give her the best of care, the best of doctors, and the best of everything within my means, and even beyond my means. And if I had to do the same thing over again, which I hope to God I never have to, I wouldn't have done it any differently. My conscience is clear. I tried to give her the best.

A year after Mrs. Lottso's death, the family structure had deteriorated. Mr. Lottso was living alone in a single room—"My bachelor quarters," he wryly commented. He was separated from his sons; one had dropped out of high school and enlisted in the army; the other had married, moved to another city, and was working part time while he attended barber's school. Depressed and isolated, Mr. Lottso was alone with his memories. He had no plans to remarry. He told us, "Remembering how she suffered tears my heart out, but my conscience is clear. I did all I could. I think she's in peace now."

The four categories of the impact of the patient's illness on the spouse,

TABLE 50. EMOTIONAL IMPACT OF THE ILLNESS UPON THE SPOUSE, BY ACCOMMODATION

Patients	N	Impact on Spouse			
		Minimal	Moderate	Extensive	Catastrophic
A. BY ACCOMMODATION*					
Private	65	39%	22%	28%	12%
Semiprivate	54	39	32	22	7
Ward	42	14	31	29	26
Total	161				
B. BY SERVICE†					
Medical	74	18	32	35	15
Surgical	87	45	23	18	14
Total	161				

* Private compared to semiprivate, $p > .05$; private compared to ward, $p < .05$; semiprivate compared to ward, $p < .05$.
† $p < .05$

defined and illustrated above, are summarized in Table 50. The impact of the illness on the spouse was related significantly to accommodation in two of the three sets of comparisons presented in section A of this table: The effects were different on the families with a spouse housed on the wards than on those in semiprivate and private accommodations; there were no meaningful differences in the impact of the illness on the spouses of the semiprivate and private patients. There were few differences in the proportion of spouses who were affected moderately or extensively from one accommodation to another. The sharp differences were found at the two extremes.

Viewed from the perspective of the service on which the patient was treated, the impact on the spouse differed significantly; the greatest difference was concentrated among the minimal reactions. The effect of the illness on the spouse was greater among the medical patients for the two categories of moderate or severe impact, but there was no difference between the two services in the proportion who experienced a catastrophic effect. There were no meaningful differences by sex.

The impact of the illness on the spouse was influenced by the nature of the illness. Organic illness produces either temporary or continuing physiological and structural changes in the body; this fact is so well known to physicians and laymen it hardly needs to be either defended or illustrated. However, the way we summarized physical effects on the patients does need to be explained. First, we made an assessment of the discernible physical effects of the illness on the patient. Then we classified our assessments into one of four categories: *none, slight, moderate,* or *severe.* The physical effects of the illness were nonexistent or undiscernible in the *none* group. Among persons who had been treated for uncomplicated restorative surgery, the effects were negligible and, thus, they were rated as *slight.* Persons who were recovering from myocardial infarctions and compromised pulmonory functions as well as breast amputations were classified in the *moderate* category. All persons who died between admission and the home interview and persons with limb

TABLE 51. PHYSICAL DISABILITY OF THE PATIENT AND EMOTIONAL
IMPACT OF THE ILLNESS ON THE SPOUSE

Physical Disability of Patient	Emotional Impact on Spouse			
	Minimal	Moderate	Extensive	Catastrophic
None	75%	52%	26%	8%
Slight	14	12	26	4
Moderate	11	27	26	25
Severe	—	9	22	63
N =	(51)	(44)	(42)	(24)

$p < .05$; $\bar{C} = .66$.

amputations, chronic congestive heart failure, advanced carcinomatosis, and incapacitating chronic pulmonary disease were given a rating of *severe* physical effect. In short, the physical ratings summarized in the left-hand stub of Table 51 were based upon the degree to which the disease had compromised the body's capacity to perform in a healthy manner. The ratings of the emotional effects of a patient's physical disability on the spouse, shown in the headings of the columns of Table 51, are the ones we defined earlier and summarized in Table 50. Separate analyses of the interrelationships between the physical disability of the patients and the emotional effects of the illness on the spouse by accommodation, service, and sex revealed that in each type of comparison, the two were strongly associated with one another. Therefore, we present only the summary for the 161 patients and their spouses.

The percentages in Table 51 show a strong relationship between the extent of physical disability a patient had and his spouse's emotional reaction to the illness. Stated briefly, when a patient had no physical disability the emotional effect of the illness on the spouse was minimal; when the patient had a severe physical disability the spouse exhibited a strong emotional reaction.

TABLE 52.   PERFORMANCE DISABILITY OF THE PATIENTS AND THE EMOTIONAL IMPACT ON THE SPOUSE

Performance Disability of Patients	Emotional Impact on Spouse			
	Minimal	Moderate	Extensive	Catastrophic
None or slight*	42%	8%	—	—
Moderate	42	79	46%	8%
Severe	16	13	54	92
N =	(51)	(44)	(42)	(24)
$p < .05$; $\bar{C} = .76$.				

* The 21 patients who did not have a performance disability were combined with the group of *slight* disability for the chi-square analysis.

While there was a high association between the physical handicap resulting from the illness and the spouse's emotional reaction, the relationship was even stronger when we examined the data from the perspective of the patient's ability to perform his usual family and work roles. The corrected coefficient of contingency of .76 in Table 52 reveals that the emotional reaction of the well spouse to the sick spouse was linked closely to the level of the sick person's inability to perform his usual roles in the family after the development of the illness.

We examined the possible interrelations between the emotional impact of the illness on the spouse and three factors which could conceivably have an influence on the way spouses reacted to their sick mates: maladjustment in the family, sex of the patient, and pre-illness mental status of the patient. Family maladjustment and pre-illness mental status of the patient were inter-related but neither was related to the impact of the illness on the spouse. We infer that the spouses had learned to live with one another's idiosyncracies before the illness became a central problem. Likewise, the sex of the patient did not appreciably influence the reaction of the spouse; this finding means that when the patient was a male the emotional effect on the wife was not essentially different from what it was when the sexes were reversed. We conclude that illness upset the symbiotic balance of a spouse pair to about the same extent regardless of whether the sick member was the husband or the wife. In the psychic economy of the nuclear family each spouse played a reciprocal role to the other. Illness upset the accustomed functions of one member of the pair and the other member reacted emotionally to the situation.

In Chapter 15 we pointed out that forty spouses were widowed between the time we selected the family for study and the end of data collection. Thirty-nine of the forty deaths resulted from a chronic disabling disease; one individual died unexpectedly from an illness that was unrelated to that for which he had been hospitalized when he was selected for this study. Two persons who were hospitalized for chronic diseases died unexpectedly from complications of their diseases during the hospitalization in which they had been chosen for study. The death of the other thirty-seven had been expected for varying lengths of time. We now consider the reactions of the surviving spouse to the fact of death.

Death represented a permanent break in a network of human relations which had extended over a period of years. In some seven families out of ten the spouse pair had remained intact from the time of marriage until it was broken by death. In all instances, death represented the loss of a key person in the family, either the husband and father or the wife and mother. It required the surviving family members to readjust their lives physically, emotionally, and socially to the loss. The chronically ill persons had suffered extensively and intensively from organic diseases for varying lengths of time. Death, while it marked the end of life for them, brought relief from suffering. The spouse especially, but other family members also, had endured the complications of the disease and its effects on them personally, as well as the prolongation of life and its attendant sufferings through the treatment of the patient's disease; although treatment kept the patient alive longer it did not always bring relief from either physical or emotional pain. The continuation of life and suffering was accompanied also by added expenses the family had to meet whether or not they were able to bear the burden.

The real feelings of the surviving spouse were difficult to plumb because of the emotional turmoil associated with death and because the widowed person did not like to share his or her emotions. Although it was awkward to interview the surviving spouses, we found them willing to communicate to our neutrally sympathetic ears their reactions to the illness and death of their loved ones. Sometimes veiled in circumlocutions, sometimes in denials, sometimes in real sorrow and deep emotional pain, they told us either directly or indirectly that death was a relief from their grief-filled life with a chronically ill, incurable spouse.

Release from the threat of the illness was expressed by all of the surviving spouses of persons who had died from chronic illnesses. A sense of relief was expressed cautiously as a rule, since to rejoice openly was viewed as inappropriate behavior. Openly verbalized expressions of relief were linked with the suffering of the dead person—"He is better off now, considering how he suffered." "There was no good life left." "Who wants to live with all that suffering."—rather than with the surcease from emotional pain for the survivor. However, a few spouses phrased their release from tension in terms of the welfare of the family—"It was horrible for all of us especially near the end."

A second type of reaction, observed in the statements of the surviving spouse about life with the now dead person, was focused around the social roles the deceased had played in the network of family relationships. From the stories the surviving spouse had told, we became aware that the spouse's death was often a welcomed event. By relating the difficulties of living with the dead person the survivor may have been asking indirectly—*Can you blame me for not being broken up over the loss of my spouse?*

Each of the surviving spouses of the thirty-nine patients who died of chronic disease expressed a sense of relief that the long struggle with death was over. Each felt a sense of release from strain that had lasted an indeterminate period of time. In addition, 59 per cent voiced a distinct feeling of freedom from complicated family strife. In these families the dead spouse had been a key figure in the turmoil which encompassed the family. The surviving spouse realized this fact and it entered into his or her response to the bereavement.

The figures in Table 53 show a strong relationship between the surviving spouse's statement on how he or she felt about the dead spouse's part in family conflict and the degree of maladjustment in the family. The greatest concentration of persons who voiced a sense of release from family turmoil occurred in families we rated as severely maladjusted.

The life history of the late Mrs. Ingraham was related to us by her husband and her two adolescent children, as well as by Mrs. Ingraham, herself,

TABLE 53. FAMILY MALADJUSTMENT AND EXPRESSED SENSE OF
RELIEF AT DEATH OF SPOUSE

	Family Maladjustment		
Reaction at Death of Spouse	None or slight*	Moderate*	Severe
Expressed relief	—	17%	84%
Did not express relief	100%	83	16
N =	(2)	(12)	(25)
$p < .05$; $\bar{C} = .88$.			

* None or slight category combined with moderate maladjustment
category in the chi-square analysis.

before her death. She was the only child of well-to-do parents who married
late in life. She lived in a "Victorian" household, cared for by servants and
raised by a domineering maiden aunt who controlled the family fortune, a
passive bachelor uncle, and her mother, widowed early in her marriage, whom
Mrs. Ingraham described as a woman with a "will of steel." Each member
of this truncated family attempted to direct the child, demanding much and
complaining of their disappointment when she rebelled. Caught in this vortex
of competing family forces she began to fantasize over her dead father, believing he was the only person in her life who had been kindly and understanding.

After graduation from a well-known woman's college Mrs. Ingraham,
much against the wishes of her mother, aunt, and uncle, married a man of
limited means and ambition. In many ways she was an annoyance to her husband: She disliked housework and shopping for groceries; when she found
she was pregnant for the second time she moved into a room of her own and
never again permitted Mr. Ingraham to have sexual intercourse with her.
Although she had a considerable income which she shared with her husband
and children, she always attached disconcerting "strings" to her giving which
strained family relations. She was "cool," "distant," yet "indulgent" with
her family.

Following the birth of her second child, Mrs. Ingraham developed lupus
erythematosus. This disease advanced slowly before it took a serious turn.
For ten years she was treated by a general practitioner, but Mrs. Ingraham did
not completely believe any doctor and regulated much of her treatment and
medication herself. Although she consulted specialists in several cities, she
was the one who decided when and where she would be hospitalized and
how often she would take the medications she chose to take. In due time she
managed to get prescriptions for steroid drugs from more than one physician,

taking them in very large amounts until her bones became decalcified. She suddenly developed a spontaneous fracture of the leg as she stepped out of her car, and it was for this injury that she was hospitalized.

The physician anticipated no problems since Mrs. Ingraham's disease, although chronic in nature, was essentially mild. Mrs. Ingraham, however, prepared her will and included within it detailed instructions concerning her death and memorial services. (She stipulated that her body was to be cremated and her ashes sprinkled on her father's grave.) She continued to be distant to her family, directing her children not to visit, as she had been at odds with them before the hospitalization. She did not develop a trusting relationship with her physician or her nurses. During the hospitalization, an attempt was made to remove the steroids, upon which she had become dependent. Complications developed and suddenly and unexpectedly she died, more from the treatment of the disease than from the disease itself.

The feelings of the family toward this woman were discovered during the home visit. Initially, their sense of relief at her death was hidden but as the visit continued the family described her domineering ways and her most unsatisfactory performance as wife and mother. Mr. Ingraham told us:

> Considering all these things, perhaps it's best this way. I carried out her wishes to the letter, but she never was a happy woman. This was very hard on us. I'm almost ashamed to say it, but in less than a month after her death the children and I are closer than we ever were before. We have always been close but strangely now we are even closer. No one has cried, not even the girl, about her death, except momentarily. The children are continuing in school and they're doing all right. Of course, what we'll do in the future it is too early to tell.

A similar case is the story of Mr. Banes who had been a successful salesman. Unfortunately, he was in a business in which the use of alcohol was an accepted part of the selling process. Gradually, the drinking became a problem undermining Mr. Banes' health and his ability to work regularly. Over a period of seven years his health failed and, as his illness progressed, his income was reduced. To supplement the family income Mrs. Banes found a job as a secretary, at first part time then later full time, but her salary was not sufficient to make up for Mr. Banes' loss of income and it was wholly inadequate to meet the medical expenses that began to mount.

The relationship between Mr. and Mrs. Banes had not been satisfactory since Mr. Banes had become a chronic alcoholic. She found life with him unpleasant and told us, "The story of my life would read like a serial of tragic dramas." The one satisfying aspect of her life was their only child, a teen-age son in high school who was planning to go to college.

Mr. Banes had long feared hospitals and distrusted physicians. As a consequence, when he had his first heart attack, Mrs. Banes had to argue with him for two days before he agreed to call their family physician. He refused the hospitalization recommended by the physician and remained at home while he recovered from the attack. A second heart attack, which occurred two years later, was treated in the same fashion. Eventually, congestive heart failure developed, as well as diabetes and iatrogenic hypothyroidism, and Mr. Banes lost his job. Because of his disability he had to accept dependency upon his wife, but he refused to see doctors or go to the hospital. Mrs. Banes became the sole financial and emotional support of the family, working outside the home all day, nursing her husband and performing all the chores of the homemaker in the early mornings and evenings. As Mr. Banes tended to sleep in the day when he was alone and be wakeful and lonely at night, Mrs. Banes sat up with him a good part of every night. For nine months she carried out this exhausting routine until Mr. Banes deteriorated noticeably. A major break then occurred in the relationship between the spouses. Mrs. Banes felt she could no longer meet her husband's demands. Mr. Banes begged to be left at home, but Mrs. Banes requested assistance from their family doctor who referred them to the hospital.

Mr. Banes had been unemployed for almost a year and there was no medical insurance, but the Baneses had expected semiprivate accommodations "at the very least" and the concern of their own doctor. However, this physician had made an accurate assessment of their financial position and the probable prognosis of Mr. Banes' illness; he did not telephone the hospital. Mr. and Mrs. Banes came to the hospital alone and were directed to the emergency service. Upon examination, the medical admitting officer recommended Mr. Banes be admitted to the hospital.

Both spouses were shocked when Mr. Banes was given a bed on the ward accommodation. The hospital admitting officer suggested that Mrs. Banes consult the Welfare Department concerning the payment of the hospital bill and funds on which to live. Mrs. Banes was distraught at the implication that she and her husband were "welfare cases," but she consulted the Welfare Department and was told the family would have to be destitute before they would be entitled to welfare support.

Since Mr. Banes had never been hospitalized before, the members of his committee assumed he was in the beginning phases of chronic congestive heart failure, and they were optimistic. They told him, "You'll get up and walk out of here," and they told Mrs. Banes at first that her husband was doing well. She reported to us, "They keep encouraging me, telling me he's coming along okay, but I can't see it."

Mrs. Banes came regularly to visit her husband during his hospitalization and attempted to look attractive for him, but she was so ashamed of the implications of the ward accommodation that she did not permit any friends to visit him. Mr. Banes became convinced that his wife had abandoned him to his fate. He had little confidence in the young physicians in charge of his care. He told us the hospital is a place from which "most people go out in a pine box." As the hospitalization wore on, it became apparent that Mr. Banes would not leave the hospital alive. At this point the physicians changed their story to Mrs. Banes and she began to doubt their reports. She wondered if he had cancer but she did not ask the doctors. One day when she came to visit she was startled to find his bed in the ward empty and felt relief at the thought he had died. When she discovered that he had been taken to the X-ray department for further examination she became worried about the cost and complained to us, "What good will X rays do him now?"

By the time death arrived, Mrs. Banes had become very confused. She could not understand the conflicting reports of the doctors. Humiliated by her enforced association with welfare clients, the ward service, and the changing opinions of the committee physicians, she refused permission for a post-mortem examination. She was unmoved by the intern's pleas and said that she had had enough and her husband had had enough. She told us, "I may take a slow boat to China and forget the whole thing."

Sobered by many years of marital discord and relieved of the burden of a chronically ill husband, Mrs. Banes resolved to make the most of her limited resources. Since her income was small, her son gave up a tuition scholarship to a famous university and attended a local college where they could afford the living expenses. Regarding their hospital and other debts and the expenses of college, Mrs. Banes said, "My son is a nice young man. He is understanding and helpful. We will make out with the help of God."

A similar case was that of Mr. Gordon, part of whose story is told in Chapter 11. Mr. Gordon had had trouble in both his family of orientation and his family of procreation. Ten years before his death he divorced his first wife, with whom he had had one son, and married again. Although he worked steadily and was popular at work, he was in the habit of drinking heavily and was unreliable in his relationship with his second wife. Actually, he was a man who wanted to be liked but had little to offer his wife and other family members. He considered his home primarily a place to sleep; each evening after work he went to a tavern where he stayed and drank until closing time. Mrs. Gordon felt more like a widow than a wife. However, she depended upon her husband for financial support and she appreciated his gesture of paying for an annual two-week vacation in Florida for her. Mr. Gordon felt close to his son and two grandsons and to his sister who became fond of Mrs. Gordon. They understood her problems and were sympathetic.

Whenever there was a family gathering on a holiday, Mr. Gordon drank heavily and became provocative. He teased his grandchildren and nieces and nephews until they cried. He realized this often led to family fights but he seemed not to be able to control his behavior for which he usually apologized later to members of the family. Mrs. Gordon suffered from his actions and relied upon his family to help her deal with his drinking and abusiveness.

At the time of Mr. Gordon's death, Mrs. Gordon went immediately to stay with his family, as he had suggested, and arranged with them for the burial. She had ample money from the insurance policy to live comfortably. As soon as the first payment from the insurance company arrived, she bought a new car so she would be free to visit family and friends. Both Mrs. Gordon and his family promoted a legend of Mr. Gordon as a willing, productive worker who "couldn't help it if he was born Peck's bad boy." The family felt relief from his provocations and were enjoying the fruits of his years of work; they began to tell humorous stories of his life which included "high weekends," barroom brawls, and constant rampages within the family. A year after his death Mrs. Gordon told us:

> I couldn't be happier. I have my car and I live with his sister and her family. They look out for me like I was one of their own. I visit his son and grandchildren most evenings. I never went back to the place we had after he died. I never wanted to. His family took care of all that.

The experiences of these three families are illustrative of the sense of release some families exhibited after the death of a husband or wife who suffered from a chronic illness. The surviving spouse and others in the family had come to realize long before the death that when the person was healthy he represented both an asset and a liability. When stricken with chronic illness, however, the assets eroded; the liabilities increased, and were often compounded. In a family burdened by complicated interpersonal relations, fights, and quarrels, as both the Ingraham and the Gordon families were, the underlying strife, characterizing family relationships before the onset of illness, was exacerbated. The feelings family members had about one another in life carried on in the memories of the living after death had broken family ties.

Summary

In order to assess an individual's reaction to his or her spouse's illness, four categories of emotional impact were developed—minimal, moderate, extensive, and catastrophic. The impact of the illness on the spouses of ward patients was significantly greater than that on the spouses of semiprivate and private patients. There were few differences from one accommodation to another in the proportion of spouses affected moderately or extensively, but there were sharp differences at the two extremes. Although the impact on the spouses of medical patients was more often moderate or severe than among the spouses of surgical patients, there was no difference between the two services in the proportion of spouses who experienced a catastrophic effect.

Analyses of the relationship between physical disability of the patient and emotional effects of the illness on the spouse revealed a strong relationship between the kind of physical disability and the emotional impact. Moreover, the emotional reaction of the well spouse to the sick spouse was associated closely with the level of the sick person's ability to perform his usual roles in the family. There was a strong relationship between family maladjustment and an expressed sense of relief at the death of the patient.

A COMPREHENSIVE STUDY OF INTERDEPENDENCE BETWEEN illness in a family and the economic burden it created would have required detailed data on the direct and indirect costs of illnesses over the years. The direct costs would have included expenditures on all types of health services—physicians, dentists, nurses, hospitals, insurance, medicine, transportation to and from doctors' offices and hospitals, and so on—for every member of the family. Indirect costs would have included loss of income from illness and estimated value of the contributions of nongainfully employed members to the economy of the family and of relatives and friends to the care of the sick. In brief, to make a detailed study of the burden of the illness on a family would have required far more data than we gathered in this study.

In this chapter we draw attention to *selected aspects* of the general problem of the economic effects of illness on a family. We are concerned with the economic burden on the family of a spouse's illness rather than with the broader issues mentioned above. Four questions are posed and answered: (1) *How much did it cost to be hospitalized?* (2) *How was the hospital bill paid?* (3) *What economic effects did this illness have on the family?* (4) *How much did a terminal illness cost?*

Three sources of data were drawn upon to answer these questions. Answers to the first and second questions were based upon the financial records of the hospital. The third and fourth questions were answered from information the family members gave us regarding the impact of the illness on the family from its beginning through the convalescence. For those patients whose illness experiences ended in death, our estimates of the cost of the terminal illness were derived from conversations with the surviving spouse and other responsible adults in the family who were conversant with the costs of the illness.

The exact amounts charged each patient during the hospitalization were made available to us by the accounting office of the hospital. The charges are summarized into eight groups: room and board, laboratory, X rays and X-ray therapy, drugs, operating room, other diagnostic procedures, other therapies, and miscellaneous. All patients were charged for board and room, but other charges were levied only if a particular service was rendered. Thus, the number of patients who were billed for a given service can vary from one group to another. For those receiving a given service, the average amount charged for each item in each accommodation is given in Table 54. Almost all patients were billed for laboratory tests so that the means in this category are a reflection of the three divisions of the study group. On the other hand, only 54 per cent of the private, 55 per cent of the semiprivate, and 41 per cent of the ward patients were charged for the operating room, anesthesia, or the recovery room. The result is that the several means for each accommodation are based upon a varying number of charges; the number of patients who were charged particular amounts for a given service influenced the t-test. This point is essential to understanding the comparisons of the means in each series of items. To correct for this the pooled variances of each group

TABLE 54. MEAN DOLLAR CHARGES FOR LISTED ITEMS BY ACCOMMODATION AND SERVICE

Category	Mean Charges			Significant at 5% Level
	Private	Semiprivate	Ward	
A. BY ACCOMMODATION				
Room and board	$365	$284	$318	P-SP, P-W*
Laboratory	124	85	158	SP-W
X ray and X-ray therapy	77	81	56	SP-W
Drugs	30	26	49	P-W, SP-W
Operating room	124	116	168	P-W, SP-W
Other diagnostic procedures	22	16	29	SP-W
Other therapies	27	50	74	P-SP, P-W
Miscellaneous	18	15	34	P-W, SP-W
Mean of all items	$666	$547	$723	P-SP, SP-W
B. BY SERVICE	Medicine	Surgery		Significance
Room and board	$371	$288		p < .05
Laboratory	154	91		p < .05
X ray and X-ray therapy	81	59		p < .05
Drugs	36	32		p > .05
Operating room	78	134		p < .05
Other diagnostic procedures	26	16		p < .05
Other therapies	72	34		p < .05
Miscellaneous	15	26		p < .05
Mean of all items	$691	$598		p < .05

* P-SP, private compared with semiprivate; P-W, private compared with ward; SP-W, semiprivate compared with ward.

were used when the means of only two groups were compared to determine if they differed significantly.

The significance of difference for each group of items for each accommodation is shown in the fourth column of Table 54, section A. For example, the mean amount patients were charged for X ray and X-ray therapy in each accommodation was: private, $77; semiprivate, $81; ward, $56; the mean charges for X ray and X-ray therapy were significantly higher for semiprivate patients in comparison with ward patients. They were not significantly greater than we would expect by chance at the 5 per cent level of probability for the other two sets of comparisons—private compared to semiprivate and private compared to ward. Potentially, each type of charge could differ from the other two accommodation comparisons. Actually, there was a significant difference for at least one accommodation group in comparison with one of the others, but in none of the eight groups of items for which charges were made was any one of the three accommodation groups significantly different from the two others. The mean of all items differed significantly when the private patients were compared with the semiprivate patients; likewise, there was a significant difference when we compared the semiprivate patients with the ward patients. Overall, the lowest mean cost was in the semiprivate and the highest in the ward accommodation. These findings reflect the differences in the severity of illnesses of patients and, to a lesser extent, differential charges for room and board in the different accommodations.

The mean charges for each group of items by service are shown in Table 54, section B. These charges differed significantly for seven of the eight sets of items. The charge for room and board was higher for the medical patients because they were hospitalized longer than surgical patients; they had more laboratory tests and also were subject more to X rays and, therefore, to higher charges. The operating room, anesthesia, and recovery room charges, naturally, were concentrated more heavily in the surgical group. The balance shifted to the medical patients in other diagnostic and therapy charges. The charges for drugs did not differ from one service to the other. Overall, it cost more to be hospitalized on the medical than on the surgical service.

The mean number of days patients were hospitalized did not differ significantly by accommodation, as a glance at Table 55 shows. However, the mean charges per day of hospital care did. The ward patients were charged more than the semiprivate patients but not significantly more than the private patients.

The differences between the length of stay in the hospital and the mean charges per day were significant between the medical and the surgical services. Medical patients stayed in the hospital longer than surgical patients, but the cost per day was higher for the surgical patients.

TABLE 55. RELATIONSHIP OF MEAN DOLLAR CHARGES PER
PATIENT DAY TO DAYS OF HOSPITALIZATION, BY
ACCOMMODATION AND SERVICE

Patients	Length of Hospitalization	Charges per Day
A. BY ACCOMMODATION		
Private	11 days	$60
Semiprivate	10	55
Ward	12	61
Significant	—	W-SP*
B. BY SERVICE		
Medicine	12 days	$56
Surgery	9	63
Significance	p < .05	p < .05

* W-SP, ward compared with semiprivate.

The 161 patients received bills totalling $106,245 for the services the hospital had rendered during the single admission we studied intensively. From the viewpoint of the hospital, accounts were settled through payments and allowances; payments were made to the hospital by the patient or his family, his insurance company, or welfare; allowances were made to meet the conditions of a particular patient or the contractual agreement between the hospital and a third-party payer.

In Table 56 we present only the overall data on sources of payment since no significant difference was found between accommodation, service, and sex. Practically all Blue Cross payments were derived from contracts between employers and the Blue Cross association in the state. Other insurance included that issued primarily by private insurance companies to individuals and families. As in the case of Blue Cross, some of this insurance was established by conditions of employment. Approximately 71 per cent of the charges levied by the hospital were paid by insurance policies of one kind of another. Welfare payments constituted but a small portion of payments. Only four

TABLE 56. SOURCE OF PAYMENT OF HOSPITAL BILL

Source of Payment	Amount Paid	Percentage of Bill
Patient and/or family	$21,690	20%
Blue Cross	50,558	48
Other insurance	24,676	23
Welfare	1,382	1
Hospital allowances	4,126	4
Balance due	3,813	4
Total	$106,245	100%

patients had part of their bills paid by the local or state governments. No patient had his entire bill paid by a public welfare agency. Allowances were a bookkeeping device used by the hospital to adjust any differences that arose between what a patient's insurance policy paid for a specified service and what the hospital charged. They were spread over the three accommodations and both services. Some patients were entitled to discounts as a prerogative of their employment with the hospital. Also, physicians on the staff were given a discount on the portion of their bill not covered by insurance.

The estimated charges for the hospitalization, over and above any insurance payments, were generally collected in cash before an elective admission of a ward patient. (However, particularly on the medical service, most ward patients required urgent admission.) Other patients, usually semiprivate, who appeared as poor credit risks also were asked for an advance payment by the admitting officer. All other bills were due upon discharge.

Among our patients, the time of the payment of the bill was related to the accommodation on which the patient was housed: Three out of four private and semiprivate patients but only 55 per cent of the ward patients paid all of their bill within 30 days after discharge. The private patients were most likely to pay their bills within six months after discharge, while the ward patients had the highest percentage of unpaid bills after two years. Over all, 3.6 per cent of the aggregate of hospital bills was not paid at the end of a two-year period after discharge.

Among the private and semiprivate patients, the length of time elapsed after discharge until the bill was paid was linked significantly to physician sponsorship. Patients whose sponsorship was committed or casual paid their bills more promptly than those who were sponsored by the semicommittee, as shown in Table 57. The connection between sponsorship of the patient by a physician and the length of time after discharge until his bill was paid was a facet of the status system. We demonstrated in Chapter 8 that a physician's

TABLE 57.   SPONSORSHIP AND TIME OF PAYMENT OF HOSPITAL BILLS, PRIVATE AND SEMIPRIVATE PATIENTS

Time Interval from Discharge to Payment of Bill	Physician Sponsorship*		
	Committed	Casual	Semicommittee
0–30 days	83%	82%	57%
31–180 days	17	9	13
7 months–2 years	—	9	30†‡
N =	(24)	(65)	(30)
p < .05			

* Committed and casual sponsorship combined in chi-square analysis.
† Includes one private patient whose bill was not paid.
‡ Includes three semiprivate patients whose bills were not paid.

sponsorship was associated with a patient's socioeconomic status; thus, the patient's capacity to pay his hospital bill was related likewise to his socioeconomic status. (This aspect of the problem is discussed later in this chapter.)

Two years after discharge from the hospital, the patients had not paid all of their bills; by accommodation they were: private, one; semiprivate, three; and ward, six. Ideally, the bill should have been paid when the patient was discharged from the hospital, but when this did not occur, and it did not in about one half of the discharges, the financial officer attempted to reach a definite understanding with the family as to when and how the bill was to be paid. Negotiations with the family were often drawn out and costly to the hospital, but as long as there appeared to be a reasonable expectation of payment the hospital waited. Payments as small as $1 a week were accepted from families with meager resources. The hospital placed a bill with a collection agency reluctantly; however, when a family did not pay and failed to show plans for payment, the hospital had little choice but to do so.

Of the ten patients with unpaid bills, nine had died. The one patient whose bill was not paid in full and was still living was a ward patient who, at the time we finished the data collection, was working and paying $3 weekly on his bill. The unpaid portions of the bills of the five ward patients who had died were placed with a collection agency, as was the bill of one semiprivate patient who had died. The hospital bill for the one private patient, not paid two years after discharge, was paid later in small amounts by the family.

We now turn from the discussion of payment of the hospital bill to the third issue upon which we focus in this chapter—the economic impact of the illness upon the family. When an individual became ill, the economic effects on his family varied from negligible to devastating, depending upon the nature of the disease and the economic status of the family. A working-class family with few savings might lose its home and be forced to move to less desirable living quarters; the family automobile might have to be given up; a teen-ager might have to drop out of school. On the other hand, a well-to-do family could absorb the cost of an illness with little outward effect. Some wealthy families paid thousands of dollars out of pocket toward health care and were influenced only in minor ways by the payment of physicians' and hospital bills. We classified into four categories the economic effect of the illness on each family: *minor change, moderate hardship, severe hardship,* and *very severe hardship.*

Minor change entailed temporary inconsequential influences on the family's economy. Accordingly, only minor adjustments were necessary. The family was faced with a bill or series of bills which it was able to pay without lowering it. standard of living or making personal sacrifices. The Mulvey family was an example of this category. Mr. Mulvey was a top executive in an international trading company with a salary of $75,000 a year plus bonuses and a share of profits from the business. He was admitted to the hospital for diagnosis and treatment of gastrointestinal complaints. He occupied the most expensive single room in the hospital. At discharge, he paid $116 while Blue Cross paid the balance of the $418 hospital bill; his Blue Shield policy paid the specialist, in large part, for his services. Mr. Mulvey told us that, unless his illness were prolonged, the costs of hospitalization and medical care were inconsequential to him. Mr. and Mrs. Mulvey gave more thought to the new car they were about to purchase for one of their sons than they did to the hospital bill. As far as this family was concerned, inherited wealth combined with earned income assured their way of life. Even the loss of their breadwinner would not radically change their mode of living.

Families facing *moderate hardship* had to make minor adjustments in their living conditions, recreation, and so forth. If the economic losses did not continue they could usually recover their prehospitalization standard of living. Typical of this category is the Kana family. Mr. Kana was a tool designer with an income of $9,500 per year. This family lived modestly and had accumulated some savings for the schooling of their two children. They had the most comprehensive of Blue Cross and Blue Shield insurance. Mrs. Kana suffered from high blood pressure, a minor stroke, blood clots in one eye, heart disease, diabetes, and thyroid disease. Complications from these conditions gave rise to numerous hospitalizations in this and other cities. Over the years, many doctors were used to provide the necessary care. During the ten years prior to the current admission to the hospital, the Kanas had spent, in addition to insurance premiums, an average of $750 annually for medical care for Mrs. Kana and a smaller amount for other family members. The consistent expenditures on Mrs. Kana's health care resulted in the diversion of family funds from savings for old age, a better home, vacations, and social activities. Mr. Kana's one recreation was a men's church club. He was aware of the drain on his finances but with each new physician seen he hoped a "cure or improvement" would appear. The bill for the current hospitalization was $611, of which $125 was paid by the family at the time of discharge and the balance was paid by insurance. The Kanas looked upon these expenditures as unpleasant and unwelcome, but they were far more concerned about Mrs. Kana's health than about the expenditures for her care.

When an illness required a family to consume a large part of its assets to meet the costs of caring for the sick person, the family was classified in the *severe hardship* category. Almost always, the family had to make substantial readjustments in its standard of living sometimes resulting in major sacrifices in the lives of one or more members. (We rate as a major sacrifice, for example, a family member having to leave high school or college to take a job to help the family meet medical bills.)

The Saxon family was severely handicapped financially and personally by a member's illness. Mr. Saxon was employed as a semiskilled machine operator in a metal products factory where he earned $100 per week. After marriage, the Saxons lived in an apartment; when they had saved enough money for a down payment on a home they bought a six-room house in a new development in a suburban town, from which Mr. Saxon commuted to work in the family car. They purchased life insurance to supplement his veterans' insurance. Mr. Saxon was handy with tools and he liked to garden and take care of the home His one outside recreation was a fishing club sponsored, in part, by his fellow workers in the factory. Their two children were happy and did very well in school.

Four years before the present hospitalization Mrs. Saxon began to have pains in her back and a numbness in her right leg. She consulted her family doctor, a general practitioner, who diagnosed her symptoms as arthritis. She took the medication he prescribed for three months without any surcease of symptoms. The doctor then recommended she see a dentist for a "focal infection." This resulted in an extraction of all her teeth and the acquisition of dentures. After three months more had passed without any substantial improvement she was admitted to a general hospital in a nearby city for surgery for "a slipped disk." The fusion of the spine in the lumbar area resulted in partial paralysis of both lower limbs, but by persistence and grim determination Mrs. Saxon learned to walk again. A year later she was admitted to the same hospital for pneumonia and arthritis. Steroid therapy was prescribed and administered to her regularly for almost two years until she began to complain of and was hospitalized for a series of vague symptoms which included muscular weakness, stomach pains, fatigue, and inability to do the housework. After six weeks of her third hospitalization, the physician recommended that she be transferred to this hospital as a special case for "staff care" because her symptoms were "interesting." The committee assigned to her decided after four or five days of tests that she was suffering from lupus erythematosus which was associated with arthritis, pericarditis, central nervous system involvement, anemia, and chronic gall bladder disease.

From the first day of the 45-day hospitalization here, both Mrs. and Mr. Saxon were worried about the expenses of her care. The room and board charges on the ward were $28 per day, while medicines, tests, and treatments were billed as separate items. As the days and weeks of hospitalization dragged on and Mrs. Saxon did not improve, Mr. Saxon became grim. He had spent all the savings they had accumulated in the sixteen years of their marriage on doctors' bills, hospitals, and medicines before Mrs. Saxon had been transferred to this hospital. He knew the medical insurance he held at the factory would cover a large part of the charges but he would still be responsible for some 20 to 25 per cent of the costs. There was no alternative but to drop out of his fishing club and borrow on his life insurance.

Six weeks after admission here, the medical resident decided there was little more the hospital could do for Mrs. Saxon although she was not ready to return home. He asked the social service department to have her transferred to a convalescent hospital in the suburban town in which the Saxons lived. Mr. Saxon arranged, through a friend in the fishing club, for the town ambulance to take Mrs. Saxon to the convalescent hospital without charge. The hospital bill came to $1,200 of which insurance paid $980 and Mr. Saxon paid $220.

For the six months Mrs. Saxon was in the convalescent hospital, Mr. Saxon and the children carried on at home. Mrs. Saxon's mother who had come to keep house during the earlier hospitalization had to return to her home several hundred miles away. The boy, now 15, found a part-time job which threw the burden of dishwashing, house cleaning, and minor chores on his 12-year-old sister. Mr. Saxon continued to supervise the family, commute to work daily, help with the housework, and visit his wife four or five evenings a week. Gradually, Mrs. Saxon's symptoms abated and she learned to walk again. When she finally left the convalescent home, Mr. Saxon was down to the last $50 of a loan from the credit union at the factory.

Mr. Saxon told us the family was at the "end of the rope" financially. The bill at the convalescent hospital was over $2,000. The factory-sponsored insurance policy paid $1,800 but Mr. Saxon did not have the balance. In this crisis the convalescent hospital cancelled the remainder of the bill and marked it paid. During the many months of hospitalization, the family had dropped behind in its mortgage payments on the house. The car broke down and Mr. Saxon had to pay $100 for repairs so he could get back and forth to work, visit Mrs. Saxon, and run errands. The house needed painting badly, the driveway was breaking up, the cement was scaling off the sidewalk, and the lawn was full of weeds. Mr. Saxon apologized for all these things. He told us he hoped "to get on my feet," "fix things up," and "send the boy on through high school."

Two years after Mrs. Saxon's return from the convalescent hospital she was markedly improved; she was able to do her own housework and occasionally to go out socially. Mr. Saxon had succeeded in keeping the family intact. Although the family had suffered severe hardship because of the costs of Mrs. Saxon's illness, they were recovering both emotionally and financially. Nevertheless, Mrs. Saxon suffered from a disease which was likely to become worse and eventually claim her life. Therefore, the economic outlook for the family was uncertain.

Families classified as suffering *very severe hardship* either were impoverished by illness or had borne such economic burdens that it was unlikely their members would be able to recover the standard of living to which they had been accustomed before the patient's illness. The Eastons were a family of this type. They had managed to buy a home on time payments, raise five children, three of whom they sent through high school, and keep a car until a series of illnesses devastated their financial standing. Within five years Mrs. Easton was hospitalized three times—for pneumonia, for a hernia repair, and most recently for breast cancer. The family was able to afford semiprivate accommodations and a private physician although the expense was enormous for Mr. Easton who earned $86 a week as a factory worker. He was not able to keep up the payments on their home, and the family had to move into a rented flat. However, with Mrs. Easton's recovery, only two children still dependent upon them, and Mr. Easton's high seniority in his union, the family began to "get back on our feet" financially. Then illness struck again! Mr. Easton, who was now 49 years old, developed fever and shortness of breath. The family physician, a general practitioner, diagnosed the illness as "the grippe" and told him to take aspirin and cough medicine. When this did not reduce the fever Mr. Easton went to another general practitioner. After five weeks of similar treatment during which the symptoms came and went, Mr. Easton began to feel pain in the right side of his chest. The second physician then advised him to seek help from the hospital clinic. After an examination and chest X ray at the clinic, he was admitted to the hospital for evaluation of a right upper-lobe infiltrate. During the 17-day hospitalization, neither Mr. nor Mrs. Easton was given a diagnosis or told the probable outcome of Mr. Easton's illness. He was discharged and told to return as an outpatient for X-ray therapy. The medical records noted a diagnosis of epidermoid carcinoma of the right lung.

The hospitalization cost $1,024, of which $300 was paid by the family and the difference by Blue Cross and the union insurance. This expenditure exhausted the Eastons' small family savings account. Mr. Easton was not well enough to return to work and, since the $30 a week in sickness compensation from the factory was not sufficient to meet the needs of the family, Mrs. Easton attempted to find a job. She said she would have taken "any old job," but prospective employers looked at her sallow complexion and 90-pound frame and did not want to hire her. The older married children who were struggling to make ends meet and to raise their own families could offer no assistance. In an effort to help the family, the teen-age son found a job after school and on weekends.

Eight weeks after his discharge Mr. Easton was readmitted to the hospital for removal of the chest mass. After the operation the resident told Mr. Easton that they "took the entire lung but everything looks good in there." This completed the exchange between the surgeon and his patient. An assistant resident joked with Mr. Easton and said, "Everything went very well. We were very pleased with how things turned out inside. Dr. ―― [the resident] will tell you all about it when he has time, but you don't need to worry." Although Mr. Easton did not talk with the surgeon again in the twelve days before he was discharged, he told us he had confidence in the ability of the doctors in the hospital to help him.

Ten days later, the resident in thoracic surgery wrote to Mr. Easton's employer:

> Mr. Easton was seen yesterday in our clinic and an additional insurance form has been forwarded to you for him. His progress has been entirely satisfactory and we would anticipate that he would be able to return to employment in four weeks. In view of the fact that the entire lung on one side was removed, it is our opinion that he will not be able to return to his former job which involved considerable heavy lifting and would recommend a lighter form of employment be offered to him, if available.

At this time bills for Mr. Easton's medical care began to mount. The second hospitalization cost slightly more than $1,000 and there were also unpaid bills from two general practitioners, the outpatient department of the hospital, and several pharmacies, as well as for electricity, food, and other necessities. The Eastons had no funds even to start to pay these bills. Their economic problems were complicated by other problems. The building to which they had moved was scheduled to be torn down for redevelopment. Mrs. Easton persuaded the authorities to postpone the demolition of the house for several weeks until the city relocation office found a flat which they could afford. The family was distraught. In a short time, they had moved from a working-class, residential area of single homes to a rented flat in an old, remodeled house in a slum area. They disliked their new neighbors and were resented and disliked in turn. The son hated the new school and was harassed by the neighborhood boys for his academic interests. The daughter was pushed off the sidewalk, cursed, and beaten by the slum girls; she vented her anger on the teachers in the new school and lost interest in her studies.

Instead of recovering from the surgery as predicted, Mr. Easton grew weaker. He was totally incapable of working; Mrs. Easton could not find a job. They pursued his employer's insurance company for payment of the hospital and medical bills as well as for a disability pension, but the letter from the surgical resident, stating that Mr. Easton should be able to return to work shortly, shut off further consideration of his case. The problem was compounded by the departure from the hospital and the area of this surgical resident upon whose judgment of Mr. Easton's case the other physicians relied. Because these doctors chose to discount the grave prognosis which they never told to Mr. Easton and persisted, instead, in encouraging him, the family was cut off from any form of financial assistance to which they might have been entitled. Even an application for social security benefits on the basis of disability was turned down after correspondence between the Social Security Administration and the hospital physicians. Eventually, in order to survive they had to apply to the city Welfare Department for assistance. In due time, a small allowance for food and partial payment of rent and electricity bills was granted. The son dropped out of high school to join the army; the daughter longed for the day when she too would be old enough to drop out.

The Eastons were bewildered. They were aware of the optimistic reports of the hospital physician, but these reports were not realistic to them. They had contributed for many years toward sickness and accident insurance and unemployment benefits and felt that they were entitled to receive some assistance. They could not understand the disapproval of their social security application. They knew Mr. Easton had cooperated fully in all tests and examinations and had accepted the therapy prescribed; they thought the doctors should have effected a "cure." Their family was broken up; they were besieged by bill collectors; they were depressed, lonely, and bitter. Mr. Easton told us:

> I told them [the hospital] that I have no money and they could do anything they wanted with the bill. I'm sorry, but I can't do anything about it now. Right now, we are dragging on the bottom. I guess our next step will be to find a place in the poorhouse.

Mr. Easton's illness progressed over a period of time. In his disillusionment with the doctors, he sought no treatment. Finally, his chest pain became severe and he was brought to the Emergency Room of the hospital by a former neighbor. He was kept waiting in severe respiratory distress for a doctor. After examining him, a resident wrote in the medical record:

> This patient has been here for two hours. He has rales throughout his chest. He is severely ill. Does it take two hours to decide to admit him to this hospital? Please admit him to the medical service.

Twelve hours later Mr. Easton died from pneumonia and emphysema. Mrs. Easton refused permission for a complete postmortem examination but did permit a limited examination of Mr. Easton's chest. No tumor was found within the chest itself and no determination could be made of whether or not malignancy was to be found elsewhere in the body.

A combination of forces worked against this family: They were uneducated people although quite intelligent, but they were powerless in the hands of their "family doctor," the hospital, committee sponsorship, employers, and welfare agencies. Although the young physicians who attended Mr. Easton meant only to be optimistic, they misled the Eastons about the diagnosis and prognosis of the disease. They also misled the agencies that might have assisted this family in their distress. Through illness, the Easton family was overcome by medical, social, and economic deprivations and finally by poverty and death.

TABLE 58. ECONOMIC IMPACT OF THE ILLNESS ON THE FAMILY, BY ACCOMMODATION

| Economic Impact on Family | Patients | | | |
	Total	Private	Semiprivate	Ward
Minor change	40%	57%	35%	21%
Moderate hardship	31	32	32	29
Severe hardship	20	8	28	29
Very severe hardship	9	3	6	21
N =	(161)	(65)	(54)	(42)

Private compared with semiprivate, $p < .05$; private compared with ward, $p < .05$; semiprivate compared with ward, $p > .05$.

Our judgments of the economic impact of the illness on the 161 families in the study are summarized in Table 58. The illness had little effect economically on the families of a majority of private patients; moderate hardships were distributed approximately in equal proportions in all accommodations; relatively few families of private patients suffered severe hardship as a result of the illness, but approximately one family out of four in the semiprivate or ward accommodations suffered severe hardships as a consequence of the illness. Very severe hardships clustered, in large part, among ward patients, with 50 per cent suffering either severe or very severe hardships, while only one in three of semiprivate patients and one in nine of private patients suffered to a comparable extent.

The sex of the patient was not related to the economic effects of the illness on the family. This finding may appear incongruous since one would assume that the illness of middle-aged men who were heads of households would have a definitely different effect on the family capacity to cope with an illness than the illness of a female spouse. Presumably if the male were ill and had to be hospitalized the family would suffer more economically than if the wife were ill. This common belief is derived from the assumption that the male is the breadwinner in the family. However, among these families the role of the male as breadwinner was not as influential as one might assume.

Many of the well wives were working when the husband became ill, or they found gainful employment outside the home after he became ill. A compensating factor also was the presence of children old enough to be able to help in a crisis. However, when a husband became severely disabled by illness, his wife was not able to work, and the family was of relatively low socioeconomic status (as illustrated by the story of the Eastons), the impact of the illness was devastating.

The service on which the patient was treated revealed no statistically significant differences in the economic impact of the illness on the family when we compared patients on the medical service with patients on the surgical service.

Families who had a difficult time meeting daily, weekly, and monthly bills under normal circumstances were faced with a formidable crisis when a serious illness struck. For those of lower socioeconomic status the effect could be impoverishing. When an illness was terminal and the family members were unable to meet the costs of that illness, they were overwhelmed by its catastrophic effects.

Of the forty patients who died, five families out of six were able to report relatively accurate figures on the charges to the family by physicians, hospitals, pharmacies, rest homes, and so on; the other families could give us only sketchy data. On the basis of what we knew of the illness, the hospitalization, the physicians the patient had seen, and other information given to us by the surviving spouse or a grown child, we made estimates of the probable cost of the illness for these few families. The calculated and estimated costs of the last illnesses range from less than $1,000 to over $25,000.

The median charges for the terminal illness were $2,500 for ward patients, $3,500 for private patients, and $4,500 for semiprivate patients. The small number of semiprivate patients who died may have elevated the median because expenditure on the terminal illness for three of the seven was more than $5,000 each.

The families of deceased private patients met all obligations associated with the terminal illness. Six of the seven families of semiprivate patients paid bills for the terminal illness although in one case the patient's fraternal association aided the widow in the payment of bills for her husband's last illness. The families of seven of the fifteen ward patients who died were able to pay for the many items connected with terminal illness; the other eight families were given some assistance by public and private welfare agencies. Some agencies gave voluntarily, while others were coerced into underwriting the costs of a particular illness. In Mr. Easton's case, for example, a voluntary health association heeded Mrs. Easton's pleas for help by giving her $300 to pay for her husband's radiation treatments. When Mr. Easton was hospitalized for the last time the bill for his previous hospitalization had not been paid. In effect, the hospital unwillingly underwrote the costs of his terminal hospitalization. In another case, a convalescent hospital admitted a patient under the impression that the Welfare Department would pay the bill. However, the patient was not cleared for payment at that time or later; the family was completely unable to pay, and the convalescent hospital was "stuck with the bill."

When families were unable to pay for medical assistance and were forced to seek help from a welfare agency, they often felt the investigation that followed was undignified. Families feared that being forced to ask for aid from an outside agency would strip them of self-respect and would lay open the family's private affairs to prying eyes. When public relief was granted it was given in small amounts and usually grudgingly.

Summary

The economic impact on the family of the illness of a spouse was broken down into four aspects—the cost of the hospitalization, how the hospital bill was paid, the economic effects of the illness on the family, and the cost of the terminal illness for families in which the patient died.

For the eight groups of items which made up the cost of the hospitalization, the lowest mean cost was in the semiprivate accommodation and the highest in the ward accommodation. The costs of hospitalization on the medical service were higher than on the surgical service. There was no significant difference by accommodation for the mean number of days patients were hospitalized. Ward patients were charged more than semiprivate patients per day of hospital care but not significantly more than private patients. Medical patients stayed in the hospital longer than surgical patients, but the cost per day was higher for the surgical patients.

No significant difference was found between accommodation, service, or sex on sources of payment of hospital bills. However, the time of payment of the bill was related to the accommodation on which the patient was housed. There was a significant link between physician sponsorship (and, thus, with socioeconomic status) and payment of bills.

The economic effect of the illness on the family was classified into four categories—minor change, moderate hardship, severe hardship, and very severe hardship. In comparing accommodations, the less severe effects on families were found among private patients. There were no significant differences between effects of the illness on families of ward patients and those of semiprivate patients. The sex of the patient was not related significantly to economic effects of the illness on the family, nor was the service upon which the patient was treated.

Family obligations to pay the costs of the terminal illness were met for all private patients, 86 per cent of the semiprivate cases, and only one half of the ward patients. One half of the families of ward patients were unable to pay and had to seek help from a welfare agency.

PART **VI** A LAST LOOK

WE BEGAN THIS RESEARCH WITH THE ASSUMPTION THAT the care hospitalized patients received was modified by factors other than their physical disease. To test this assumption we studied a sample of medical and surgical patients selected during a single episode of illness. We limited the sample to white persons between the ages of 40 and 64 years who had been admitted to a general hospital; each patient selected for study was conscious on admission, a resident of the state, and married and living with his spouse. These specifications were imposed for reasons of necessity and convenience outlined in Chapter 2, pp. 15–16. Within the limits specified above, each patient was selected randomly from the larger universe of persons who might have been chosen had not chance intervened.

The data were assembled from many sources. The major ones were: personal face-to-face interviews with patients, physicians, nurses, spouses of the patients, and other family members; observations in the hospital; the medical records of the patients; and visits to the homes of the patient. The sample was compared with the universe of patients to determine if there were significant differences between the patients in the study and the patients who were not selected. No significant differences were found between the two groups on any of the items available for comparison. We conclude that our sample is representative of all patients who met our specifications. Therefore, we may generalize from the study group to the universe from which they were drawn.

At the time we designed the study, we conceived of the patient as the central figure in a core group composed of the physician, the nurse, and the patient's spouse. Each member was involved directly in the processes entailed in the care of the patient. Associated with this central group, in one way or another, is a peripheral set of figures—hospital administrators, ancillary staff in the hospital, faculty and students in the School of Medicine, and other specialized personnel who are a vital part of the operation of the hospital. Professional and personal interactions tied the members of the core group to the members of the peripheral group. In order to detect influences on patient care which might arise from interactions within the core group and from interactions between members of the core group and peripheral figures, we interviewed persons in the central group as well as those on the periphery. In short, we did not rely entirely upon patient-centered data.

In the presentation of the findings of the study we have examined the diverse facets of the conceptual model from different perspectives. In this chapter we shall present the major problems we found which characterized human relationships as they related to the care of the patients.

From the hour of the patient's admission until his discharge the hospital provided the theater in which the drama of patient care was played. The most salient characteristic of the hospital was its system of accommodations. In turn, the structure of human relations was molded to fit the physical plant. Perhaps it would be more accurate to state that the physical plant was constructed to enable the social system of the community to function in the hospital without too much distortion.

The three types of accommodations provided by the hospital were linked to the status system of the community. Private rooms were furnished for patients of private practitioners who could pay for both the room and the physician. One patient per room was the rule in the private accommodations; moreover, the rooms were separated physically from the two lesser types. Patients who were housed in the private rooms ranked higher in social status than those in the other accommodations. The semiprivate accommodations provided from two to four beds per room. The patients who used these accommodations ranked lower in the socioeconomic system than those in the private rooms. These patients, like the patients in the private rooms, paid for both their beds and the physicians who sponsored them in the hospital. Patients admitted to the ward accommodations occupied the lowest social positions in the community. They had no professional ties to private practitioners while they were in the hospital; they were sponsored by the hospital as "service patients" and placed under the care of the faculty, house staff, and students in the School of Medicine.

Admitting officers and other staff members related themselves to the patients and their families in terms of their conception of the community's status system and the family's position in it. Each group regularly took into consideration the social position of the patient in order to define the kind of relationship that was necessary or desirable. However, relatively accurate perception of social status was obligatory only on the part of the admitting officer who had the responsibility for screening patients so that the hospital was protected against excessive financial losses in their care. It is not clear why the attitudes and performances of other members of the hospital staff reflected the social status of the patients. Perhaps status in itself was important enough to command the attention of nurses and other staff members, or it may have been a reflection of the importance the staff attached to the hospital's accommodations and physician sponsorships which were so indicative of social position.

Physician sponsorships influenced the ways physicians dealt with patients in the different accommodations. Although having a personal physician did not always ensure that physician's attention it did protect the patient against some of the resented practices found in the ward accommodations where patients were more often the tools of learning than the objects of concern in the eyes of those who cared for them. The phrase "clinical material" is symbolic of this situation. Thus, when patients could not pay for an elective admission in advance, if they were not "sick enough" or not "good teaching cases" they might be rejected. Once admitted, this clinical material was found by students and staff to be personally unattractive. Exposure to the realities of poverty, disability, and destitution was a shock to most medical students and house staff who came from a distinctly different social group than the ward patients.

On the wards suspicion, distrust, and confusion were extreme and common. The performances of physicians tended to keep alive this distrust. The patient hoped for the best care and an explanation of what was being done. Although he may have been given optimal treatment, if he did not get an explanation of what was being done he often felt that he was being used as a "guinea pig." He thought that the physicians did not "talk my language." In fact, physicians often misinformed the patient concerning his illness and the intended treatment. In some instances, young physicians were embarrassed when they realized that they had carried out without sufficient justification the most elaborate of diagnostic and treatment maneuvers. They recognized that a consultation with selected specialists might have obviated some of the procedures which were expensive and painful for the patient. At other times, they questioned the humanity of some diagnostic and therapeutic measures.

From their varied experiences, direct and indirect, patients and their families developed a lore of their own concerning the ward accommodation. This lore was often inconsistent with the facts, but the belief was nonetheless real. Family members lacked the knowledge to initiate an investigation to determine the facts for themselves. The student physicians were seldom sensitive to fears and suspicions. Staff who dealt with the family members were often unaware of these concerns. If they became aware of them, they commonly attributed them to personality flaws rather than to experiences in the ward accommodations. Ward patients and their families may have been mistaken in their beliefs, but the fact remains that their suspicions and distrust were derived from experience and perceptions of experience.

As an observer moved about the hospital he could note that senior physicians and private-duty nurses were frequently present on private floors, less often seen on semiprivate divisions, and conspicuous by their absence from the wards. On the other hand, students of all types appeared in larger and larger numbers as one went from the private to the less costly types of accommodation. In accordance with this observation, the medical, nursing, and ancillary staff students were found most frequently on the wards.

The illness conditions of the patients were also related to the accommodation structure. Generally speaking, the ward patients were the sickest; they had the highest mortality rates; semiprivate patients were least ill; the private patients were intermediate.

Persons often sought the advice of family members, nurses, pharmacists, and others for the treatment of minor ailments. However, for health problems viewed as major, a physician was usually consulted. To be hospitalized required a physician's evaluation and recommendation. The patient, through his history and the presentation of his body for examination, provided the physician with the information essential for diagnosis, treatment, and prognosis. Communications of patients and physicians, however, were selective so that the information sought by one and supplied by the other was usually incomplete and often misleading.

The patient was confused about his symptoms and fearful about his illness. He frequently delayed reporting his symptoms because he feared not only illness but the physicians whom he saw. He suspected that they might fail to understand him, keep the truth from him, tell him unpleasant truths, or discover embarrassing things about him. The patient often informed the physician selectively, describing his physical symptoms but not his emotional state, since it was acceptable, though unpleasant, to be physically ill but not acceptable to be mentally ill. Thus, the patient presented a limited history of his problem, yet he and his physician believed that this history was adequate for diagnostic and treatment purposes. In many instances it was not adequate.

The physician focused his interest on physical disease; he was usually not concerned with personal and social influences in relation to the disease. He altered his communications with patients to meet their expectations and, at times, to protect himself from patients and family reactions. Between them, the patient and the physician defined the patient's problem and determined what information was important in the diagnosis and treatment of his disease. This definition, however, rarely took into account the presence of emotional or family disturbances and the extent to which they influenced the patient's symptoms. Psychiatric diagnoses were rarely applied; psychiatrists were in-

though some high-status patients were made to feel this was so. House staff were always present; they took histories and examined patients. In a crisis they were the first to attend to a hospitalized patient. They supplemented the private practice of medicine, but, since they viewed themselves primarily as students, they did so reluctantly when they thought their learning was being compromised. They exerted considerable influence medically. What they lacked in experience was usually more than made up by the simple fact of their presence. The patient's own physician, in contrast, was a visitor. *We suggest that the use of house staff as essential manpower in the care of patients was as important a supplement to private practice as it was a necessity to learning and career development of young physicians.* We infer that private practice has been unable or unwilling to provide an equally acceptable alternative to fill the growing need for medical manpower in the care of hospitalized patients.

One of the salient points revealed in this research is *the separation of surgeons and internists from the everyday concerns of their patients.* These physicians need to return to the mainstream of society. In brief, the extant physician-patient relationship: (1) ruled out a systematic appraisal of personal and family influence upon the etiology of symptoms, the diagnosis of illness, and patient management; (2) was profoundly influenced by the social position of the patient; and (3) was rarely a simple one-to-one relationship in the hospital but rather a varied association involving private physicians and house staff in the semiprivate and private accommodations and medical students and house staff in the wards.

The nurse-patient relationship was limited by expectations of physicians, the hospital, and patients. Physicians expected nurses to follow their orders and provide for the daily living requirements of the patients. The physicians realized that registered nurses were in short supply; thus, they accepted the ancillary staff as necessary for the completion of routine tasks. Patients, for the most part, gave little indication that they expected the nurse to make more than minor decisions concerning their care; they looked to the physician for all the major decisions requisite to the treatment of their illness; those few who sought assistance for personal problems preferred the attention of the physician rather than that of the nurse. Both patients and nurses were keenly conscious that the physician was the primary person who was legally and professionally responsible for the care of the patient. Accordingly, the physician made diagnostic and treatment choices with which, for the most part, patients, families, and nurses complied.

The physician looked upon the nurse as a personal assistant. She followed his orders which generally included direct assistance with diagnostic and treatment procedures, administration of medications, and the collection of specimens from patients. To be sure, there were selected tasks the registered nurse was required to do herself, including preparation and administration of medications, keeping of appropriate records, and reporting the patient's condition to the physician. (The registered nurse, along with others, may be held legally accountable for her performance in patient care.)

The hospital administrator relied upon the registered nurse to carry out physicians' orders and supervise the staff on her division. The head nurse, or her alternate the charge nurse, occupied the most senior position of those who stayed "on the floor" where patients were housed. She clearly was the central figure in getting things done for patients. Without her, the operation of the hospital's patient-care divisions as they now exist would collapse. With the limited supply of registered nurses, there was minimal time for them to spend with patients beyond that required to carry out the physicians' orders. The registered nurse spent about the same amount of time in interaction with patients as physicians did. She knew comparatively little about the medical problems of patients and almost nothing about their personal problems though she may have been aware that personal and family difficulties existed. Under these conditions, the patient and nurse could not develop a problem-solving relationship centered upon the patient as a person. Neither patients nor physicians wanted the nurse's role to be anything beyond the relatively passive one of providing a technical service in an atmosphere of "tender loving care." Thus, *the nurse-patient relationship was technical, administrative, and task oriented; it was not person oriented.*

The nurse-physician relationship was an integral part of the patient-care process. This relationship as well as that between the patient and the nurse was determined largely by choices within the physician-patient relationship. Nurses rarely discussed patients with doctors; they carried out their orders in the treatment of the disease and reported progress in the fight against illness. Apart from limited and often only written messages, *there was no communication between the physician and the nurse.* We are in agreement generally with the medical resident who responded to our question with the blunt statement: "There is no nurse-physician relationship in this hospital."

The time spent by staff registered nurses on the divisions where out patients were housed was exceeded by that spent by the private-duty nurses. The private-duty nurse confined her attention to the patient who employed her. Her employers were, in very large part, housed on the private accommodations. Few of the administrators, physicians, and staff nurses were comfortable with the relationship of the private-duty nurses to the hospital or the patient. Even more distressing was the belief that the majority of private-duty nurses were out of touch with modern patient care. Even a portion of the private-duty nurses realized their limited competence in the hospital of today. Our data reveal further that the private-duty nurse generally had too much time to spend usefully on one patient and used her free time to manipulate hospital nurses, physicians, family members, and even patients. The objective of these machinations was to ensure for the private-duty nurse her survival in a changing medical setting. *We believe her talents could be better used in a more effective organization of the hospital.*

We turn now from the complex of interactional relationships which characterized the principal persons involved in the care of patients to more general considerations. The problems we have highlighted in the care of patients within the inner core of patient-professional relations are linked, in turn, to the larger framework of the Medical Center. The composition of the Medical Board, discussed in Chapter 3, revealed the diverse professional interests of physicians who practiced in the hospital. It included representatives from the School of Medicine, private practitioners in the community, and hospital administrators. Although the administrators were responsible to the hospital's Board of Directors they had little authority over the private practitioners or faculty in the School of Medicine. The administrators relied primarily on nurses to carry out their policies, but the nurses took their orders from the physicians. Thus, the prime authorities in directing patient care were the physicians, ranging from private practitioners who spent comparatively little time on the patient-care divisions to house staff and medical students. Senior professors in the School of Medicine and most private practitioners appeared often enough to give some direction to patient care in the different services. Thus, they had some awareness of what was occurring and could maintain a position of greater strength vis-à-vis the administrators on the Medical Board. These physicians did not have a continuing presence on the patient-care divisions, however; they left the care of patients to house officers and head nurses. The nurses were not capable of directing the division in the interest of patient care because they were not trained to practice medicine. The house officers performed very well at times, but they did not have the full authority to direct patient care, were not seasoned physicians, and viewed patients more as tools of learning than objects of care and compassion.

The central purpose of the hospital—the care of patients, especially the personal aspects of that care—was not controlled directly or effectively by the hospital or by anyone. The two groups of physicians who presumably were most able to direct patient care were not in a position to do so although their representatives were the most powerful members of the Medical Board. It was a case of greater authority and lesser responsibility that was attributable to the working relationships between the three institutions represented on the Medical Board—organized medicine, medical education, and the hospital.

At the level of patient care the leadership was so varied and inconsistent that nurses and house officers were often confused about what was needed or wanted. At best, the house officers and nurses who had overall concern for a patient-care division may have had a senior physician who understood their problems, but under existing conditions their performance was hindered by the division of leadership at the top and the absence of senior medical leadership at the level of individual patient care. The physicians were often in conflict with nurses and hospital administrators. Moreover, the differing groups of physicians were often in conflict with each other. In brief, each group looked out for itself and understood inadequately the problems it created for members of other groups in giving patient care.

Physicians and nurses did not work closely together except in surgical and selected other procedures. On the patient-care divisions they did not communicate with one another as much as they did among themselves: Physicians talked with physicians; nurses talked with nurses. It was unusual for nurses and physicians to visit patients together or to inform one another and the patients about what was planned and why. In those few cases in which a registered nurse possessed personal information about a patient's problems relevant to his care, this knowledge was not shared with the physician or used in the patient's behalf. The chief link between physicians and nurses was the "doctor's order book," a one-way communication. Communications were limited usually to what was required in the staff's technical performance in the diagnosis and treatment of disease. This is a rather narrow framework and is only part of the care of patients. *Confusion on the floor of the patient-care divisions was the net result.*

Physicians were reluctant to admit to confusion except in the unusual case. The nurses knew there was confusion, but they were impotent to do anything about it. The patients knew there was confusion and a measure of disorganization; while they gave little indication of awareness of their own or others' contributions to the confusion they saw and felt, they volunteered the information that they were the victims of this confusion. Though reactions may have been withheld by the patients or not perceived by professionals, patient resentments were common. They were centered primarily upon disappointment in the physician, especially in his failure to communicate. Also, patients were suspicious of flaws in the physicians' technical performance. Finally, patients were sensitive to problems of disagreement and incoordination in their care. When the conditions of poverty, low social status, committee sponsorship, and personal and family turmoil were combined, as they so often were on the wards, the results were spectacularly tragic for the patient and his family.

In brief, we found that no patient, person, or set of persons was consistently at the center of the human group in the hospital. The center of concern shifted from time to time as conditions and persons required in the light of their respective powers and objectives at the moment.

The outcome of the treatment administered during hospitalization was examined from a number of different points of view. First, ward patients had poorer prognoses than those in other accommodations; their mortality during and after hospitalization was significantly greater than that of semiprivate patients. This finding was more or less expected, considering the urgency for admission by accommodation. Second, success of treatment varied by service but not by accommodation or sex. Treatment of medical patients was less satisfactory than that of surgical patients. This difference resulted primarily from the existing conditions: Therapy by internists was most often palliative, symptomatic, or otherwise limited, whereas therapy offered by surgeons was more curative for surgical conditions. More medical patients had symptoms, even diseases, which were related directly to the whole adaptive scheme of their work and their families. The task of treating these patients involved presumably an appraisal and some therapeutic manipulation of the patient's family and his way of life. Such an undertaking was not attempted. Instead, *ad hoc* diagnoses and corresponding treatment were offered with limited or no success.

The subjective feelings of patients were related to the severity of the physical illness and disability; they were not related to accommodation, service, or sex. We conclude that patients and their families had life problems which disabled in various ways but were accepted as a part of the life the patients led. When patients developed sick bodies the new problems may have aggravated the existing situation, but the chief impact subjectively was to increase the burdens. The extent of the burden was directly related to the severity of the illness and physical disability.

Although patients and physicians focused upon physical disease, personal and social attributes produced disability as great as that caused by physical disease. Of the 155 patients discharged alive, 14 per cent were not disabled, 24 per cent were disabled from physical disease, 44 per cent were disabled from psychosocial disturbances, and 18 per cent were disabled from a combination of these causes. While patients sought relief from the physical and emotional pain resulting from these psychosocial disturbances, they did not expect physicians to diagnose and treat them as such.

In the face of a poor prognosis, the personal and social realities for the patient and his family were usually discounted or ignored. All parties concerned concentrated on the treatment of the physical disease, but in these situations the impact of the illness on the patient and his family was profound and disconcerting. Patients, family members, nurses, and physicians failed to communicate; they guessed at what was being said. Isolation, suspicion, and distrust were common.

At the same time that the treatment of disease consumed the energies of the physicians and nurses, patients and their families faced not only problems of disease but also the trials of living together. Families were relieved when the burdens of caring for a chronically ill and disabled member were ended by death. They were relieved also when death brought an end to the persistent burdens of family maladjustment caused by the patient. Among the survivors, death was rarely viewed as totally bereaving.

Another impact on families concerned costs of the illness. While the costs of hospitalization did not vary greatly from one accommodation to another, the ward patients, consistent with their more severe illness, had the highest mean charges. The payment of hospital bills was related to accommodation and sponsorship (an expression of socioeconomic status). Families of ward and semiprivate patients often faced severe economic hardship; they could not and did not pay their bills. In the case of death, one half of the families of ward patients were obliged to endure the indignity of seeking help from a public agency.

Ward patients tended to be more ill and their families poorer. Less attention was centered upon these persons than upon those in other accommodations. The result was less chance for a successful adaptation to the adversities of the patient's illness. The impact of the illness upon the spouses of the ward patients was more extensive than that upon the spouses of semiprivate and private patients. We attribute these findings to a combination of family, illness, and treatment differences.

Before leaving this research, we are impelled to draw attention to the implications of some of our findings. In this last look at our subject we confine our remarks primarily to the hospital and the persons who care for patients in it—physicians, nurses, and hospital administrators. Only incidentally do we focus attention upon the patient and his family and the organization of medicine in the community. Attention is drawn to the hospital because it was here that the patient received concentrated care. Moreover, the hospital and the School of Medicine are discrete institutions which generate and transmit knowledge and influence the standards of present and future care of the sick both inside and outside the hospital. We are conscious of the interconnectedness of the care of the sick in the hospital, in the private practitioner's office, and in the family. Sickness is too broad a problem and of too crucial importance to society for us to lose sight of the forest as we look at the trees.

From this vantage point our first question is: *Can physicians treat disease in the perspective of patient and family realities, or are they capable of treating disease only in a more abstract sense?* We have reason to state that patients and families, in spite of the difficulties for them, were far more desirous of treatment in this perspective than were physicians willing to provide it. This judgment applies to the practice of medicine in private offices as well as in the hospital. It is possible that a combination of forces had set the observed patterns. Confidence is placed in what succeeds. In the past one hundred years the most spectacular successes in treating disease have been based upon applications from the physical and biological sciences. At the same time social and environmental influences upon health have been neglected.

The consequences of this narrow focus were apparent in the case of the majority of patients, but they were particularly impressive in two situations: First, for 26 per cent of the semiprivate and private patients cared for on the medical service, the diagnoses applied had little or nothing to do with the patients' problems. Moreover, these diagnoses were usually inapplicable, always led to complications of existing problems, and produced no therapeutic benefits. The second situation involved patient and family efforts to cope with a poor prognosis and death. Here, evasion of truth, conspiracies of silence, and misrepresentation of the problem were commonplace. The confusion which followed added much to the already existing burdens of the patient and his family. We realize patients and families were involved in the cause of the confusion, but we emphasize that the professionals passively ignored or added to the chaotic situation.

The strains between practitioners, patients, and families were at least partially the result of the practitioner's limited conceptualization of and corresponding action toward the problems of patients. These strains were seen in the hospital because physicians set the pattern of performance of the house staff and of nurses in the care of patients. Some physicians were aware of these problems, but they were divided in their views of a solution. One senior faculty member commented: "We should see this from the patient's point of view and work from there." Another disagreed:

> I like things the way they are. We are training researchers first, practitioners second. Those who enter practice are usually the second-rate students and some say we should teach them how to practice. But I feel we shouldn't waste our time on them. They can learn how to practice in a short time, later on. They won't do much harm in the meantime because given the nature of people and chronic disease they really can't do much good.

Some physicians believed that only the physically ill should be hospitalized. Others thought this approach was unrealistic since patients cannot be so simply divided beforehand. Our data support the latter view.

We believe physicians should be taught a cosmopolitan view of normality and deviance. They should accept most if not all deviance (and there is much of it) as a part of the adaptive patterns of patients and families and should function as counsellors within these adaptive schemes. The role of the counsellor desired by the patients and families, according to our interpretation, extends at least as far as diagnosing the patient's problem whether or not disease exists in an organic sense. Being sick or well, according to the physician's definition of these terms, may have no meaning to the patient or may have, at times, a different meaning. The physician should find out how the patient views his situation. He should function as a kindly and cautious Socratic teacher who uses what the patient is, knows, and desires in making his choices of advice, information, diagnosis, and treatment to be given to the patient. Within this framework, we believe there would be the mutual communication necessary for a more useful conceptualization of the patient's problems.

We found the professionals often insulated themselves against the stream of stimuli from patients and families who wanted immediate attention, understanding, and finally action in the management of the patients. It is our view that "scientific" medicine has been used appropriately and successfully in the management of some patients in this study, but it also has been used inappropriately in the care of others. Sometimes, the therapeutic choices did not apply to the problem, or "scientific" medicine was used as "insulating" medicine between patients and physicians. In that process the physician assumed superior knowledge and discounted or even ignored the report of the patient.

The training of practitioners, especially early training, took place primarily in the ward accommodation where patients were not assertive; for the most part, students could and did continuously ignore the patients. Given the environment of the School of Medicine with its focus on disease, it is understandable that the medical student looked upon the patient only incidentally as a social and human being. Because of limited support from the community for the care of the sick poor and the simultaneous requirement that the hospital must care for these persons at least at a minimal level, medical and nursing students often became unwilling participants in what they considered to be inadequate care of the poor. They seemed less conscious of a possible relationship between inadequate care and ineffective learning—a relationship strongly suggested by our findings.

We are critical of the care ward patients received. These poor people hoped for adequate care and the hospital attempted to provide it, but the attempt was limited. We think many sick poor were turned away from the hospital because they were not sick enough, were weak teaching cases, or could not afford the schedule of charges which the hospital had to maintain to remain solvent. Against their wishes many were investigated without their under-standing who was probing or why. Their personal and social problems which were often severe prior to illness were aggravated with the illness. Those who cared for them found them uninteresting but their diseases usually con-venient for learning. Although their diseases technically were treated as effectively as those of patients in other accommodations, the ward patients generally were viewed as ignorant, unintelligent, and unworthy of devoted service. Few persons in authority were aware of the ways physicians and hospital staff interacted with ward patients and their families inside or outside the hospital.

Along with the educational, nursing, and administrative changes suggested below, *Shouldn't there also be a senior medical authority for each ward divi-sion to ensure that patient care is improved and the rights of patients pro-tected?* Even putting these humanitarian concerns aside, *are practices found in the ward accommodations suitable as a patient-care model for students of the health professions?* We think not, for the very neglect of personal and social influences upon disease, diagnosis, and care found in *all* accommoda-tions may be viewed as extensions of the ward model.

Such a medical authority as we suggest may be necessary also in the semi-private and private accommodations to ensure the improvement of patient care and the optimal teaching of the increasing numbers of persons who re-ceive training here. We believe such a position is needed to improve train-ing through better patient management in a personal sense. Moreover, while we did not study the technical performances of medical and nursing staff in caring for patients as systematically as we did the interpersonal relation-ships, we learned from direct observations and reports of physicians and nurses that not all of their performances were as they should have been. We believe that physicians generally, or perhaps a few in particular, should assume more active and continuing roles in the hospital care of patients—care which in today's expanding technology and specialization is likely to become more extensive and complicated. Direction of patient care largely by absentee senior physicians may be inconsistent with excellence in hospital services. Given the complex of technical, personal, and organizational conditions we have described, *can senior physicians be successful private entrepreneurs or professors and at the same time effective leaders in hospital patient manage-ment?* We must answer this question negatively, at least in the framework of patient care we describe in this book.

Because of the lack of clarity of medical leadership there was much am-biguity and confusion on the patient-care divisions. The nurses attempted to resolve this and "keep things going," but they were not in a position to settle conflicts and provide the necessary leadership. Given these limitations, nurses were dissatisfied in the roles set for them as medical technicians and minor hospital administrators. Yet it was the nurse on the scene who expedited patient care, and she also probably took the brunt of expressed patient dissatisfaction.

The nurse, however, was not the only person who feared or refrained from action in the face of problems. The practitioners acted to protect their position as physician to the patient, but they were not always free to use their best medical judgment. Many physicians responded to the demands of the sick persons or their families even when such demands had little to do with solving the patient's problems; such demands commonly involve hospitalization, a "dictated" diagnosis, and inappropriate therapy. The physician feared loss of status and income as well as involvement in the problems of patients. He was not trained to deal with the life problems of patients even though the patients and particularly his professional organizations may have believed he was. The result was that *the problems of many patients were subordinated to the physician's efforts to protect the physician-patient relationship as he defined it.*

It is possible that a senior medical director of each division could pull together fragments of medical, personal, and social data from patients, family members, practitioners, nurses, and house staff to provide more adequate care of patients. We believe such an innovation offers promise of improved patient care and increased satisfaction for nurses who then might have sufficient medical leadership and protection to assume more responsibility for both the technical and personal care of patients. (In so doing, she also might find herself elevated to a new, stable position as a medical auxiliary with built-in career opportunities. This would contrast sharply with her current blocked mobility.)

The medical leadership of each division should be free to reflect the true nature of patient problems and to propose solutions. The Medical Center might bring about a demonstration service from which patients, families, and community practitioners can benefit in their efforts to solve health problems inside the hospital. *Is not this a suitable, indeed a necessary, task for a teaching hospital? If not in a teaching hospital, then where can such an innovation be tried?*

Originally, we thought "the problems of nursing" were those of low morale and personnel shortages. Our data demonstrate that these problems did exist; they were serious and chronic. However, we no longer think these and other issues that involve nurses can be solved within the profession of nursing. The registered nurses and ancillary staff were under partial control of physicians. Their roles were defined as administrative, technical, or routine. They could not concentrate upon individual patients for lack of time; they were not encouraged by physicians to do so and at times were not even permitted to do so. The patients identified with physicians and often repelled the efforts of nurses to help them. Recognizing the importance of the nurse in the routine running of the hospital, in providing for sick persons, and in satisfying patients and physicians in their current patterns of defining and dealing with patients, we have no specific recommendations regarding the reorientation of hospital-paid nurses unless medical leadership changes as mentioned above. However, with such changes medical and administrative authorities should allow and require nurses to assume roles of close relationship with patients and offer them, along with physicians, suitable career opportunities in that role.

For the sake of the individual private-duty nurse and particularly for the care of hospitalized patients both as individuals and as a group, we believe the private-duty nurses should become an integral part of the hospital's nursing staff. The performance of the private-duty nurses was costly, wasteful, and problematic. Their tendency toward obsolescence was marked. Their efforts were not concentrated where the greatest need existed. Private-duty nurses denied, discounted, or ignored these problems. Their aim was to maintain themselves as private entrepreneurs. However, the parties who controlled private-duty nurses in the hospital—patients, their families, hospital administrators, and physicians—would not permit them to act as free professionals. *We believe the private-duty nurse should be incorporated fully into the hospital's nursing services;* her direction, supervision, and continuing development as a nurse should be formally controlled by the hospital. The aim of our recommendation is to rescue the private-duty nurse from exclusion from the hospital and in so doing improve the lot of the patient. This situation can be ameliorated by management changes. Considering the situation of the private-duty nurses, it is reasonable to ask if their services were worth approximately the $1,000,000 annually paid them by patients in this hospital. *Should not some changes be made?*

Nursing shortages were not less important than morale. While we recognize that shortages have many determinants, we here call attention to some factors which impressed us throughout this research: The hospital-paid registered nurses determined when they would work even if they did not control the working conditions. Nurses had alternatives available to them. The shortage gave them the advantages of a seller's market. If they were married they could usually depend on their husband's income and did not have to work regularly. If they were single and without dependents they could become private-duty nurses, seek employment in more promising situations, or leave the profession for other kinds of work. They were not anxious about employment because employment was readily available. The hospital, on the other hand, was dependent upon them and most anxious to purchase their services. However, cultural constraints exercised by the hospital, physicians, and above all the patients limited the salaries the hospital offered the nurse for her services. The hospital-paid nurses manipulated their employment just as private-duty nurses manipulated theirs. The effect on patients in both cases was the same—*nursing care was erratic and usually inadequate.* It is likely to remain so unless sweeping changes are brought about.

We do not see the basis for a solution to the manpower and morale problems in the present system. In this connection we ask: *Can women be wives and mothers and at the same time provide all the manpower, leadership, and stability in a vital sector of a growing health industry?* We must answer this question negatively, but we find no basis to believe there is anything in nursing which is uniquely feminine, any more than we find attributes in medicine which are uniquely masculine. Although the nursing profession has recognized the need for men in the field, recruitment has been minimal. *We suggest a new career in the health field—the medical auxiliary.* Should not suitable schools be opened to prepare men and women for careers in the health field which involve direct care of patients? Should such schools replace nursing schools? We think that either nurses or others should develop a career under a title which will attract both men and women. A title so uniquely feminine as *nurse* will not suffice as an appeal for men to enter a field so vital to health care.

Since it is necessary that men meet societal expectations of family support, suitable career and economic advances must be offered to ensure success of recruitment and stability within the role. In our view, such a new role could be satisfying to men and women, but to be sufficiently popular to attract many, and thus possibly reduce the manpower crisis in the health field, attractive career opportunities are essential. Such a condition, in our view, is more likely to exist if the suggested auxiliaries are strongly linked to patients and physicians and aviod roles which should be taken only by administrators and their assistants.

In brief then, we suggest that (1) health professionals be trained to deal systematically with the personal and social factors which affect the diagnoses and treatment of patients; (2) continuing senior medical leadership focus on the care of patients in each patient-care division; (3) nurses be responsible largely to this medical leadership; and (4) medical auxiliaries eventually replace nurses and be given more responsibility and career opportunities in patient care.

The authors are mindful of the dollar costs which may be entailed in these suggestions but are equally aware of the high costs of inefficiencies and deficiencies of the current care of patients. We are aware also of probable resistance to change and the uncertainty of the consequences. Finally, although we have reasons to believe that our findings may apply in other similar settings, further research is necessary on this point. These reservations led us to ask questions and offer suggestions rather than make recommendations. However, we believe that the synthesis of the data reported in this book provides several guidelines for innovation while constituting, at the same time, a humbling and sobering opportunity for hospital trustees, medical educators, hospital administrators, practitioners of medicine and nursing, patients and their families, and thoughtful citizens to consider the issues we have raised in this research. This is the challenge we offer. Shall we complacently continue to "walk backward into the future," congratulating ourselves on how much better medical care is today than it was in the early part of this century, or will our challenge be met? *The answer is basically a society-wide issue rather than a problem for medical professionals alone.* Sickness is inextricably linked with society and society will have to look to itself for the solution.

INDEX

Accommodation (hospital), 22, 36–37, 38, 53, 74, 270–271, 366
  adjustment (family) and, 102
  age and, 90
  and admission process, 108, 110, 112, 116–118
  and autopsy, 326–329
  and death, 307
  and impact of illness, 336–337, 359, 378
  and length of hospitalization, 350
  and mental status, 204–205
  and need for admission, 152–155
  and nurse assignment, 67–69, 368
  and nurse-patient relationship, 220–222, 225–229, 230–231, 237–246
  and nurse-physician relationship, 73–75, 218–220, 222–223
  and payments, 351–352
  and physician-patient relationship, 108, 121–122
  and psychiatric consultation, 209–210, 368–369
  and satisfaction, 229–231, 279–282
  and socioeconomic status, 116–123, 336
  and sponsorship, 110–111, 145–148
  and treatment, 40, 75–76, 84, 77–78, 294–295
  and visiting, 260–261
  attitudes about, 40, 115–116, 120–122
  charges by, 348, 350
  education and, 93
  fears by, 278–279
  sex and, 90
Adjustment (family)
  and accommodation, 102
  and death, 340–345
  and emotional impact, 338
  and mental status, 248–250
  defined, 94
  in families, 94–103, 249

  See also: Empathy; Manipulation; Mental status
Administrators (hospital), 44–88
  and faculty, 46–47
  and house staff, 48–50, 57–58
  and medical students, 46–47, 61
  and nurses, 69, 70, 71–72, 80–82, 84–85
  and private physicians, 53–58, 61–62
  role of, 5–6, 44
Admission (to hospital), 7, 16, 37–39, 71, 107–118
  and accommodation, 110, 112, 152–155
  and family, 107–108, 113
  and socioeconomic status, 116–118, 366
  diagnostic process in, 7, 38, 113, 151–155
  financial process in, 7, 37, 38, 39, 114–116
  need for, 151–155
  officers, 37, 38, 39, 113–116, 154–155, 206, 366
  See also: House staff
Age of patients by accommodation and sex, 24, 90
Ancillary personnel
  interaction time, 236–237
  role of, 5–6, 86
  See also: Licensed practical nurses; Nurse's aides
Anxiety (in hospitalization), 273
  causes of, 282–286
Autopsy, 320–329
  See also: Death

Care (of patients)
  and house staff, 56, 120, 121, 143, 148, 159, 316, 318–358, 372–373
  defined, 6
  nurse satisfaction with, 229–231
  of ward patients, 380
  patient satisfaction with, 230–231, 279–282

387

ABOUT THE AUTHORS

RAYMOND S. DUFF was born in 1923 on a potato farm in northern Maine near the Maine–New Brunswick border. His ancestors, who were of Scotch and English origin, came to Maine over a few generations through the Maritime Provinces. His early years were spent primarily at work on the farm or in a one-room elementary school. After high school and two years of college he spent three years in the Army during World War II, leaving with the rank of Second Lieutenant, Field Artillery. With the help of the G.I. Bill, he was able to set out on a career in medicine. In 1952, he received his M.D. from the Yale University School of Medicine and his Master of Public Health degree in 1959.

Dr. Duff is Associate Professor of Pediatrics at Yale University.

From 1956–1960, he was Director of Ambulatory Services at Yale–New Haven Hospital and in 1955–56 was Director of the Bureau of Medical Services of the New Haven Health Department.

Dr. Duff lives in Woodbridge, Connecticut, with his wife, Glenna Joyce, and three daughters.

AUGUST B. HOLLINGSHEAD was born in Lyman, Wyoming, in 1907. He graduated from Fremont High School and received his A.B. in 1931 and his M.A. in 1933 from the University of California at Berkeley. He received his Ph.D. from the University of Nebraska in 1935.

Dr. Hollingshead has been the William Graham Sumner Professor of Sociology at Yale University since 1963.

He was professor in the department of sociology, Yale University, from 1947–1963 and served as Visiting Professor at the University of London in 1957–58.

Since 1950, he has been Consultant in the Surgeon General's office of the U.S. Public Health Service.

In addition, Professor Hollingshead has taught at the University of Indiana at Bloomington (1936–39) and was a visiting professor at the University of California at Berkeley (1946–51).

Professor Hollingshead and his wife, Carol, live in Woodbridge, Connecticut.

Format by Katharine Sitterly
Set in Intertype Garamond
Composed, printed and bound by The Haddon Craftsmen, Inc.
HARPER & ROW, PUBLISHERS, INCORPORATED